S. Haykin

INTERNATIONAL SERIES OF MONOGRAPHS ON
ELECTRONICS AND INSTRUMENTATION
GENERAL EDITORS: D. W. FRY AND W. A. HIGINBOTHAM

VOLUME 8

SPACE-CHARGE WAVES
And Slow Electromagnetic Waves

OTHER TITLES IN THE SERIES
(FORMERLY PERGAMON SCIENCE SERIES ELECTRONICS AND WAVES)

SPACE-CHARGE WAVES
WAVES
And Slow Electromagnetic Waves

by

A. H. W. BECK, B.Sc.(Eng.), A.M.I.E.E.
Standard Telecommunications Laboratories Ltd.

PERGAMON PRESS
LONDON · NEW YORK · PARIS · LOS ANGELES
1958

PERGAMON PRESS LTD.
4 & 5 Fitzroy Square, London W.1

PERGAMON PRESS, INC.
122 East 55th Street, New York 22, N.Y.
P.O. Box 47715, Los Angeles, California

PERGAMON PRESS, S.A.R.L.
24 Rue des Écoles, Paris V^e

Library of Congress Card Number 58–10735

Set in Times New Roman by Santype Ltd., Salisbury
Printed in Great Britain by Wyman and Sons Ltd.
London, Reading and Fakenham

CONTENTS

PREFACE

MICROWAVE valves, as we know them today, are the product of extensive research carried out in considerable secrecy during the Second World War. It is hardly surprising that many different theoretical treatments were evolved, some of fairly general application, others not. It is now realized that the most satisfactory treatment is the general one based on the application of two fundamental laws of electrodynamics, Maxwell's equations and the Lorentz force law, combined with the principle of the conservation of charge which itself is a consequence of Maxwell's equations. As our knowledge progressed it became clear that it was unnecessary to use the full apparatus of the Maxwellian approach, which in most cases gives far more knowledge than we need. Instead, one may direct attention to the interaction of two wave systems: the first, that observed on the circuit in the absence of an electron beam; the second, that on the beam in the absence of circuit waves. The purpose of this book is to examine this idea and to illustrate it by describing the operation of most known microwave valves in these terms.

The book starts with a brief qualitative description of the major types of microwave valve so as to acquaint the reader with the broad phenomena to be described. A very compressed account of Maxwellian electrodynamics is then given. Next comes the application to the solution of the circuit problem. This problem may be succinctly expressed as that of providing electromagnetic waves with phase velocities very much less than that of light and field systems which lead to the largest possible electric fields in the direction of the electron beam. The reader is then asked to master Appendix 6 which deals with the several ways in which long, heavy-current electron beams are maintained in more or less cylindrical form. The following two chapters deal with the beam waves. Chapter 4 considers the general space-charge wave problem in several geometrical arrangements and for different beam-forming means. The effects of changes of mean velocity are discussed and analogies with transmission lines and filters are drawn. Power flow theorems are derived. The general theory of plasmas is also included as it is felt that the valve engineer has something to learn from the theoretical physicist dealing with high-current gas discharges and vice versa. Chapter 5, which contains a good deal of original matter, exposes the difficulties of determining the amplitudes of the infinite series of space-charge waves which are excited in general boundary value problems and gives the solutions as far as they are known. Next come four chapters on the application of the methods in the theory of various kinds of valve. Here the more widely used devices are emphasized. The very important problem of inherent noise is dealt with in the final chapter.

The Appendices deal with some matters which seemed inappropriate in the main text, such as measurements on circuits, the theory of the maintenance of electron beams and Llewellyn's electronic equations. The remaining Appendices cover some special mathematical analyses and other material involving heavy algebra, whose absence improves the text.

In the past I have been accused of using too advanced mathematics. This is incorrect. I am an engineer and not a mathematician, as will be obvious to mathematicians, and I only use mathematics to get the results required. I should be delighted if one had only to count on one's fingers to do this, but the hard and inescapable fact is that one has to use a certain amount of mathematics. The amount is really rather limited, the main items being a knowledge of the solutions of Bessel's equation and the simpler properties of Bessel functions together with a little matrix algebra. This is no harder than, say, elementary trigonometry, and any reader who is convinced he needs the knowledge could master it in a couple of days of concentrated work. To my mind it is a symptom of one of the many things wrong with British technological education that I should need to write this paragraph. American readers should disregard these sentences.

I hope this book will be useful to several classes of reader; to research students and young physicists and engineers starting to work in the microwave tube industry, to teachers as a statement of our present level of understanding, as an indication in which directions research should go and also as yet another example of the application of Maxwellian theory. Theoretical and experimental workers in several allied fields may find useful viewpoints or may be able to throw light on the unsolved problems. Lastly, more senior valve engineers will obtain a broad picture of the field and may improve their understanding of specific devices.

The literature has been surveyed up to, roughly, the end of 1957 and, while I make no claim to have included everything, I believe that all major advances are referred to.

Many people have helped me and I offer them my sincere thanks. Among my colleagues at S.T.L. Dr. E. A. Ash has read the book and has helped me to clarify several difficult points. Mr. P. E. Deering has worked with me on the lengthy and boring computations involved in multi-mode theory. The authors and organizations who have allowed reproduction of data and illustrations are separately thanked. My wife has typed the manuscript, criticized my English, and corrected the proofs. Without her the book would not have been written.

Finally, I wish to thank the management of Standard Telecommunication Laboratories, Ltd. for permission to publish the work.

ACKNOWLEDGEMENTS

THE Author and Publishers wish to acknowledge the co-operation of the following in giving permission for the reproduction of many illustrations: *Proceedings of the Physical Society*, *Proceedings of the Institute of Radio Engineers*, *Journal of Applied Physics*, *Journal of Electronics*, *Annales de Radioelectricité*, *Proceedings of the Institution of Electrical Engineers*, Cambridge University Press and the Hughes Aircraft Co.

ERRATA

p. 21. Eq. (20) For $\frac{\partial H_x}{\partial x}$ read $\frac{\partial H_z}{\partial x}$.

p. 32. Eqs. (73) and (74). For $\left(\frac{q'_n r}{a}\right)$ read $\left(\frac{q'_m r}{a}\right)$.

p. 70. Eq. (82). For $\tan^2 \frac{I_0}{2}(I_0 + \sin I_0)$ read $\tan^2 \frac{\Phi_0}{2}(\Phi_0 + \sin \Phi_0)$

p. 101. Eq. (1). For $j\omega\mathbf{B}$ read $-j\omega\mathbf{B}$.

p. 101. Eq. (4). For $jk\omega\mathbf{E} + \mathbf{J}_1$, read $jk/c\mathbf{E} + \mu_0\mathbf{J}_1$.

p. 101. Eq. (8). Insert E_z after $(\beta^2 - k^2)$.

p. 102. Eq. (16). For $\beta_{1,2} = \pm jk$ read $\beta_{1,2} = \pm k$.

p. 107. Eq. (32). For $-j\eta$ read $-j\eta\omega I_0$.

p. 111. Eq. (45). For bsn $(\gamma_r b - \gamma_r c)$ read Bsn $(\gamma_r b - \gamma_r c)$.

p. 125. Eq. (104). For $-\cos Z_1$ read $\cos Z_1$.

p. 126. Delete minus signs in the matrix equations preceding Eq. (106).

p. 152. In Eq. (201) and in the first term of Eq. (203), for $(\omega - \gamma u_0)$ read $(\omega - \gamma u_{0q})$.

p. 167. Fig. 4. Interchange captions defining solid and dotted lines.

p. 172. Eq. (36). Invert second expression for W_n.

p. 210. Last line of page. For $(\alpha_2 M)_{\text{opt}}$ read $(S\alpha_1)M_{\text{opt}}$.

p. 294. Owing to a change of notation, late in the preparation of the book, no distinction is made between the D.C. and A.C. velocities. Denote A.C. velocities by $\tilde{u}_a$, $\tilde{u}_b$. Then, in Eqs. (6), (8), (10) and (12), for u_b, u_a read $\tilde{u}_b$, $\tilde{u}_a$. In Eqs. (7), (9) and (11) for u_a read $\tilde{u}_a$.

p. 341. Eq. (9). For W_c read W.

GENERAL INTRODUCTION

In this book my aim is to present a unified treatment of the small-signal behaviour of microwave valves. Here, the term microwave is not to be interpreted in any pedantic sense but has its broadest meaning and comprises the frequency range from roughly 1 kMc/s to the highest frequencies which can, at present, be generated as coherent radiation. This limit, in 1956, is somewhat in excess of 100 kMc/s. I exclude from the treatment valves such as triodes and tetrodes which depend on space-charge control grids. The small-signal theory of these devices was established by the end of the nineteen thirties and their future development is now a question of improved manufacturing technique. Treatments are given of all the devices which depend on velocity-modulation of an electron beam. These include klystrons, travelling-wave tubes, backward-wave oscillators and less well-known devices such as velocity-jump and space-jump amplifiers, scalloped-beam amplifiers, resistive-wall amplifiers and space-charge wave tubes. Magnetron oscillators are not discussed because their study takes us completely outside the field of small-signal phenomena and because considerable numbers of books already exist in which magnetron performance is treated in detail, although, one is forced to add, without the complete success one would like to see. The restriction to small-signal conditions should perhaps be explained. First, this condition is not too restrictive to be useful. For example, in klystrons, small-signal conditions obtain up to electronic efficiencies of over 40% and the output efficiency of a klystron working under these conditions at the lower end of our frequency range could well be over 35%. Secondly, the study of large-signal behaviour is becoming the prerogative of the computer working with high-speed machines. While I would not wish to deny the utility of the computational approach, I feel it is a matter for regret if we abandon the search for improved theories too easily. Computational programmes only give the answers to the questions asked. They do not suggest new questions, nor do they give an indication of where the inadequacies in our understanding lie. The computer is a good servant but a bad master. Therefore I hope that a restatement, re-examination and extension of existing small-signal theories may lead to further progress with large-signal theory. Lastly, small-signal theory is relevant to all the problems which one encounters in working at the upper limit of our frequency range. All valves for these frequencies except, perhaps, some magnetrons, are small-signal devices.

Most of this introductory chapter is devoted to a brief survey of the qualitative behaviour of the various types of valve mentioned above. Before starting this survey, I think it useful to give a very short history of the development of the theory of transit-time devices. In doing this I should like to make it clear that I am writing not as a scientific historian but as a working researcher who has developed along with the subject. Others, with an equal knowledge of the facts, might legitimately place the emphasis differently.

1.1. DEVELOPMENT OF TRANSIT-TIME THEORY

In the early development of valves or vacuum tubes, if you prefer it, the velocities of electrons in free-space under the influence of electrode potentials of a few hundred volts were sufficiently large to ensure that effects due to the time of transit between one electrode and another were negligible. Owing to the rapid development of broadcasting and short-wave radio communication, the operating frequency limit of transmitters and receivers was pushed up with the consequence that it became obvious that the valves of the period exerted a severe damping effect on the tuned r.f. circuits to which they were connected. These effects were partially due to lead inductances and stray capacitances, which could be reduced by improved constructional techniques, but, by the end of the nineteen-twenties, it was realized that effects due to the finite electron velocities were also important. The earliest fairly successful attempts at a theory of these effects are due to BENHAM,[1] closely followed by MÜLLER,[2] LLEWELLYN,[3] BAKKER and DE VRIES[4] and many others. These authors start with the consideration of a system of plane-parallel electrodes, infinite in lateral extent, so that the electrons move parallel to the z axis and they include only effects due to electrostatic fields. This approach is, of course, natural by virtue of the actual structures with which they wished to work. Llewellyn, who

[1] BENHAM; *Phil. Mag.*, 1928, **5**, 641; 1931, **11**, 457.
[2] MÜLLER; *Hockfrequenz u. Elektroakust*, 1933, **41**, 156.
[3] LLEWELLYN; *Proc I.R.E.*, 1933, **21**, 1532; B.S.T.J., 1935, **14**, 632.
[4] BAKKER and DE VRIES; *Physica*, 1934, **1**, 1045; 1935, **2**, 683.

carried the theory to its present form, uses electromagnetic theory to establish the relation

$$\dddot{Z} = \eta \frac{\mathbf{I}}{\epsilon_0} \tag{1}$$

where $\mathbf{I}$ is a function of t, but not of z. Equation (1) can then be integrated over the path of an electron to obtain the acceleration, velocity and position of the electron in terms of the instant of observation and the time of origin. The d.c. conditions yield a value for the transit time when no a.c. fields are present and the a.c. conditions can be calculated by perturbation of the d.c. conditions. More details are given by LLEWELLYN[5] and BECK[6]. This theory, systematically applied, yields a set of equations, known today as the Llewellyn electronic equations (Appendix 12), which give precise values for the a.c. currents, voltages and velocities at any plane in terms of the (known) values at an earlier plane. Slightly modified forms of the equations are due to BAKKER and DE VRIES,[7] which have the advantage that the transit angle functions are of modulus one.

The Llewellyn electronic equations are capable of solving the small-signal problems of grid-controlled valves. They do not apply to multi-velocity electron beams, except, as is fortunately the case in practice, when the velocity range is negligible by comparison with the mean velocity. Nor do they apply when electrons are given such large velocity swings that overtaking occurs, i.e., $\mathbf{I}$ in Eq. (1) has to be considered as a single-valued function of z and t. The equations could be elaborated to cover cylindrical diodes and triodes but the extension would be mathematically cumbersome and has not been done.

Meanwhile, electron devices which did not depend on space-charge control were worked on. The first of these was the magnetron, invented by Hull in 1921. The second was the Barkhausen-Kurz tube in which oscillations at high frequencies were generated in a cylindrical triode operated with positive grid and negative anode. The theory of these valves, at least in the structural forms in which they first appeared, is complicated and it is hardly surprising that only a rather incomplete picture of the details of their operation was obtained. A book by GROOS[8] may be taken as a good

[5] LLEWELLYN; *Electron Inertia Effects*, Cambridge University Press, 1941.
[6] BECK; *Thermionic Valves*, Cambridge University Press, 1953, Section 7.4.
[7] BAKKER and DE VRIES; *loc. cit.*
[8] GROOS; *Theorie und Technik der Dezimeterwellen*, S. Hirzel, Leipzig, 1938.

account of the state of knowledge in this field in the middle and late thirties.

The break-through really began with the invention by the HEILS'[9] of the generator which bears their name. This device is a genuine velocity-modulation tube but in its original form did not use a cavity resonator. The Heils' paper did not give much in the way of a theory of the device, but work was going on at the same time in several American laboratories and resulted in the almost simultaneous publication of papers describing the klystron (VARIAN and VARIAN[10]), the velocity-modulated tubes of HAHN and METCALF[11] and the inductive output amplifier of HAEFF.[12] The theory of the klystron was treated by ballistic methods by WEBSTER[13] and the theory which we shall use and develop very extensively in this book was given by HAHN[14] and RAMO.[14]

During the war klystrons, both of the straight-through and reflex type, were extensively developed in all the combatant countries. Large numbers of theoretical studies were made, mainly based on the extension and improvement of the Webster theory. Almost all workers, including myself, were relatively insensitive to the space-charge wave theory of Hahn and Ramo. There were probably several reasons for this, among which are the following: first, the treatment given by Hahn was formidable in the extreme, it included relativistic effects and was very general in nature whereas Webster's treatment was very simple and his physical model was easy to understand. Secondly, the forms of valve developed were similar to those of the Varian–Webster–Hansen group and differed greatly from those of Hahn and Metcalf, so that there was a tendency to regard Webster's theory as the only theory which applied to this design of valve. Thirdly, the conditions of excitation of the electron beam are not made very clear in the Hahn theory, while gap theory was very extensively developed and easily taken into the ballistic theory. Lastly, the Webster theory is valid for electron beams which are short in comparison with one quarter space-charge wavelength. This condition was obeyed for all the wartime valves, which used electrostatic focusing and short electron beams. The Webster theory therefore agreed with measurements at least well enough to serve as a valuable aid to design. Several books and major

[9] HEIL and HEIL; *Z. Phys.*, 1935, **95**, 752.
[10] VARIAN and VARIAN; *J. Appl. Phys.*, 1939, **10**, 321.
[11] HAHN and METCALF; *Proc. I.R.E.*, 1939, **27**, 106.
[12] HAEFF; *Electronics*, February 1939, 30.
[13] WEBSTER; *J. Appl. Phys.*, 1939, **10**, 501.
[14] HAHN; *Gen. Elect. Rev.*, 1939, **42**, 258; 497. RAMO; *Phys. Rev.*, 1939, **56**, 276.

articles[15-18] describe the state of knowledge at the end of the war and none makes other than cursory mention of the Hahn–Ramo theory. However, towards the end of the war KOMPFNER[19] invented the travelling-wave tube and PIERCE[20] gave an initial theory which has been widely accepted. This theory is fundamentally a ballistic theory and has to be supplemented by space-charge wave theory when the beam current exceeds very moderate values. Moreover, the practical work which went into the design of long, magnetically focused electron beams was applied to high-gain high-powered klystron amplifiers. These valves no longer behaved according to Webster's theory unless extensive approximate corrections were introduced. It was gradually realised that these corrections simply amounted to the insertion of results of space-charge wave theory and the present state of affairs may be expressed as a situation in which gap theory, developed on ballistic lines or on the Llewellyn electronic equations, is wedded to space-charge wave theory in an acceptable way. This book is an attempt to systematize the theory of several different types of valve along these lines.

To conclude this historical sketch, it should be pointed out that newer tubes, such as velocity-jump amplifiers and space-jump amplifiers, have been invented which depend entirely on space-charge wave ideas for their functioning.

We now describe the physical principles of some of the valve types mentioned above.

1.2. THE KLYSTRON

Klystrons have been described in a great deal of detail in the references cited. A two-cavity klystron amplifier consists of an electron beam which traverses an input resonant cavity (buncher), a space free of a.c. fields (drift space) and an output cavity (catcher). The beam is finally collected on a heat-dissipating electrode (collector). In ballistic terminology the operation of the device is as follows: suppose that an a.c. voltage is imposed on the terminals

---

[15] HARRISON; *Klystron Tubes*, McGraw-Hill, 1947.
[16] HAMILTON, KUPER and KNIPP; *Klystrons and Microwave Triodes*. M.I.T. Series V.7, McGraw-Hill, 1948.
[17] BECK; *Velocity Modulated Thermionic Tubes*, Cambridge University Press, 1948.
[18] PIERCE and SHEPHERD; *Bell Syst. Tech. J.*, 1947, **26**, 460.
[19] KOMPFNER; *Proc. I.R.E.*, 1947, **35**, 124.
[20] PIERCE; *Proc. I.R.E.*, 1947, **35**, 111.

B

of the buncher gap, electrons passing the gap in one half-cycle are accelerated, those in the other decelerated. The emergent beam is said to be velocity modulated. In the drift tube, accelerated electrons catch up with those decelerated in the preceding half-cycle so that there is an increase in electron density at the position in space of a reference electron which passed the gap centre at the instant when the field changed from negative (decelerating) to positive. As the beam progresses down the drift tube the local increase in density round the reference electron becomes more pronounced and a bunch is formed. When the bunch passes the catcher gap it induces an opposing electric field in the catcher resonator which slows all the electrons in the bunch, thereby converting battery energy into a.c. energy. The tighter the bunch and the fewer electrons left in unfavourable phases, the more efficient the energy conversion becomes.

This picture, which is that of the simplest Webster theory, is incomplete. As the beam becomes bunched in the drift space, retarding forces due to the repulsion forces between the electrons are set up. Immediately the beam is disturbed from its uniform state the repulsion forces start to grow and to reduce the change in velocity due to the modulation process. The new situation has to be described by space-charge wave theory. If we picture an electron beam and imagine that all the electrons are given the same initial a.c. velocity at a specified plane, electromagnetic theory can be used to show that space-charge waves are set up on the beam, in much the same way that waves are set up on a dielectric rod. We may thus picture the beam as a conductor on which the waves propagate. The space-charge waves arise in pairs, one wave of each pair having a phase velocity slightly greater than the electron velocity, the other slightly less. The difference depends on the plasma frequency of the electron beam and on the geometry of the system. The plasma frequency is defined through

$$\omega_p{}^2 = \frac{\eta I_0}{\epsilon_0 u_0 \Sigma} \tag{2}$$

and the propagation constants of the space-charge waves are

$$\gamma_1 = \frac{\omega + F\omega_p}{u_0}, \qquad \gamma_2 = \frac{\omega - F\omega_p}{u_0} \tag{3}$$

where F is the factor depending on the geometry. The actual determination of F is detailed in Chapter 4. As we shall see, practical systems for exciting space-charge waves on beams require that the initial conditions be fulfilled by infinite series of pairs of space-charge waves, each pair with a different value of F, but for the moment we consider a single pair, for simplicity. Then, the initial condition in our klystron is that the beam is suddenly given an initial velocity modulation at the catcher gap centre while the a.c. beam current is zero at the same plane. The explicit relations giving the travelling wave forms of the a.c. velocity and the a.c. current waves are then written down and superposed to give the initial conditions $u_1 = u_{10}$, $i_1 = 0$ at $z = 0$. This gives standing wave expressions for a.c. velocity and current of the form

$$u_1 = u_{10} \cos \frac{F\omega_p}{u_0} z \exp j\left(\omega t - \frac{\omega z}{u_0}\right) \tag{4}$$

$$i_1 = j\frac{I_0 u_{10}}{u_0} \cdot \frac{\omega}{F\omega_p} \sin \frac{F\omega_p}{u_0} z \exp j\left(\omega t - \frac{\omega z}{u_0}\right) \tag{5}$$

Equation (5) allows us to determine i_1 at any distance from the buncher and therefore to calculate the voltage and power induced into a catcher at such a point. In particular i_1 as a function of z reaches the maximum value at $\sin (F\omega_p/u_0)z = 1$.

$$z = \frac{\pi}{2} \cdot \frac{u_0}{F\omega_p} \tag{6}$$

The space-charge wavelength is $2\pi u_0/F\omega_p$, so Eq. (6) tells us that the current reaches its first maximum at one-quarter space-charge wavelength distance from the buncher gap, and there is nothing to be gained by making z greater than this value. This is directly contrary to simple ballistic theory which states that transconductance varies linearly with z. Moreover, at the plane of maximum current the a.c. velocity $u_1 = 0$, so that all the electrons instantaneously have their original d.c. velocity u_0. This fact actually greatly simplifies the detailed calculation of the output power.

It should be noted that the present theory tells us nothing about the maximum value which can be given to u_{10}, which we require to know before we can calculate the maximum power output. This is a consequence of the fact that the theory is linearized or small-signal. The ballistic theory, however, does give an answer to this question and one of our problems is how to make best use of these answers to supplement space-charge wave theory.

1.3. THE TRAVELLING-WAVE AMPLIFIER

Here again the physics of the device has been thoroughly described elsewhere[21-23] and we can be brief. The original, and most common form today is that in which a magnetically focused beam traverses a long thin helix (Fig. 1). The helix is coupled at input and output to wave guides, using one of a large variety of methods for effecting an impedance transformation. The fact that the wave

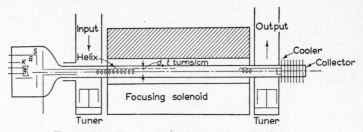

FIG. 1. Travelling-wave amplifier—schematic diagram.

travels $\pi\, dt$ cm along the helix to progress 1 cm along the axis reduces the axial phase velocity to the electron velocity. When this is the case, the electrons travel approximately in-phase with the wave so that electrons which reach the beginning of the helix when the field is accelerating tend to catch up with electrons which reached the beginning of the helix at earlier times when the field was decelerating. This is similar to the klystron case except that in the T.W.A. the electrons bunch in a weak field which acts for a long time instead of being velocity-modulated by a strong field acting only for a short time. Consider now the situation when the beam exhibits some bunching or, in other words, when the r.f. current wave has started to build up. The phase of the bunches is such that their centres move with the planes where the fields change from negative to positive. Now, if the beam and field are not precisely in synchronism, the bunches will either move forward through the field or backward. If they move forward they will move into a decelerating field which will extract energy from all the electrons in the bunch, and since this number is greater than the average electron density a net loss of power from the beam and gain by the circuit results. The effect of space-charge forces is again to reduce the velocities

[21] PIERCE; *Traveling-Wave Tubes*, Van Nostrand, 1950.
[22] KOMPFNER; *Rep. Progr. Phys.*, 1952, **15**, 275.
[23] BECK; *Thermionic Valves*, Cambridge University Press, 1953.

acquired under the influence of the circuit field and it turns out that the condition for maximum gain is when the circuit wave has a phase velocity equal to the velocity of the slow space-charge wave, which we see from Eq. (3) is somewhat less than the electron velocity, as it should be from our physical reasoning.

Here again, space-charge wave theory corrects and extends ballistic theory and has to be used to obtain agreement between theory and practice unless the beam currents are so small that the space-charge wavelength is much greater than the circuit length. It is immediately obvious that this is more stringent than the equivalent klystron condition as the circuit is much longer.

1.4. THE VELOCITY-JUMP AMPLIFIER

This tube depends for its operation on the behaviour of space-charge waves and the fact, which is proved later, that if we pass a velocity modulated electron beam through a gap across which there is a d.c. field but no a.c. field, the a.c. velocities before and after the gap are related by

$$\frac{u_2}{u_1} = \sqrt{\frac{V_1}{V_2}} \tag{7}$$

Thus, if $V_1 > V_2$ the a.c. velocity is increased by the square root of the voltage ratio. The velocity jump amplifier was invented by

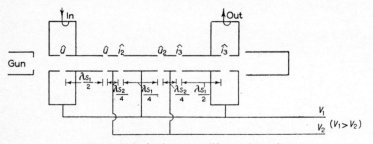

FIG. 2. Velocity-jump amplifier—schematic.

TIEN, FIELD and WATKINS[24],[25]. A possible form of the device is shown in Fig. 2. The operation is as follows: the beam is velocity modulated in a cavity resonator at a high potential V_1. Space-

[24] TIEN, FIELD and WATKINS; *Proc. I.R.E.*, 1951, **39**, 194.
[25] TIEN and FIELD; *Proc. I.R.E.*, 1952, **40**, 688.

charge waves are set up in the drift tube. The beam is allowed to drift for one half space-charge wavelength so that it passes through the stage of full current modulation back to full velocity modulation once more, as can be seen from Eqs. (4) and (5). At this point is located a d.c. velocity jump in the downward direction so that in the second drift tube bunching takes place according to Eq. (5) with the initial velocity $u_{10}\sqrt{(V_1/V_2)}$. The beam drifts one quarter wavelength to reach a current maximum and is there jumped back to the original velocity. It can be shown that the a.c. current is unaltered. The beam next drifts one quarter-wavelength at potential V_1, so that it is fully velocity modulated at the next gap. After this gap the a.c. velocity is $u_{10}(V_1/V_2)$ and the beam drifts another quarter wavelength to be fully current-modulated at a greater amplitude. Finally, it is stepped up to the full velocity and allowed to drift for a half wavelength before traversing the output gap. In the construction described the initial and final half-wave drift tubes are essentially matching devices which allow one to operate with both sides of the modulation gaps at the same, high d.c. potential. This is desirable from several viewpoints.

Clearly, the gain of the amplifier is higher than the gain of a klystron of the same length by a factor which depends on V_1/V_2. The actual increase is $20 \log_{10} (V_1/V_2)^{3/2}(F_1/F_2)$ dB, and this can be quite a large amount. Unluckily, the inclusion of higher-order waves makes the gain less attractive and this, together with the practical disadvantage that large voltage jumps upset the magnetic focusing, have prevented the device from being used.

1.5. THE SPACE-JUMP AMPLIFIER

This amplifier seems to have been independently invented by several workers, including BIRDSALL and WHINNERY[26] and the author[27]. It depends on the observation that the last tube improves on the klystron even if $V_1 = V_2$ when F_1 is made greater than F_2. These quantities, as has already been said, depend on the geometry and, in particular, on the ratio of beam diameter to the diameter of the surrounding tunnel. A detailed examination of the problem shows that we have to expand the tunnel suddenly at the plane of a current maximum. The current has to be continuous at the discontinuity in the wall and this requirement is equivalent to changing

[26] BIRDSALL and WHINNERY; *J. Appl. Phys.*, 1953, **24**, 314.
[27] BECK; *Brit. Pat.*, 743593.

the velocity to $u_1 \cdot (F_2/F_1)$. If the large diameter is several times the beam diameter $F_2 \to 1$. F_1 can be made quite small so that useful gains result.

This device is very simple and one can envisage constructions

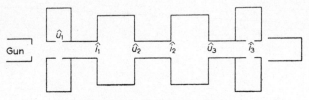

FIG. 3. Space-jump amplifier—schematic.

suitable for use at high frequencies. It is not subject to any disturbance in the beam focusing, but, once more, the effect of higher order modes is to render it less attractive. Experimental work[28] has shown that practical results can be obtained.

1.6. SCALLOPED-BEAM AMPLIFICATION

MIHRAN[29] has described an even simpler version of the above scheme. It is illustrated in Fig. 4. An electron beam is injected from a shielded electron beam into a magnetic field. The conditions at entry are purposely chosen to be completely different

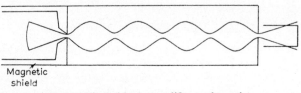

Magnetic shield

FIG. 4. Rippled-beam amplifier—schematic.

from the Brillouin condition which gives uniform, cylindrical flow, so that the beam shows a very large ratio of maximum to minimum diameter, or, in other words, well-marked scallops. The variation in d.c. electron density along the beam implies that ω_p is a function of the space co-ordinates so that the effective plasma wavelength

[28] BIRDSALL; *Proc. I.R.E.*, 1954, **42**, 1628.
[29] MIHRAN; I.R.E., P.G.E.D., Ed-3, 1956, 32.

varies as it did in 1.5. The magnetic field is adjusted until the scallops appear in the correct positions to obtain amplification.

1.7. RESTIVE-WALL AMPLIFIERS

The simplest type of resistive-wall amplifier can be visualized as a two-cavity klystron in which the internal wall of the drift tube is given a high surface resistivity. A tube working in this way has been described by BIRDSALL, BREWER and HAEFF[30]. The physical principle involved is that both the slow and the fast space-charge waves lose power to the resistive walls. The fast wave loses power in the ordinary way, by decreasing in amplitude. The slow wave carries a negative power and so to lose power its amplitude has to increase. If buncher and catcher are far enough apart, the catcher receives only a slow wave of large amplitude which is capable of inducing a large current in the catcher.

1.8. DOUBLE STREAM SPACE-CHARGE AMPLIFIERS

This type of amplifier consists, in its simplest form, of two cavities, both traversed by two electron beams of slightly different velocities, as sketched in Fig. 5, where we show a version in which an outer,

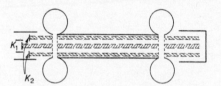

FIG. 5. Two-beam space-charge wave amplifier—schematic.

annular beam interacts with an inner, solid beam. Amplification of this sort was simultaneously discovered by several workers including HAEFF[31], NERGAARD[32] and PIERCE and HEBENSTREIT[33]. The coupling between the beams is expressed by Poisson's equation

$$\nabla^2 V = -\rho/\epsilon_0 \qquad (8)$$

since the space-charge density ρ is a scalar quantity, and is the

[30] BIRDSALL, BREWER and HAEFF; *Proc. I.R.E.*, 1953, **41**, 865.
[31] HAEFF; *Proc. I.R.E.*, 1949, **37**, 4.
[32] NERGAARD; *R.C.A. Rev.*, 1948, **9**, 585.
[33] PIERCE and HEBENSTREIT; *Bell Syst. Tech. J.*, 1949, **28**, 33.

sum of the densities of the two beams at any point. Analysis shows that the condition for amplification is that the slow space-charge wave on the faster beam should have nearly the same phase velocity as the fast space-charge wave on the slow beam.

Haeff and Pierce and Hebenstreit have described working experimental tubes with high values of gain. However, the tubes were very noisy and gave rather low outputs and efficiencies. Presumably for these reasons, little further development work has been carried out in spite of the structural simplicity of the tubes.

Another version of this device was also described by Haeff. Here, a cylindrical electron beam of high-current density was confined by a magnetic field so that the axial electrons had a considerably lower axial velocity than those on the beam periphery. This constituted one species of multi-velocity flow. Amplification was observed and was thought to be a consequence of the mechanism discussed for the two-beam case. More careful theoretical studies[34] indicate that the multi-velocity beam should not operate in this way and later experiments[35] suggest that the observed gain may have been due to feedback by secondary electrons returning from the collector.

1.9. BACKWARD-WAVE OSCILLATORS

We now come to a device which ranks in practical importance immediately after the klystron and the T.W.A. This is the backward-wave oscillator which is characterized by extremely broadband electronic tuning; that is, the oscillation frequency depends on the electron velocity and can be varied over a wide range as much as one octave or more. Two variants exist. In the first the magnetic field is along the electron beam and is used for focusing only. In the second, usually called a "carcinotron," the beam moves in crossed electric and magnetic fields, as in a magnetron. In this case the electron velocity depends on the magnetic field and the details of the behaviour are different but the major phenomena are the same.

The story of the invention of this valve is in doubt, but it is thought that Kompfner first suggested at least the B.W.O. The French C.S.F. laboratories were first to publish, and they described the "carcinotron M"[36] in 1952. In the summer of the same year

---

[34] KENT; *J. Appl. Phys.*, 1954, **25**, 32.
[35] BEAM; *Proc. I.R.E.*, 1955, **43**, 454.
[36] GUENARD, DOEHLER, EPSZTEIN and WARNECKE, *C. R. Acad. Sci., Paris*, 1952, **235**, 236.

Kompfner, who had recently left England to join the staff of the Bell Telephone Laboratories, described how an existing type of millimetre-wave T.W.A. (the Millman tube)[37] could be operated as a B.W.O. The valve has since been the subject of intensive research, but this work is dealt with later in the book. Here we only attempt to give a qualitative understanding of the operation.

First, however, it is convenient to summarize the different variants of the T.W.A. and B.W.O. These are shown in Fig. 6. Fig. 6(a) shows the conventional T.W.A. with magnetic focusing field along the beam. Fig. 6(b) shows the analogous B.W.O. Here, the helix

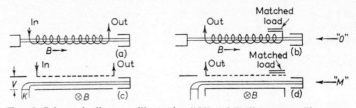

FIG. 6. Schematic diagrams illustrating "O" and "M" type travelling-wave amplifiers and backward-wave oscillators.

is terminated at the collector end by a non-reflecting load. The power output is taken from the end of the helix nearer the gun. Fig. 6(c) shows the crossed field T.W.A. or magnetron amplifier. Fig. 6(d) shows the analogous B.W.O. in which once more the circuit is terminated in a matched load, the power being taken out at the gun end. In French, the top two are termed "O" devices, i.e., Tube à propagation d'ondes "O" and "carcinotron O" while the lower two are T.P.O. "M" and "carcinotron M". We shall use the following terminology which is the normal Anglo-American one: travelling-wave amplifier 6(a), backward-wave oscillator 6(b), magnetron amplifier 6(c), carcinotron 6(d).

We now discuss the operation of the forward and backward-wave valves. We have already seen that if the electron velocity is made nearly equal to the circuit phase-velocity, we obtain amplification in a helix type T.W.A. Closer analysis shows that to obtain such amplification it is necessary that the circuit be of such a configuration that the phase velocity is in the same direction as the group velocity† which, in low attenuation circuits, is the velocity

---

† The detailed physics of the interaction is discussed fully, when we come to the mathematical theory. This is because the discussion requires a knowledge of the behaviour of the circuit space-harmonics. These are dealt with in Chapter 3.

[37] MILLMAN; Proc. I.R.E., 1951, 39, 1035.

of energy propagation. Now, we decide the direction of the group velocity by the way we excite the circuit, for example in Fig. 6(a), by connecting a generator to the input we ensure that the energy travels to the right and the group velocity is in that direction. To obtain travelling-wave amplification the phase velocity and the electron velocity must be in the same direction. We normally call this situation one in which both phase and group velocity are positive.

Not all circuits have the property that both velocities are positive and even very simple ones can have the inverse property, that the phase velocity and group velocity are in opposite directions. In ordinary radio engineering such circuits are those that introduce a phase lag. The low-pass filter Fig. 7(a) has phase and group velocities positive while in the high-pass filter Fig. 7(b) they are

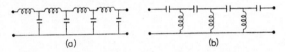

(a)   (b)

FIG. 7. Low-pass and high-pass filter configurations.

of opposite sign. On the other hand, an electron beam can still interact strongly with such a circuit if the electron velocity is nearly equal to, and is in the same direction as, the phase velocity. Now, in the backward-wave devices we make use of this type of inter-action. We assume that due to noise a small r.f. voltage is generated across the load. This voltage propagates towards the gun, yet the phase velocity is in the opposite direction, that of the electron flow, so that the noise voltage is amplified. The amplified noise builds up until the non-linearities of the system prevent further growth and a stable oscillation results. The frequency determining mech-anism is simply the condition that the circuit velocity $\doteqdot$ electron velocity and if the electron velocity is altered, the frequency of oscillation changes until this condition is restored. If we can design the circuit so that the phase velocity is a slowly changing function of frequency, relatively small changes of beam voltage will cause large alterations in frequency. In some practical situations this is desirable, in others not. One of the problems of B.W.O.s is to adjust the circuit parameters so as to obtain optimum operating characteristics for the particular purpose in hand.

The reader will have realized that there is a major electronic difference between the B.W.O. and the T.W.A. In the B.W.O. the beam encounters strong r.f. fields at entry to the circuit, while these decay cosinusoidally along it. Bunching and space-charge debunching are therefore important even close to the start of the circuit, but the r.f. field decreases as the r.f. beam current increases. In the T.W.A., on the other hand, the r.f. beam current and the r.f. field both increase in the left to right direction and both are large at the output. For this reason the large signal behaviour of the B.W.O. is somewhat simpler than that of the T.W.A.

1.10. THE CASCADE BACKWARD-WAVE AMPLIFIER

We conclude this chapter by noting that there are large numbers of possibilities for the construction of other tubes, by combining devices of the types described, in one envelope, along a single beam. As an example we use the Cascade B-W amplifier described by CURRIE and WHINNERY.[38] A schematic of this valve is shown in Fig. 8. It depends on the fact that a backward-wave oscillator

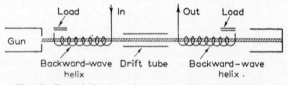

FIG. 8. Cascade backward-wave amplifiers—schematic.

behaves as a regenerative amplifier for d.c. beam currents below the value necessary to start a stable oscillation. Study of the single circuit device indicates that, to obtain significant gain, it is necessary to work close to the starting-current and that it is therefore difficult to ensure stability. In the double circuit useful gains are obtained for currents which are only about half the starting current. Two other advantages are that the two circuits are properly matched and it is possible to design them so as to obtain a constant gain over a wide band. Finally, the break between the circuits ensures that there is no direct coupling between input and output.

The frequency of the amplifier is adjusted by altering the d.c. beam voltage so that this valve can be characterized as a voltage tuneable, narrow-band high-gain amplifier.

---

[38] CURRIE and WHINNERY; *Proc. I.R.E.*, 1955, **43**, 1617.

MAXWELL'S EQUATIONS AND WAVE EQUATIONS

2.1. MAXWELL'S EQUATIONS AND OTHER BASIC LAWS

In this chapter we propose to give a highly condensed account of Maxwellian electromagnetic theory, especially as it is applied to the study of wave propagation along waveguides. Conventional waveguides exhibit phase velocities greater than the velocity of light or guide wavelengths longer than the free-space wavelength. In slow-wave structures the phase velocity is less than c, so that interaction can be obtained with electron beams moving with practical velocities, i.e., velocities corresponding to energies of less than 500 keV. Clearly, the guide wavelength in these cases is less than the free-space wavelength and we shall find that the slow-wave structures actually used are many wavelengths long. We propose mainly to bring out the differences and similarities of the two types of propagation and refer the reader to the works mentioned in the bibliography for more detailed accounts.

The general vector forms of Maxwell's equations are

$$\operatorname{div} \mathbf{D} = \rho, \qquad \operatorname{curl} \mathbf{E} = -\frac{\partial \mathbf{B}}{\partial t}$$

$$\operatorname{div} \mathbf{B} = 0, \qquad \operatorname{curl} \mathbf{H} = \mathbf{J} + \frac{\partial \mathbf{D}}{\partial t} \qquad (1)$$

Here, $\qquad \mathbf{D} = \epsilon \mathbf{E}, \quad \mathbf{B} = \mu \mathbf{H}, \quad \mathbf{J} = \sigma \mathbf{E}$

where ϵ = permittivity
μ = permeability
σ = conductivity.

For the solution of problems in electron dynamics we need to add the two following relations, the Lorentz force law

$$\mathbf{F} = -e[\mathbf{E} + (\mathbf{V} \times \mathbf{B})] \qquad (2)$$

and the equation of continuity, or conservation of electric charge

$$\nabla \cdot \mathbf{J} + \frac{\partial \rho}{\partial t} = 0 \tag{3}$$

The divergence relations of Eq. (1) follow from Eq. (3) but it is usual to state them explicitly.

Finally, we shall often need to obtain expressions for the power flow associated with electromagnetic waves. This is done by use of the Poynting vector

$$\mathbf{S} = \mathbf{E} \times \mathbf{H}$$

S gives the energy density associated with the wave so that the total flow of energy is given by forming the surface integral $\int_s (\mathbf{E} \times \mathbf{H})_n \, ds$. The derivation of this result is as follows. From (1) we can form

$$\mathbf{H} \operatorname{curl} \mathbf{E} - \mathbf{E} \operatorname{curl} \mathbf{H} = \operatorname{div} (\mathbf{E} \times \mathbf{H})$$

therefore $\quad \operatorname{div} (\mathbf{E} \times \mathbf{H}) = -\mathbf{E} \cdot \mathbf{J} - \mu \mathbf{H} \cdot \dfrac{\partial \mathbf{H}}{\partial t} - \epsilon \mathbf{E} \cdot \dfrac{\partial \mathbf{E}}{\partial t} \tag{4}$

We integrate (4) over a specified volume V bounded by surface s and obtain

$$\int_s (\mathbf{E} \times \mathbf{H})_n \, ds = \int_v \mathbf{E} \cdot \mathbf{J} \, dV - \frac{\partial}{\partial t} \int_v (\tfrac{1}{2}\epsilon E^2 + \tfrac{1}{2}\mu H^2) \, dV \tag{5}$$

In (5) the first term of the R.H.S. is the work performed in one second by the currents impressed on the system, the second term being the total stored energy in the volume, $\frac{1}{2}\epsilon E^2$ in the electric field and $\frac{1}{2}\mu H^2$ in the magnetic field. These quantities are equal. When the fields are represented by complex quantities we have to use the following definition

$$\mathbf{S} = \tfrac{1}{2}\mathbf{E} \times \mathbf{H}^* \tag{6}$$

where the star notation denotes the complex conjugate of **H**.

In our work we are always concerned with fields which have a periodic time variation, $\mathbf{E} = Ee^{j\omega t}$, $\mathbf{H} = He^{j\omega t}$. Thus, the operator $\partial/\partial t$ simply means "multiply by $j\omega$" and Eqs. (1) become

$$\operatorname{curl} \mathbf{E} = -j\mu\omega\mathbf{H}, \qquad \operatorname{curl} \mathbf{H} = \mathbf{J} + j\omega\epsilon\mathbf{E} \tag{7}$$

This procedure involves no loss in generality, because any time dependence whatsoever can be expressed as a Fourier series of exponential terms. Moreover, we shall always be concerned with waves propagating along the axis of co-ordinates which we take as the z axis. The appropriate wave functions are

$$\exp{(j\omega t - \Gamma_n z)} \tag{8}$$

where Γ_n is the propagation constant.

Now
$$\Gamma_n = \alpha_n + j\beta_n \tag{9}$$

α_n = attenuation constant for the nth mode
$\beta_n = \omega/v_{pn}$ = phase constant.

Using (8) a positive value of α means an attenuated wave, a negative value an amplified wave. In general, for all the cases in which we are interested $\beta \gg \alpha$ and $\Gamma \doteq j\beta$. We note that, by definition, the phase changes by 2π for each wavelength moved along the wave, thus $\beta = 2\pi/\lambda_g$ radians/unit length, while α is unlikely to have such a large value. With wave functions of the form (8) $\partial/\partial z = -\Gamma_n \doteq -j\beta_n$.

2.2   EXPLICIT FORMS FOR RECTANGULAR AND CYLINDRICAL CO-ORDINATE SYSTEMS

We now write down the explicit forms of the Maxwell equations.

2.2.1.   Rectangular co-ordinates (x, y, z)

$$\left.\begin{aligned}
\frac{\partial E_z}{\partial y} - \frac{\partial E_y}{\partial z} &= -j\mu\omega H_x \\
\frac{\partial E_x}{\partial z} - \frac{\partial E_z}{\partial x} &= -j\mu\omega H_y \\
\frac{\partial E_y}{\partial x} - \frac{\partial E_x}{\partial y} &= -j\mu\omega H_z
\end{aligned}\right\} \tag{10}$$

$$\left.\begin{aligned}
\frac{\partial H_z}{\partial y} - \frac{\partial H_y}{\partial z} &= j\omega\epsilon E_x + i_x \\
\frac{\partial H_x}{\partial z} - \frac{\partial H_z}{\partial x} &= j\omega\epsilon E_y + i_y \\
\frac{\partial H_y}{\partial x} - \frac{\partial H_x}{\partial y} &= j\omega\epsilon E_z + i_z
\end{aligned}\right\} \tag{11}$$

$$\frac{\partial B_x}{\partial x} + \frac{\partial B_y}{\partial y} + \frac{\partial B_z}{\partial z} = 0 \tag{12}$$

$$\frac{\partial D_x}{\partial x} + \frac{\partial D_y}{\partial y} + \frac{\partial D_z}{\partial z} = \rho \tag{13}$$

2.2.2. Cylindrical polar co-ordinates (r, θ, z)

$$\left.\begin{aligned}
\frac{1}{r}\frac{\partial E_z}{\partial \theta} - \frac{\partial E_\theta}{\partial z} &= -j\mu\omega H_r \\[2mm]
\frac{\partial E_r}{\partial z} - \frac{\partial E_z}{\partial r} &= -j\mu\omega H_\theta \\[2mm]
\frac{1}{r}\frac{\partial}{\partial r}(rE_\theta) - \frac{1}{r}\frac{\partial E_r}{\partial \theta} &= -j\mu\omega H_z
\end{aligned}\right\} \tag{14}$$

$$\left.\begin{aligned}
\frac{1}{r}\frac{\partial H_z}{\partial \theta} - \frac{\partial H_\theta}{\partial z} &= j\omega\epsilon E_r + i_r \\[2mm]
\frac{\partial H_r}{\partial z} - \frac{\partial H_z}{\partial r} &= j\omega\epsilon E_\theta + i_\theta \\[2mm]
\frac{1}{r}\frac{\partial}{\partial r}(rH_\theta) - \frac{1}{r}\frac{\partial H_r}{\partial \theta} &= j\omega\epsilon E_z + i_z
\end{aligned}\right\} \tag{15}$$

$$\frac{1}{r}\frac{\partial}{\partial r}(rB_r) - \frac{1}{r}\frac{\partial B_\theta}{\partial \theta} + \frac{\partial B_z}{\partial z} = 0 \tag{16}$$

$$\frac{1}{r}\frac{\partial}{\partial r}(rD_r) - \frac{1}{r}\frac{\partial D_\theta}{\partial \theta} + \frac{\partial D}{\partial z} = \rho \tag{17}$$

2.3. TYPES OF WAVE

Three general types of wave may be encountered. These are:

(1) Transverse-electromagnetic (TEM) waves, in which neither **E** nor **H** has longitudinal components.

(2) Transverse electric (TE) waves, in which only **H** has longitudinal components.

(3) Transverse-magnetic (TM) waves, in which only **E** has longitudinal components.

All possible solutions of Maxwell's equations can be formed by linear combinations of elementary solutions of these three types and such combinations are often necessary to satisfy boundary conditions, even for a single mode. TEM waves cannot exist in hollow pipes but comprise the most important solutions in coaxial cables, two-conductor problems, etc. The TE waves and TM waves are more interesting in our problems and we now consider the separation into TE and TM waves.

2.3.1.   TE and TM waves in a non-conducting region

For TE waves we put $E_z = 0$ and $\sigma = 0$, to obtain

$$\frac{\partial E_y}{\partial z} = j\mu\omega H_x, \qquad \frac{\partial E_x}{\partial z} = -j\mu\omega H_y \tag{18}$$

$$\frac{\partial E_y}{\partial x} - \frac{\partial E_x}{\partial y} = -j\mu\omega H_z \tag{19}$$

$$\frac{\partial H_z}{\partial y} - \frac{\partial H_y}{\partial z} = j\epsilon\omega E_x, \qquad \frac{\partial H_x}{\partial z} - \frac{\partial H_x}{\partial x} = j\epsilon\omega E_y \tag{20}$$

$$\frac{\partial H_y}{\partial x} - \frac{\partial H_x}{\partial y} = 0 \tag{21}$$

$$\frac{\partial E_x}{\partial x} + \frac{\partial E_y}{\partial y} = 0 \tag{22}$$

$$\frac{\partial H_x}{\partial x} + \frac{\partial H_y}{\partial y} + \frac{\partial H_z}{\partial z} = 0 \tag{23}$$

We now restrict ourselves to plane waves (at any instant of time all points in a plane oscillate in the same phase) of the form (8). Equation (18) then gives

$$-\Gamma E_y = j\mu\omega H_x, \qquad \Gamma E_x = j\mu\omega H_y \tag{24}$$

The wave impedance is defined as

$$Z_H = \frac{E_x}{H_y} = \frac{j\mu\omega}{\Gamma} \tag{25}$$

We now use (24) in (20) to obtain

$$\left.\begin{aligned}
\frac{\partial H_z}{\partial y} &= -\left(\frac{\Gamma^2 + \omega^2\epsilon\mu}{\Gamma}\right)H_y \\
\frac{\partial H_z}{\partial x} &= -\left(\frac{\Gamma^2 + \omega^2\epsilon\mu}{\Gamma}\right)H_x
\end{aligned}\right\} \tag{26}$$

Using (24) with (19) or (23)

$$\frac{\partial H_x}{\partial x} + \frac{\partial H_y}{\partial y} - \Gamma H_z = 0$$

and putting in results from (26)

$$\frac{\partial^2 H_z}{\partial x^2} + \frac{\partial^2 H_z}{\partial y^2} + (\Gamma^2 + \omega^2\epsilon\mu)H_z = 0 \tag{27}$$

C

To solve a problem Eq. (27) has to be solved using the specified boundary conditions, H_x and H_y are determined from (26) and E_x and E_y from (24). Put in another way, if we assume a solution containing one arbitrary constant for H_z, all the remaining field quantities can be expressed in terms of the same arbitrary constant.

If we follow exactly the same procedure in the cylindrical case we obtain

$$\left.\begin{aligned}
\frac{\partial H_z}{\partial r} &= -\left(\frac{\Gamma^2 + \omega^2 \epsilon \mu}{\Gamma}\right) H_r \\
\frac{1}{r}\frac{\partial H_z}{\partial \theta} &= -\left(\frac{\Gamma^2 + \omega^2 \epsilon \mu}{\Gamma}\right) H_\theta
\end{aligned}\right\} \tag{28}$$

$$\begin{aligned}
E_\theta &= -\frac{j\mu\omega H_r}{\Gamma} \\
E_r &= \frac{j\mu\omega H_\theta}{\Gamma}
\end{aligned} \tag{29}$$

with the wave equation

$$\frac{\partial^2 H_z}{\partial r^2} + \frac{1}{r}\frac{\partial H_z}{\partial r} + \frac{1}{r^2}\frac{\partial^2 H_z}{\partial \theta^2} + (\Gamma^2 + \omega^2\epsilon\mu)H_z = 0 \tag{30}$$

In the TM cases the wave equations are given by (27) and (30) if H_z is replaced by E_z throughout. The remaining components are also found from the above results by replacing H_x and H_y by E_x, E_y and so on, $Z_E = E_x/H_y = \Gamma/j\omega\epsilon$ in this case. The field component H_z is to be regarded as the driving force for TE waves and the component E_z is the driving force for TM waves, although in practical systems the actual driving component, determined by the method of coupling to the generator, is likely to be one of the other components. For example, in a waveguide excited by a loop in one end wall, the driving component is H_x, while a probe in a waveguide couples to E_y.

2.3.2.　TEM waves in non-conducting media

We now complete our résumé of results by considering TEM waves. These are of less importance to us in the major part of our study but cannot be ignored. As an example, we may remark that some slow-wave structures will permit a TEM wave to propagate under certain conditions and this will introduce irregularities into the behaviour of the structure. Precisely this behaviour is found in the case of the helix, and T.W.T.s using helices may oscillate unless the TEM mode is suitably suppressed. On the other hand, in, for example, interdigital lines, the TEM mode is the wanted one.

We first consider the uniform plane wave propagation in rectangular co-ordinates. This, and the TEM mode assumption, means that

$$E_z = H_z = 0$$

$$\frac{\partial}{\partial x} = \frac{\partial}{\partial y} = 0$$

From Eqs. (10) and (11)

$$\frac{\partial E_x}{\partial z} = -j\mu\omega H_y, \qquad \frac{\partial H_y}{\partial z} = -j\omega\epsilon E_x$$

or

$$\frac{\partial^2 E_x}{\partial z^2} + \omega^2 \mu\epsilon E_x = 0 \tag{31}$$

also

$$\frac{\partial^2 H_y}{\partial z^2} + \omega^2 \mu\epsilon H_y = 0 \tag{32}$$

The solutions are of the form $E_x = E \exp(-\Gamma z)$ where $\Gamma = j\omega\sqrt{(\epsilon\mu)}$. If the wave propagates in air or a vacuum $\epsilon = \epsilon_0$, $\mu = \mu_0$ and $\Gamma = j\omega/c$, where c = velocity of light. This result is, of course, to be expected.

We easily show that $H_y = (\epsilon/\mu)^{1/2} E_x$. The wave impedance is $E_x/H_y = (\mu/\epsilon)^{1/2}$. This ratio is 377 Ω for free space.

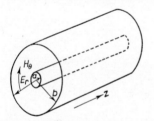

FIG. 1. Notation for TEM mode on coaxial line.

Turning now to cylindrical systems let us set up the equations for the TEM mode on a coaxial line (Fig. 1). Here E_z, H_z, H_r and E_θ are all zero and we find

$$\frac{\partial E_r}{\partial z} = -j\mu\omega H_\theta, \qquad \frac{\partial H_\theta}{\partial z} = -j\omega\epsilon E_r$$

together with

$$\frac{1}{r}\frac{\partial}{\partial r}(rH_\theta) = 0$$

i.e.,

$$rH_\theta = \text{const.} \tag{33}$$

If the total current flowing on the conductors is I and the current density on the outer conductor is J_b we have

$$I = \int_0^{2\pi} J_b . b . d\theta = 2\pi b . J_b$$

But
$$H_\theta(b) = J_b$$

Therefore
$$H_\theta = \frac{I}{2\pi r} \tag{34}$$

Now
$$\frac{E_r}{H_\theta} = \sqrt{\frac{\mu}{\epsilon}} \quad \text{or} \quad E_r = \sqrt{\frac{\mu}{\epsilon}} . \frac{I}{2\pi r}$$

Forming the Poynting vector we have

$$S_z = \tfrac{1}{2} E_r H_\theta^* = \frac{1}{2} \sqrt{\frac{\mu}{\epsilon}} \frac{I I^*}{(2\pi r)^2} \tag{35}$$

and the power flow along the line is

$$P = \int_a^b \mathrm{Re}\, S_z . 2\pi r . dr = \sqrt{\frac{\mu}{\epsilon}} . \frac{|I|^2}{4\pi} \ln \frac{b}{a} \tag{36}$$

To discuss Eq. (36) further let us derive the peak voltage difference between the conductors. This is

$$V = \int_a^b E_r . dr = \sqrt{\frac{\mu}{\epsilon}} . \frac{I}{2\pi} \ln \frac{b}{a}$$

But
$$Z = \frac{V}{I} = \sqrt{\frac{\mu}{\epsilon}} . \frac{1}{2\pi} \ln \frac{b}{a} \tag{37}$$

We note that P, as given by Eq. (36) $= |I|^2 . Z$, with Z given by Eq. (37). In this case, because there is a unique definition of V, the impedance defined as the ratio V/I is identical with the impedance defined on a power basis.

2.4. THE BOUNDARY CONDITIONS IN ELECTROMAGNETIC PROBLEMS

The problems of field propagation which interest us are all classical boundary value problems involving fields propagating in the vicinity of either metallic conductors or dielectric walls. It is convenient to state the boundary conditions once and for all. To do this consider the boundary surface between two regions whose constants are ϵ_1, ϵ_2, μ_1, μ_2 and σ_1, σ_2. The boundary conditions are:

A. $\mathbf{n} \times (\mathbf{E}_2 - \mathbf{E}_1) = 0$

or $E_{t_1} = E_{t_2}$ (38)

i.e., the tangential components of the electric field are equal on both sides of the boundary.

B. $\mathbf{n} \times (\mathbf{H}_2 - \mathbf{H}_1) = \mathbf{J}_s$ (39)

i.e., the tangential components of the magnetic field have a jump equal in value to the surface current density at the boundary. (We have used this condition in the last section.)

C. $\mathbf{n} \cdot (\mathbf{B}_2 - \mathbf{B}_1) = 0$

                                    $\mu_2 H_{2n} = \mu_1 H_{1n}$ (40)

The normal component of H is stationary in value at the boundary

D. $\mathbf{n} \cdot (\mathbf{D}_2 - \mathbf{D}_1) = P$

or $\epsilon_2 E_{2n} - \epsilon_1 E_{1n} = P$ (41)

Where P = surface charge per unit area. Thus, the normal component of ϵE has a jump equal to the surface charge.

E. $\mathbf{n} \cdot (\mathbf{J}_2 - \mathbf{J}_1) = -\dfrac{\partial P}{\partial t}$ (42)

Thus, if P is variable in time, the normal component of the current density is discontinuous.

We now specialize these general results, which are discussed in more detail by STRATTON.[1]

2.4.1. Region 2 is a good metallic conductor

We put $\sigma_2 = \infty$. In the good conductor $E = 0$ and therefore $H = 0$.

Then $\mathbf{n} \times \mathbf{E}_1 = 0$, $E_{t_1} = 0$ (43)

                $\mathbf{n} \times \mathbf{H}_1 = -\mathbf{J}_s$ (44)

                $\mathbf{n} \cdot \mathbf{H} = 0$ (45)

                $\mathbf{n}\epsilon_1 \mathbf{E}_1 = -P$ (46)

                $\mathbf{n}\mathbf{J}_2 = \mathbf{n}\mathbf{J}_1 - \dfrac{\partial P}{\partial t}$

---

[1] STRATTON; *Electromagnetic Theory*, p. 483. McGraw-Hill, 1941.

But, using (46) $\qquad \mathbf{nJ_1} = -\dfrac{\sigma_1}{\epsilon_1} \cdot P$

therefore $\qquad\quad \mathbf{nJ_2} = -\dfrac{\sigma_1}{\epsilon_1} \cdot P - \dfrac{\partial P}{\partial t}$

$$= -\dfrac{(\sigma_1 + j\omega\epsilon_1)}{\epsilon_1} P \qquad (47)$$

2.4.2. Region 2 is a perfect insulator

Here $\qquad\qquad\qquad \sigma_2 = 0, \qquad J_2 = 0$

From (42) $\qquad\quad \mathbf{n} \cdot \mathbf{J_1} = \dfrac{\partial P}{\partial t} = j\omega P \qquad (48)$

or $\qquad\qquad\qquad P = -j\dfrac{\sigma_1}{\omega} \, \mathbf{n} \cdot \mathbf{E_1} \qquad (49)$

The other conditions are unaltered.

2.5. APPLICATION TO WAVEGUIDE PROBLEMS

It is not our intention to give more than a very cursory account
of waveguide propagation. This would be unnecessary, first, because
the subject is exhaustively treated in many excellent books and
secondly because waveguide problems are purely incidental to the
major part of this work. The only justification for including these
phenomena at all is that by discussing the differences between
waveguides and slow wave structures we can obtain a clearer idea
of the physics of both.

2.5.1. Rectangular waveguide

The notation for the axes and dimensions is given in Fig. 2. Consider a TE mode system.

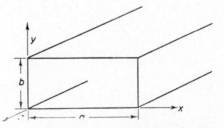

FIG. 2. Notation for rectangular waveguide.

Equation (27) is separable and leads to simple harmonic solutions. Equation (44) shows that H_z must be finite at $x = y = 0$ so we put

$$H_z = A \cos k_1 x \cos k_2 y \tag{50}$$

where $k_1{}^2 + k_2{}^2 = \Gamma^2 + \omega^2 \epsilon \mu$.

From (26)

$$H_y = A \frac{k_2 \Gamma}{k_1{}^2 + k_2{}^2} \cos k_1 x \sin k_2 y \tag{51}$$

$$H_x = A \frac{k_1 \Gamma}{k_1{}^2 + k_2{}^2} \sin k_1 x \cos k_2 y \tag{52}$$

From (24)

$$E_y = -A \frac{j\omega\mu k_1}{k_1{}^2 + k_2{}^2} \sin k_1 x \cos k_2 y \tag{53}$$

$$E_x = A \frac{j\omega\mu k_2}{k_1{}^2 + k_2{}^2} \cos k_1 x \sin k_2 y \tag{54}$$

We next use the boundary conditions.

$E_x = 0$ at $y = 0, b$ therefore $k_2 = n\pi/b$, n an integer
$E_y = 0$ at $x = 0, a$ therefore $k_1 = m\pi/a$, m an integer

Different TE modes correspond to different values of m and n. However, n and m determine Γ through

$$\Gamma^2 = \left(\frac{m\pi}{a}\right)^2 + \left(\frac{n\pi}{b}\right)^2 - \omega^2 \epsilon \mu \tag{55}$$

Now, if Γ is positive, only a damped wave decreasing exponentially with distance is set up. (The wave function is $\exp(-\Gamma z)$.) So, for propagation we must have $\Gamma = j\beta$, $\Gamma^2 = -\beta^2$, and

$$\beta^2 = \omega^2 \epsilon \mu - \left[\left(\frac{m\pi}{a}\right)^2 + \left(\frac{n\pi}{b}\right)^2\right]$$

The cut-off frequency, below which propagation is impossible, is given by $\beta = 0$, or

$$\omega_c = \frac{1}{(\epsilon\mu)^{1/2}} \left[\left(\frac{m\pi}{a}\right)^2 + \left(\frac{n\pi}{b}\right)^2\right]^{1/2}$$

For an evacuated or air-filled guide $\epsilon\mu = \epsilon_0\mu_0 = c^{-2}$

therefore

$$\omega_c = c\left[\left(\frac{m\pi}{a}\right)^2 + \left(\frac{n\pi}{b}\right)^2\right]^{1/2} \tag{56}$$

Then
$$\beta^2 = \frac{\omega^2}{c^2} - \frac{\omega_c{}^2}{c^2} = k^2 - k_c{}^2 \qquad (57)$$

since ω_c/c, ω/c are wave numbers, i.e., $k_c = 2\pi/\lambda_c$.

From the definition of β as $2\pi/\lambda_g$ we can write Eq. (57) as

$$\left(\frac{2\pi}{\lambda_g}\right)^2 = \left(\frac{2\pi}{\lambda}\right)^2 - \left(\frac{2\pi}{\lambda_c}\right)^2$$

and
$$\left(\frac{\lambda}{\lambda_g}\right)^2 = 1 - \left(\frac{\lambda}{\lambda_c}\right)^2 \qquad (58)$$

We can represent Eq. (58) by the first quadrant of a unit circle (Fig. 3), then, knowing λ, the wavelength in air and λ_c the cut-off

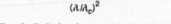

$(\lambda/\lambda_g)^2$ $r = 1$

$(\lambda/\lambda_c)^2$

Fig. 3. Relation between λ, λ_c and λ_g.

wavelength we can determine λ_g the guide wavelength. Clearly, $\lambda_g > \lambda$.

Returning for a moment to Eq. (57), the notation used therein is often introduced into the wave equations. Equation (33) could, for instance, be written

$$\frac{\partial^2 H_z}{\partial x^2} + \frac{\partial^2 H_z}{\partial y^2} + (k^2 - \beta^2)H_z = 0 \qquad (59)$$

or we may replace $(k^2 - \beta^2)$ by $k_c{}^2$ if we like.

An even more compact notation is to write ∇_t for the gradient operator applied to the transverse components only, i.e., $\nabla_t = \partial H_z/\partial x + \partial H_z/\partial y$, Eq. (59) then becomes

$$\nabla_t{}^2 . H_z + (k^2 - \beta^2)H_z = 0 \qquad (60)$$

We shall use the wave equations in this form, when discussing slow-wave structures.

We now restrict ourselves to the gravest mode and consider the power flow. From Eq. (56), since a is the broad dimension of the guide, the lowest mode is $m = 1$, $n = 0$, i.e., $k_1 = \pi/a$, $k_2 = 0$ ($m = 0 = n$ does not constitute a possible solution since Eq. (50) then gives $H_z = A$). The fields follow from inserting these values in Eqs. (50)–(54) and we observe that $H_y = 0 = E_x$. Also, $\Gamma = j \cdot 2\pi/\lambda_g$ and from Eq. (24) $E_y = (-j\mu\omega/\Gamma)H_x = -Z_H H_x$, with $H_x = jA \cdot 2a/\lambda_g \cdot \sin \pi x/a$. Using the Poynting vector, the power flow is thus

$$P = \frac{Z_H}{2} \int |H_x|^2 \, dS = A^2 \cdot \frac{a^3 b}{\lambda_g^2} \cdot Z_H \tag{61}$$

Since the power flow and the geometrical properties of the waveguide are all measurable quantities, Eq. (61) tells us how to determine the arbitrary amplitude for any given power level. Let us write down the explicit relation for E_y: it is

$$E_y = -2j\left(\frac{PZ_H}{ab}\right)^{1/2} \sin \frac{\pi x}{a} \tag{62}$$

The "voltage" across the guide is $E_y \cdot b = -2j(PZ_H b/a)^{1/2} \sin \pi x/a$. Equation (62) can be used, for instance, to estimate the maximum power handling capacity of a given guide since breakdown ensues when the field reaches a value sufficient to cause a discharge in the gas filling the guide.

The treatment follows exactly the same lines for the TM modes. The reader can easily verify that the fields are

$$E_z = A \sin k_1 x \sin k_2 y$$

$$E_y = -A\frac{\Gamma k_2}{k_1^2 + k_2^2} \sin k_1 x \cos k_2 y$$

$$E_x = -A\frac{\Gamma k_1}{k_1^2 + k_2^2} \cos k_1 x \sin k_2 y \tag{63}$$

$$H_y = -A\frac{j\omega\epsilon k_1}{k_1^2 + k_2^2} \cos k_1 x \sin k_2 y$$

$$H_x = A\frac{j\omega\epsilon k_2}{k_1^2 + k_2^2} \sin k_1 x \cos k_2 y$$

The gravest mode is, however, now $m = n = 1$ as E_z would vanish if either m or n were zero.

We now make a short digression to discuss the phase and group velocities in the guide. We have $\beta = 2\pi/\lambda_g$. But, corresponding with λ_g we have the phase velocity v_p given by $\lambda_g = v_p/f$.

Then
$$v_p = \frac{\omega}{\beta} \tag{64}$$

Using Eq. (57) we have $(v_p{}^2 - c^2/v_p{}^2) = (\omega_c/\omega)^2$ and we conclude that $v_p > c$. A more convenient relation for the computation of v_p is

$$v_p = \frac{c}{[1 - (\lambda/\lambda_c)^2]^{1/2}} \tag{65}$$

There are many equivalent definitions of the group velocity. A simple one is

$$v_g = \frac{d\omega}{d\beta} \tag{66}$$

Using Eq. (57) and the definition of v_p we find that

$$v_p \cdot v_g = c^2$$

or
$$v_g = c\sqrt{1 - \left(\frac{\lambda}{\lambda_c}\right)^2} \tag{67}$$

Therefore $v_g < c$.

Since the group velocity is a function of frequency, the waveguide is a dispersive medium. In present-day communication and radar systems bandwidths are too small and pulse widths too great to make this fact of much importance although this situation may change as the technique advances. In slow-wave structures dispersion is made use of in ways we shall study in later chapters. Sometimes, to save writing, we shall denote the phase and group velocities as p and g respectively, when no confusion can result.

2.5.2. Circular waveguides

We next proceed to treat cylindrical waveguides of circular cross-section. For our subsequent applications the circular cylindrical geometry is more important than the rectangular geometry which was only included because the wave functions, being sinusoidal, are very familiar and purely mathematical difficulties are therefore minimized.

The appropriate wave equation is Eq. (30) which we now write, (TE modes),

$$\frac{1}{r}\frac{\partial}{\partial r}\left(r\frac{\partial H_z}{\partial r}\right) + \frac{1}{r^2}\frac{\partial^2 H_z}{\partial \theta^2} + k_c^2 H_z = 0$$

This is soluble by separation, i.e., we put

$$H_z = R(r) \,.\, \Theta(\theta)$$

Then, carrying out the indicated operations and dividing through by H_z, we have

$$\frac{R''(r)}{R(r)} + \frac{1}{r}\frac{R'(r)}{R(r)} + \frac{1}{r^2}\frac{\Theta''(\theta)}{\Theta(\theta)} + k_c^2 = 0$$

Since $\Theta''(\theta)/\Theta(\theta)$ is only a function of Θ, we may put this equal to $-s^2$, obtaining

$$\left.\begin{aligned}\Theta''(\theta) + s^2\Theta(\theta) = 0 \\ R''(r) + \frac{1}{r}R'(r) + \left(k_c^2 - \frac{s^2}{r^2}\right)R(r) = 0\end{aligned}\right\} \qquad (68)$$

The standard solution of (68) is

$$H_z = (A\cos s\Theta + B\sin s\Theta)(CJ_s(k_c r) + DY_s(k_c r)) \qquad (69)$$

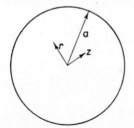

FIG. 4. Notation for circular waveguide.

H_z must be a periodic function of Θ with period 2π, so that s must be an integer, n. In our case D must then be zero because Y_s is infinite at $r = 0$. To proceed further we must use the boundary conditions. The most useful is $E_\theta = 0$ at $r = a$ (Fig. 4). From Eqs. (28) and (29) we find

$$E_\theta = \frac{j\mu\omega}{k_c^2} \cdot \frac{\partial H_2}{\partial r}$$

therefore $J'_n(k_c a) = 0$ (70)†

Let us denote the mth root of Eq. (70) by the symbol q'_{nm}, n and m both being integers.   Then

$$k_{cn,m} = \frac{q'_{nm}}{a}$$

or $$\omega_{cn,m} = c\left(\frac{q'_{nm}}{a}\right)$$ (71)

and $$\lambda_{cn,m} = \frac{2\pi a}{q'_{nm}}$$ (72)

Thus, the cut-off for the TE$_{11}$ mode is given by $\lambda c = 2\pi a/q'_{11}$ where $q'_{11} = $ first zero of $J'_1(k_c a)$ or 1·841, i.e., $\lambda_{c11} = 2\pi a/1·841$. This is the gravest mode of a circular waveguide.   The TE$_{01}$ cut-off is higher in frequency because the first zero of $J'_0(k_c a)$ is at 3·832.

The only question remaining is that of the terms $\sin n\theta$ and $\cos n\theta$. These mean, in effect, that two solutions are possible at every frequency even when the guide is excited so that only one mode is propagated.   The modes are therefore degenerate in the usual technical sense; two or more eigenfunctions correspond to a single eigenvalue. In what follows we assume that both modes of a pair are equally excited. We can now write down the explicit relations for the fields. They are

$$E_\theta = A\frac{j\omega\mu}{k_c} \exp(jn\theta) J'_n\left(\frac{q'_n r}{a}\right)$$ (73)

$$E_r = A\frac{\omega\mu}{k_c^2 r} \exp(jn\theta) J_n\left(\frac{q'_n r}{a}\right)$$ (74)

$$H_\theta = \frac{E_r}{Z_H}, \qquad H_r = -\frac{E_\theta}{Z_H}$$ (75)

---

† There is often some ambiguity in the use of the dash notation for differentiating Bessel functions. In the form used in Eq. (70) $J'_1(kr_2)$ is sometimes used to mean $(d/dr)J_1(kr) = k[dJ_1(R)/dR]$ and sometimes to mean $[(d/dR)J_1(R)]_{R=kr}$ which differ by the factor of k. The latter usage is more common and we adopt it in the sequel.

The calculation of the power flow is lengthy but typifies the work involved in such calculations when the fields involve Bessel functions. The details are therefore given in Appendix I.

The result for the TE_{11} mode is

$$P = \frac{A^2 \lambda_c^4}{8\pi\lambda\lambda_g} \cdot \sqrt{\frac{\mu}{\epsilon}} \cdot [(q'_{11}) - 1] J_1^2(q'_{11}) \tag{76}$$

Half of this power is associated with each of the (two) degenerate modes.

Turning to the TM modes we find that Eq. (69) is now satisfied by E_z and the boundary condition is simply that $E_z = 0$ at $r = a$. Therefore for TM waves the eigenvalues are given by

$$J_n(k_c a) = 0 \tag{77}$$

We denote the mth root of Eq. (77) by q_{nm} so that $k_c = q_{nm}/a$ and the radial eigenfunctions are of the form $J_n(q_{nm}r/a)$. The lowest mode is the TM_{01} for which $q_{01} = 2\cdot405$, so the cut-off frequency is higher than for the TE_{11} mode.

Writing
$$E_z = A \exp(jn\theta) J_n\left(\frac{q_m r}{a}\right) \tag{78}$$

the other field components become, using the equivalents of Eqs. (28) and (29)

$$H_\theta = \frac{An\omega\epsilon}{k_c^2 r} \exp(jn\theta) J_n\left(\frac{q_m r}{a}\right) \tag{79}$$

$$H_r = -A\frac{j\omega\epsilon}{k_c} \exp(jn\theta) J'_n\left(\frac{q_m r}{a}\right) \tag{80}$$

$$E_r = Z_E H_\theta, \qquad E_\theta = -Z_E H_r \tag{81}$$

For the TM_{01} mode,

$$P = \frac{A^2 \lambda_c^4}{8\pi\lambda\lambda_g} \cdot \sqrt{\frac{\mu}{\epsilon}} \cdot q_{01}^2 \cdot J_0^2(q_{01}) \tag{82}$$

2.6. ORTHOGONAL NATURE OF THE FIELD EXPRESSIONS

We have already stated that general solutions of Maxwell's equations can be built up from the various modes we have introduced in the preceding sections. We now discuss this possibility in more general terms and link the procedures involved with those used in various other branches of theoretical physics and in mathematics.

Let us first consider a concrete problem—a waveguide in which two of the possible modes are excited simultaneously. Then, by the superposition principle, the total field at any point is the sum of the two partial fields, which have arbitrary amplitudes A_1 and A_2. If we take TE modes in a rectangular guide we can write

$$E_x = A_1 \cos \frac{m_1 \pi x}{a} \sin \frac{n_1 \pi y}{b} + A_2 \cos \frac{m_2 \pi x}{a} \sin \frac{n_2 \pi y}{b}$$

$$E_y = A'_1 \sin \frac{m_1 \pi x}{a} \cos \frac{n_1 \pi y}{b} + A'_2 \sin \frac{m_2 \pi x}{a} \cos \frac{n_2 \pi y}{b}$$

The power flow derived from the Poynting vector is

$$\tfrac{1}{2} Z_H \cdot \int_0^b \int_0^a \{ |E_x|^2 + |E_y|^2 \} \, dx \, dy \tag{83}$$

so that cross products of the form

$$A_1 A_2 \left\{ \left(\cos \frac{m_1 \pi x}{a} \sin \frac{n_1 \pi y}{b} \right) \left(\cos \frac{m_2 \pi x}{a} \sin \frac{n_2 \pi y}{b} \right) \right\}$$

arise. Consider now the integrand with respect to x, this is

$$\int_0^a \cos \frac{m_1 \pi x}{a} \cdot \cos \frac{m_2 \pi x}{a} \, dx = c \, \delta_{m_1, m_2} \tag{84}$$

where δ_{m_1, m_2} is Kronecker's delta symbol, i.e.,

$$\delta_{m_1, m_2} = \begin{cases} 0, \, m_1 \neq m_2 \\ 1, \, m_1 = m_2 \end{cases}$$

Similar considerations apply to the sin sin integral, so we see that the cross product terms make no contribution to the result and the power flow is just equal to the sum of the powers due to the two modes considered separately. This is a consequence of the orthogonality of the trigonometric functions.

If we made the same calculation for a circular guide, the cross product terms would be of the form

$$\int_0^a r J_n \left(\frac{q'_{m_1} r}{a} \right) J_n \left(\frac{q'_{m_2} r}{a} \right) \tag{85}$$

Integrals of this type vanish when the boundary conditions are of the form $J_n(q')$ or $J'_n(q') = 0$ (Appendix 2) and again we find the powers in each mode can be separately calculated and superposed. In mathematical language the Bessel functions are an orthogonal set with weight function r. We therefore recognize the TEM, TE and TM modes as electromagnetic analogues of the normal co-ordinate system introduced by Kelvin and Tait and applied extensively in acoustics by RAYLEIGH.[2] This being the case, we can apply the whole of the extensive mathematical structure based on Hamiltonian and Lagrangian functions, leading to important variational techniques for handling slow-wave structures.

We have, so far, worked with concrete examples which demonstrate the required behaviour without any technique more advanced than ordinary integration. A general proof is not much more difficult. We write Maxwell's equations (10) and (11) in the form

$$\operatorname{curl} \mathbf{E}_n = -j\omega_n\mu\mathbf{H}_n$$

$$\operatorname{curl} \mathbf{H}_n = j\omega_n\epsilon\mathbf{E}_n$$

and consider two modes n and m.

The vector relation $\operatorname{div}(\mathbf{E} \times \mathbf{H}^*) = \mathbf{H}^* \operatorname{curl} \mathbf{E} - \mathbf{E} \operatorname{curl} \mathbf{H}^*$ gives

$$\operatorname{div}(\mathbf{E}_n \times \mathbf{H}_m{}^*) = -j\omega_n\mu\mathbf{H}_n\mathbf{H}_m{}^* + j\omega_m\epsilon\mathbf{E}_n\mathbf{E}_m{}^*$$
$$\operatorname{div}(\mathbf{E}_m{}^* \times \mathbf{H}_n) = j\omega_m\mu\mathbf{H}_n\mathbf{H}_m{}^* - j\omega_n\epsilon\mathbf{E}_n\mathbf{E}_m{}^* \qquad (86)$$

We now integrate Eqs. (86) over the whole volume of the space considered and transform the volume integral by Gauss's theorem

$$\int_v \operatorname{div}(\mathbf{E} \times \mathbf{H}) \, \mathrm{d}V = \int_s (\mathbf{E} \times \mathbf{H}^*) \cdot n \, \mathrm{d}s \qquad (87)$$

but the boundary condition can be expressed in the form $n \times \mathbf{E} = 0$ and $n \cdot \mathbf{H} = 0$ on S. Thus the R.H.S of (87) is zero and we must have

$$-\omega_n\int_v \mu\mathbf{H}_n\mathbf{H}_m{}^* \, \mathrm{d}V + \omega_m\int_v \epsilon\mathbf{E}_n\mathbf{E}_m{}^* \, \mathrm{d}V = 0$$

$$\omega_m\int_v \mu\mathbf{H}_n\mathbf{H}_m{}^* \, \mathrm{d}V - \omega_m\int_v \epsilon\mathbf{E}_n\mathbf{E}_m{}^* \, \mathrm{d}V = 0$$

This is only possible when $\int_v \mu\mathbf{H}_n\mathbf{H}_m{}^* \, \mathrm{d}V = 0 = \int_v \epsilon\mathbf{E}_n\mathbf{E}_m{}^* \, \mathrm{d}V$ if $\omega_n \neq \omega_m$. If, on the other hand, $\omega_m = \omega_n$, $n = m$ and then $\int_v \mu|\mathbf{H}_n|^2 \, \mathrm{d}V = \int_v \epsilon|\mathbf{E}_n|^2 \, \mathrm{d}V$.

---

[2] RAYLEIGH; *Theory of Sound*, 2nd Ed., Vol. 1, Macmillan, 1894.

Referring back to our discussion of Eq. (5) we see that we have proved that the stored electric and magnetic energies are equal.

We have now obtained a general proof of the orthogonality of the solutions of Maxwell's equations under the standard boundary conditions. It should be mentioned that the form of Poynting vector encountered when we calculate the loss in the walls, i.e., $S_n = \frac{1}{2} E_{\mathrm{tan}} \cdot H_{\mathrm{tan}}{}^*$ does not possess orthogonal properties. In other words when we are calculating waveguide losses and attenuations, cross-product terms should not be neglected. The position is therefore analogous to that in mechanical systems including friction not directly proportional to the velocity. In general cases this leads to considerable mathematical complication but it must be remembered that most practical waveguides are used to propagate only the dominant mode. Regions in which more complicated wave systems are excited, to satisfy the boundary conditions, i.e., obstacles, bends, etc., are usually short in comparison with the total length of guide and the series losses are of no practical importance. It is, however, a criticism of our present state of knowlege that we find it difficult or impossible to calculate losses in even quite simple structures with any degree of accuracy.

To conclude our elementary description of the orthogonal properties of electromagnetic waves, the attention of the reader must be drawn to the general mathematical theory of such properties which is encountered in connexion with the theory of Sturm–Liouville equations, a short and lucid account being that of MARGENAU and MURPHY.[3] Most of the special functions of mathematical physics are orthogonal with appropriate weight functions. Under fairly general conditions any arbitrary function can be expanded as a series of orthogonal functions. The resulting expansion approximates the original function in the mean, i.e., if $f(x)$ is the function and U_n are the orthogonal functions, w is the weight function then $\int w[f(x) - \sum_1^\infty a_n U_n]^2 \, \mathrm{d}x$ is minimized by the expansion. Moreover, the expansion is complete. Obviously, Fourier's series are the best known examples of such expansions and Fourier–Bessel expansions are also common. We shall make much use of the latter in subsequent work, as they enable us to calculate the excitations of the various allowed modes under given boundary conditions. A very readable account of the properties required is contained in CHURCHILL.[4]

---

[3] MARGENAU and MURPHY; *The Mathematics of Physics and Chemistry*, 1st. Ed., Chapter 8. Van Nostrand, New York, 1943.

[4] CHURCHILL; *Fourier Series and Boundary Value Problems*. McGraw-Hill, New York, 1941.

2.7. GENERALIZATIONS OF MAXWELL'S EQUATIONS

In some electromagnetic problems it is possible to obtain more elegant solutions by resorting to formulations of the basic equations different from those employed by Maxwell. The use of such formulations is largely a matter of taste and if one is fully conversant with, say, the Maxwellian technique, it is probably easier to steamroller one's way through a particular problem than to attack it by an elegant, but unfamiliar, method. However, these techniques are often used and it is necessary to expose at least the bare bones of the subject here. We confine ourselves to two alternative formulations, (a) the introduction of vector and scalar potentials, (b) the use of Hertzian vectors, sometimes called polarization potentials. Both these are used in our subject, the first was used by Ramo[5] in his original development of space-charge wave theory and the second has been used in developing the theory of the helix. We lean heavily on the treatment given by Stratton (see Bibliography).

2.7.1. Vector and scalar potentials

Since, in Maxwell's equations, $\nabla \cdot \mathbf{B} = 0$, $\mathbf{B}$ must always be a solenoidal vector and can therefore be expressed as the curl of another vector. We therefore write

$$\mathbf{B} = \nabla \times \mathbf{A_0} \qquad (88)$$

Equation (88) is not, however, unique for we could equally well write

$$\mathbf{B} = \nabla \times (\mathbf{A_0} - \nabla \psi) \qquad (89)$$

where ψ is an arbitrary scalar function of position. Now, the equation for curl $\mathbf{E}$ in the set (Eq. 1) gives either

$$\nabla \times \left(\mathbf{E} + \frac{\partial \mathbf{A_0}}{\partial t} \right) = 0$$

or

$$\nabla \times \left\{ \mathbf{E} + \frac{\partial}{\partial t} (\mathbf{A_0} - \nabla \psi) \right\} = 0$$

The vectors $\mathbf{E} + \partial \mathbf{A_0}/\partial t$, $\mathbf{E} + \partial/\partial t\, (\mathbf{A_0} - \nabla \psi)$, are therefore irrota-

---

[5] Ramo; *Phys. Rev.*, 1939, **56**, 276.

D

tional and are therefore expressible as the gradients of scalar functions, e.g., ϕ_0 and ϕ.

Therefore
$$\mathbf{E} = -\nabla\phi_0 - \frac{\partial\mathbf{A}_0}{\partial t} \tag{90}$$

or
$$\mathbf{E} = -\nabla\phi - \frac{\partial}{\partial t}(\mathbf{A}_0 - \nabla\psi) \tag{91}$$

whence
$$\phi = \phi_0 + \frac{\partial\psi}{\partial t} \tag{92}$$

The $\mathbf{A}$ functions are spoken of as magnetic vector potentials; a particular pair are specified by Eqs. (88) and (90) and an infinite set of others may be deduced from (89) and (92).

Consider now a medium which is homogeneous, isotropic and in which ϵ and μ are independent of the field strengths. Then $\mathbf{D} = \epsilon\mathbf{E} = -\epsilon(\nabla\phi + \partial\mathbf{A}/\partial t)$, $\mathbf{H} = 1/\mu\,\mathbf{B} = 1/\mu\,.\,\nabla\times\mathbf{A}$. If these relations are substituted back into Maxwell's equations, the curl $\mathbf{H}$ and div $\mathbf{D}$ equations give

$$\nabla\times\nabla\times\mathbf{A} + \mu\epsilon\nabla\frac{\partial\phi}{\partial t} + \mu\epsilon\frac{\partial^2\mathbf{A}}{\partial t^2} = \mu\mathbf{J} \tag{93}$$

$$\nabla^2\phi + \nabla\,.\,\frac{\partial\mathbf{A}}{\partial t} = -\frac{\rho}{\epsilon} \tag{94}$$

All the particular solutions of Eqs. (93) and (94) will lead to the same fields when subjected to the same boundary conditions but differ among themselves by the arbitrary function ψ. If we decide to choose $\mathbf{A}$ and ϕ so that

$$\nabla\,.\,\mathbf{A} + \mu\epsilon\frac{\partial\phi}{\partial t} = 0 \tag{95}$$

ψ has to satisfy, from Eqs. (89) and (92)

$$\nabla^2\psi - \mu\epsilon\frac{\partial^2\psi}{\partial t^2} = \nabla\,.\,\mathbf{A}_0 + \mu\epsilon\frac{\partial\phi_0}{\partial t} \tag{96}$$

where $\mathbf{A}_0$ and ϕ_0 are particular solutions of Eqs. (93) and (94). But Eq. (96) has removed the ambiguities and $\mathbf{A}$ and ϕ are now unique.

Using Eq. (95) in Eqs. (93) and (94)

$$\nabla \times \nabla \times \mathbf{A} - \nabla\nabla \cdot \mathbf{A} + \mu\epsilon \frac{\partial^2 \mathbf{A}}{\partial t^2} = \mu\mathbf{J} \qquad (97)$$

$$\nabla^2\phi - \mu\epsilon \frac{\partial^2\phi}{\partial t^2} = -\frac{\rho}{\epsilon} \qquad (98)$$

Equation (97) can be simplified using the vector identity

$$\nabla \times \nabla \times \mathbf{A} = \nabla\nabla \cdot \mathbf{A} - \nabla \cdot \nabla\mathbf{A} \qquad (99)$$

and in rectangular co-ordinates $\nabla \cdot \nabla\mathbf{A} = \nabla^2 \cdot \mathbf{A}$ therefore

$$\nabla^2\mathbf{A} - \mu\epsilon \frac{\partial^2 \mathbf{A}}{\partial t^2} = -\mu\mathbf{J} \qquad (100)$$

The scalar potential ϕ is measured in volts while $\mathbf{A}$ is measured in webers/metre. To use this formulation the wave Eqs. (97), (98) and (100) are solved for the appropriate initial and boundary value problem and the actual fields are subsequently derived from the defining equations (88) and (92). The basic advantage gained by introducing the magnetic vector potential and the scalar potential is that the six components of $\mathbf{E}$ and $\mathbf{H}$ are reduced to a scalar plus the three components of $\mathbf{A}$, i.e., to four, with consequent simplification. A further step in the same direction is possible, since $\mathbf{A}$ is not independent of ϕ but is connected by Eq. (90). This leads us to the Hertzian formulation.

2.7.2. The Hertzian vectors

There are two such vectors; the Hertzian electric vector $\boldsymbol{\pi}$ and the magnetic vector $\boldsymbol{\pi}^*$, sometimes called the Fitzgerald vector. The fields are given in terms of these vectors by

$$\mathbf{H} = \epsilon \frac{\partial}{\partial t} (\nabla \times \boldsymbol{\pi}), \qquad \mathbf{H} = \nabla\nabla \cdot \boldsymbol{\pi}^* - \mu\epsilon \frac{\partial^2\boldsymbol{\pi}^*}{\partial t^2} \qquad (101)$$

$$\mathbf{E} = \nabla\nabla \cdot \boldsymbol{\pi} - \mu\epsilon \frac{\partial^2\boldsymbol{\pi}}{\partial t^2}, \qquad \mathbf{E} = -\mu \frac{\partial}{\partial t} (\nabla \times \boldsymbol{\pi}^*) \qquad (102)$$

where $\boldsymbol{\pi}$ and $\boldsymbol{\pi}^*$ satisfy

$$\nabla \times \nabla \times \boldsymbol{\pi} - \nabla\nabla \cdot \boldsymbol{\pi} + \mu\epsilon \frac{\partial^2\boldsymbol{\pi}}{\partial t^2} = 0 \qquad (103)$$

or, in rectangular co-ordinates

$$\nabla^2\boldsymbol{\pi} - \mu\epsilon\,\frac{\partial^2\boldsymbol{\pi}}{\partial t^2} = 0 \tag{104}$$

The above relations apply to a homogeneous, isotropic region with constant μ and ϵ. The introduction of the Hertzian vectors is much less advantageous when free charges have to be considered so we do not pursue this topic here. The proof of the above results is as follows: we put

$$\mathbf{A} = \mu\epsilon\,\frac{\partial\boldsymbol{\pi}}{\partial t}$$

Therefore $\mathbf{B} = \mu\epsilon\left(\nabla \times \dfrac{\partial\boldsymbol{\pi}}{\partial t}\right),$ $\mathbf{E} = -\nabla\phi - \mu a\,\dfrac{\partial^2\boldsymbol{\pi}}{\partial t^2}$

These are put into the curl $\mathbf{H}$ equation and yield

$$\frac{\partial}{\partial t}\left(\nabla \times \nabla \times \boldsymbol{\pi} + \nabla\phi + \mu\epsilon\,\frac{\partial^2\boldsymbol{\pi}}{\partial t^2}\right) = 0 \tag{105}$$

ϕ is now chosen to satisfy $\phi = -\nabla \cdot \boldsymbol{\pi}$ and if Eq. (105) is integrated with respect to t, we obtain the wave Eq. (103), when the constant of integration is put equal to zero. This is allowed because it obviously does not influence the value of the fields.

We now apply these results to a cylindrical polar co-ordinate system. We shall observe how naturally the division into transverse electric and transverse magnetic modes comes about. The TM modes derive from $\boldsymbol{\pi}$ if we consider that π_r and π_θ are zero and π_z finite. The TE modes derive from $\boldsymbol{\pi}^*$ under the same conditions. We limit ourselves to the case of a homogeneous, isotropic region of zero conductivity and infinite extent, so that possible effects due to a distribution of magnetization and/or polarization outside the region, need not be considered.

We can immediately write down the expressions for the fields from Eqs. (101) and (102) by writing down the appropriate expansions of the vector operators. Then, if the subscript 1 refers to the TM modes,

$$H_{\theta 1} = -j\omega\epsilon\,\frac{\partial\pi_z}{\partial r}, \qquad H_{r1} = \frac{j\omega\epsilon}{r}\,\frac{\partial\pi_z}{\partial\theta}, \qquad H_{z1} = 0 \tag{106}$$

and

$$E_{\theta 1} = \frac{1}{r}\,\frac{\partial^2\pi_z}{\partial z\,\partial\theta}, \qquad E_{r1} = \frac{\partial^2\pi_z}{\partial z\,\partial r}$$

$$E_{z1} = -\frac{1}{r}\left[\frac{\partial}{\partial r}\left(r\,\frac{\partial\pi_z}{\partial r}\right) + \frac{\partial}{\partial\theta}\left(\frac{1}{r}\,\frac{\partial\pi_z}{\partial\theta}\right)\right] \tag{107}$$

For the TE modes (2) the expansion of $\pi_z{}^*$ gives

$$E_{\theta 2} = j\omega\mu \frac{\partial \pi_z{}^*}{\partial r}, \qquad E_{r2} = -\frac{j\omega\mu}{r} \frac{\partial \pi_z{}^*}{\partial \theta}, \qquad E_{z2} = 0 \qquad (108)$$

$$H_{\theta 2} = \frac{1}{r} \frac{\partial^2 \pi_z{}^*}{\partial z\, \partial \theta}, \qquad H_{r2} = \frac{\partial^2 \pi_z{}^*}{\partial z\, \partial r}$$

$$H_{z2} = -\frac{1}{r}\left[\frac{\partial}{\partial r}\left(r \frac{\partial \pi_z{}^*}{\partial r} \right) + \frac{\partial}{\partial \theta}\left(\frac{1}{r} \frac{\partial \pi_z{}^*}{\partial \theta} \right) \right] \qquad (109)$$

Now π_z has to satisfy the (scalar) wave equation

$$\nabla^2 \pi_z + k_0{}^2 \pi_z = 0 \qquad (110)$$

and if π_z is to be of the form $R(r)\Theta(\theta)\exp j(\omega t \pm \beta z)$ we find from Eq. (110)

$$\frac{1}{r}\left[\frac{\partial}{\partial r}\left(rR'(r)\Theta(\theta) \right) + \frac{\partial}{\partial \theta}\left(\frac{1}{r} R(r)\Theta'(\theta) \right) \right] + (k_0{}^2 - \beta^2)\pi_z = 0$$

We can then rewrite the expressions for E_{z1} and H_{z1} in the forms

$$E_{z1} = (k_0{}^2 - \beta^2)\pi_z \qquad (111)$$

$$H_{z2} = (k_0{}^2 - \beta^2)\pi_z{}^* \qquad (112)$$

The superposition of these two sets of modes will satisfy the boundary conditions on any cylindrical surface whose generators are parallel with the z axis. In particular the field can be built up of a superposition of wave functions of the form

$$\psi_n = J_n[(k_0{}^2 - \beta^2)^{1/2}r]\exp j(\omega t + n\theta \pm \beta z) \qquad (113)$$

This includes the case when $\beta^2 > k_0{}^2$, which is usually written explicitly as I_n.† If we write $\pi_z = \sum_{-\infty}^{+\infty} A_n\psi_n,\ \pi_z{}^* = \sum_{-\infty}^{+\infty} B_n\psi_n$, we obtain

$$E_z = (k_0{}^2 - \beta^2) \sum A_n\psi_n \qquad (114)$$

$$E_r = \pm j\beta \sum A_n \frac{\partial \psi_n}{\partial r} + \frac{\mu\omega}{r} \sum B_n\psi_n \qquad (115)$$

$$E_\theta = \mp\frac{\beta}{r} \sum nA_n\psi_n + j\mu\omega \sum B_n \frac{\partial \psi_n}{\partial r} \qquad (116)$$

$$H_z = (k_0{}^2 - \beta^2) \sum B_n\psi_n \qquad (117)$$

---

† The solution using Hankel functions, appropriate to radiation problems, is of no interest in our work.

$$H_r = \frac{\omega \epsilon}{r} \sum n A_n \psi_n \pm j\beta \sum B_n \frac{\partial \psi_n}{\partial r} \tag{118}$$

$$H_\theta = -j\omega\epsilon \sum A_n \frac{\partial \psi_n}{\partial r} \mp \frac{\beta}{r} \sum B_n \psi_n \tag{119}$$

In electronic problems we shall be interested in field systems for which $E_z \neq 0$, so that we may often ignore the TE fields, which we do by putting all the B_n's equal to zero. If, in addition, the field in which the electrons travel shows no θ dependence, we must have $E_\theta = 0$ which implies that all the A_n's are zero except A_0. From Eq. (118) this implies that H_r vanishes as well as E_θ, so that the only finite fields are E_z, E_r and H_θ. We shall use fields of this type rather frequently in the subsequent analysis.

The Hertzian vector formulation has been given in considerable detail because it will subsequently be used in treating the helical slow-wave structure and this structure is of such major practical importance that a full understanding of the theory is necessary.

BIBLIOGRAPHY

The literature of the subjects treated in this chapter is now very extensive. We select from it:—

1. SLATER; *Microwave Electronics*, Van Nostrand, 1950.
2. MONTGOMERY, DICKE and PURCELL; *Principles of Microwave Circuits*, M.I.T. Series, Vol. 8, McGraw-Hill, 1948.
3. STRATTON; *Electromagnetic Theory*, McGraw-Hill, 1941.
4. RAMO and WHINNERY; *Fields and Waves in Modern Radio*, Wiley, 1944.

These are mainly theoretical. A good reference with more experimental details is

5. HUXLEY; *Principles and Practice of Wave Guides*, Cambridge University Press, 1947.

3

SLOW-WAVE STRUCTURES

IN THE preceding chapter we saw that the phase velocity p of electromagnetic waves in waveguides is somewhat greater than the velocity of light in the medium filling them. If an electron beam is to interact with an electromagnetic wave over a distance, e.g., over a length equal to several wavelengths, the electron velocity must be roughly equal to that of the wave. For non-relativistic velocities the velocity of an electron falling through V_0 volts is

$$u_0 = 5 \cdot 95 \times 10^5 V_0^{1/2}$$

which is valid up to about $5 \cdot 95 \times 10^7$ m/sec. Therefore if we are to make our beams interact with waves, the latter must be slowed down by a factor which may range from about 3 to about 30. Such waves are called slow waves. In addition to the phase velocity, the ability to set up waves with a strong E_z component is of primary importance in valve design. This property is usually expressed as a "coupling impedance" and the main part of this chapter is devoted to calculating these two parameters.

Let us now consider a few typical slow-wave structures. We may distinguish two general forms:

(1) Uniform.

(2) Filter or delay line structures.

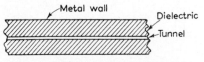

FIG. 1. Dielectric filled waveguide.

Typical examples of (1) are a waveguide filled with dielectric (Fig. 1) except for a small hole in which the beam flows. In this case $p \doteq c/(\epsilon\mu)^{1/2}$ or, practically, $c/\epsilon^{1/2}$. Since substances with fairly large values of ϵ and low loss (e.g., TiO_2) are known, this might be a practical system but careful analysis shows that it is not. A second uniform structure is the helix, which is the most broadly useful structure known today. This we discuss in some detail later.

Fig. 2 shows a variety of delay line structures. Fig. 2(a) is a disk-loaded waveguide, Fig. 2(b) a disk-loaded coaxial line with the inner line loaded, Fig. 2(c) represents either an interdigital line, in which case the end elevation is shown at c_1, or a corrugated waveguide, end elevation as at c_2. Fig. 2(d) represents the Karp

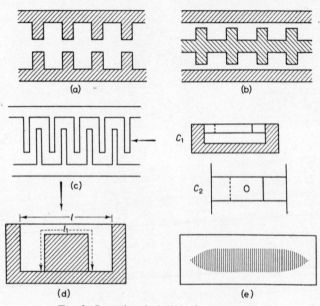

FIG. 2. Several typical delay line structures.

structure, named after its inventor. In this structure a ridged waveguide is covered by a conducting sheet in which a large number of $\lambda/2$ resonators are punched transverse to the direction of propagation. Fig. 2(e) shows this and the tapered matching sections at the ends. There are many other similar structures. All can be visualized as chain networks of elementary fourpoles in which the plane waveguide properties have been modified by loading with inductance or capacitance.

3.1. THE BRILLOUIN DIAGRAM

Our general understanding of the behaviour of slow-wave structures depends greatly on a diagrammatic representation of their properties, much used by BRILLOUIN.[1] This is a plot of ω against β, where β is the phase constant, as usual, for the structure. (Brillouin plots frequency against reciprocal wavelength, in his notation $\nu \sim a$.) From the definitions of p and g, straight lines through the origin of such a plot are lines of equal p while the tangents to the curve are lines of equal g.

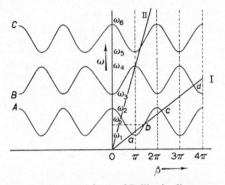

FIG. 3. A general form of Brillouin diagram.

Fig. 3 shows a Brillouin diagram drawn for a structure with no TEM mode, i.e., no propagation at zero frequency. Three pass-bands are shown; $\omega_1-\omega_2$, $\omega_3-\omega_4$, $\omega_5-\omega_6$. The straight line marked I intersects the lowest branch three times and the second branch once. Consider the intersections in turn. At a, g is small and negative, at b large and positive, at c negative and at d negative. A wave in which the group velocity is of opposite sign to the phase velocity is called a backward wave. We note that, for circuits with small values of loss/wavelength, the group velocity is the velocity of energy propagation and the sign of g determines the direction of energy flow. For example, if we connect a generator to one end of a backward-wave structure, g is directed away from the generator, p towards it; while for a forward-wave both p and g are directed away from the generator. Returning to line I, we see that there is only one forward-wave interaction, that at b, which is in the range $\pi < \beta < 2\pi$. This structure could then be used as a travelling-wave amplifier at the voltage corresponding with the slope of I, to amplify at b, however, I cuts the curve at a fairly steep angle and the ampli-

[1] BRILLOUIN; *Wave Propagation in Periodic Structures*. McGraw-Hill, New York, 1946.

fier would work substantially at a single frequency. Consider now the interaction of electrons represented by line II with the third harmonic. Here line II coincides with the $\omega \sim \beta$ plot over a considerable range of ω and wideband operation is possible. Clearly, the condition for this desirable state of affairs is simply $p = g$.†

We now introduce a few new terms, the branches of the curve A, B, C, etc., are the harmonics, as usual. The parts of the curve extended beyond $\beta = \pi$ are due to the space-harmonics or Hartree harmonics, Hartree having first isolated this concept in his work on cavity magnetrons. We characterize the particular structure yielding Fig. 3 as one in which the first pass-band extends from $\omega_1 - \omega_2$, the first space-harmonic being a backward wave and so on. For the second pass-band the first space-harmonic is a forward wave. Depending on the configuration of the structure we might equally well have had a forward first space-harmonic in the lower pass-band.

The portion of the diagram to the left of the β origin represents waves propagated in the opposite direction, left or right as the case may be. In ordinary circuit theory we are usually concerned with filter networks or transmission lines excited at one end only. In electron devices, however, the interaction takes place over the major part of the length of the circuit and not at the ends. The energy taken from the beam in the nth filter section is propagated half to the right and half to the left. We shall see, in detail, later that the direction of growth of the circuit wave depends on interference between the energy packets from the $(n - 1)$th and $(n + 1)$th sections. The existence of the oppositely directed waves is necessary to the operation of space-charge wave devices. This matter is stressed a little because books on filter theory sometimes omit the negative branches of the diagram.

It should now be clear that, if we can prepare a Brillouin diagram for any specified circuit, either experimentally or theoretically, we have all the information required to forecast the performance in interaction with electron beams, except for a knowledge of the actual field amplitudes, which is often given in the form of a coupling impedance. We can determine the voltage and frequency ranges for various interactions, find possible interfering modes and so on. Moreover, while an accurate estimate of Z_c is necessary, a semi-qualitative knowledge of the Brillouin diagram will show if the circuit is a good one or not.

---

† It is easy to prove, from the definitions of g and p, that $dp/d\beta = (1/\beta)(g - p)$.

Many other forms of diagram give similar information, but the Brillouin form is the most useful. Another common diagram is the dispersion curve in which p is plotted as a function of f or λ.

3.2. SIMPLE FILTER CIRCUITS

We recall the elementary theory of filters[2] in a form suited to our needs. Fig. 4(a) shows part of an infinite network built up from elementary π networks. The input impedance is the mid-shunt characteristic impedance Z_π. Fig. 4(b) is a similar T-based network

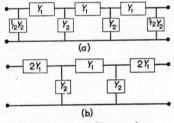

(a)

(b)

FIG. 4. π and T filter sections.

with mid-series characteristic impedance Z_r. We restrict ourselves entirely to purely reactive networks so that Y_1 and Y_2 are pure susceptances. The transmission along such networks is given by

$$V_n = V_0 \exp\left(-n\Gamma\right) \tag{1}$$

with a similar expression for the current. The propagation constant Γ, $(\Gamma = \alpha + j\beta)$ is given by

$$\cosh \Gamma = 1 + \frac{Y_2}{2Y_1} \tag{2}$$

For pure reactances Eq. (2) is real so we have, since $Y = jB$

$$\cosh \Gamma = \cosh \alpha \cos \beta = 1 + \frac{B_2}{2B_1} \tag{3}$$

$$\sinh \alpha \sin \beta = 0 \tag{4}$$

[2] For full treatments of filter theory see (in increasing order of complexity) WARE and READ; *Communication Circuits*, 3rd Ed. Wiley, 1949. SCHELKUNOFF; *Electromagnetic Waves*. Van Nostrand, 1943. GUILLEMIN; *Communication Networks*, Vol. 2, Wiley, 1935.

By definition, in the pass-band $\alpha = 0$, therefore

$$\cos \beta = 1 + \frac{B_2}{2B_1} \tag{5}$$

and B_2 must be of opposite sign from B_1. β has the range 0 to π. In the stop-band (4) shows that $\sin \beta = 0$, i.e., $\beta = 0$ or π. We now consider some specific cases.

3.2.1. Low-pass filter

Here $B_1 = -1/\omega L$, $B_2 = \omega C$ therefore

$$\cos \beta = \left(1 - \frac{\omega^2 LC}{2}\right) \tag{6}$$

The phase shift is zero at zero frequency and initially increases linearly with increasing frequency. Cut-off takes place at $\omega^2 = 4/LC$ where $\cos \beta = -1$, $\beta = \pi$. Differentiating Eq. (6) to determine the group velocity we find

$$g = \frac{d\omega}{d\beta} = \frac{\sin \beta}{\omega LC} \tag{7}$$

Thus $g = 0$ when $\beta = 0$ or π and g is positive for $0 < \beta < \pi$. When the group velocity is zero there can be no transmission of energy, which, of course, agrees with our deduction from the propagation constant. In lumped constant circuits there are no higher pass-bands, and the behaviour in the stop-band, which is important in

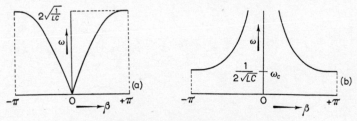

FIG. 5. (a) Brillouin diagram for a low-pass filter.
(b) The same for a high-pass filter.

filter theory, is of no importance to us. The $\omega \sim \beta$ diagram is shown in Fig. 5(a). It is clear from the figure and can easily be shown analytically, that $p \doteq g$ for low frequencies, i.e., up to about

20% of cut-off. The circuit may therefore be used for travelling-wave amplification at low frequencies and model T.W.T.s have in fact been based on this circuit, mainly for pedagogic purposes.

The characteristic impedance

$$Z_\tau = \pm \frac{1}{2B_1} \left\{ -\frac{(B_2 + 4B_1)}{B_2} \right\}^{1/2} \tag{8}$$

while $\qquad Z_\tau . Z_\pi = -B_1 . B_2 \tag{9}$

Signs are chosen so as to make Z positive in the pass-band. Putting in the values of B_1, B_2 and the cut-off frequency f_c we have

$$Z_\tau = \sqrt{\frac{L}{C}} \left(1 - \frac{f^2}{f_c^2} \right)^{1/2}$$

$$Z_\pi = \sqrt{\frac{L}{C}} \left(1 - \frac{f^2}{f_c^2} \right)^{-1/2} \tag{10}$$

Then, if we built a T.W.T. using this circuit and the beam interacted with the capacitances, the voltage acting on the beam would be related to the circuit power by

$$V^2 = 2PZ_\pi \tag{11}$$

3.2.2. The high-pass filter

Here $B_1 = \omega C$, $B_2 = \omega L$. In the pass-band

$$\cos \beta = 1 - \frac{1}{2\omega^2 LC} \tag{12}$$

Fig. 5(b) shows the $\omega \sim \beta$ plot. Here g is negative, $0 < \beta < \pi$ so the circuit is a backward-wave circuit

$$Z_\tau = \sqrt{\frac{L}{C}} \left(1 - \frac{f_c^2}{f^2} \right)^{1/2}$$

$$Z_\pi = \sqrt{\frac{L}{C}} \left(1 - \frac{f_c^2}{f^2} \right)^{-1/2} \tag{13}$$

3.2.3. Band-pass filters

The simplest band-pass filter is obtained by connecting two filters in tandem, a l.p. filter with cut-off f_l and a h.p. with cut-off f_h.

The frequencies must be arranged so that $f_l > f_h$. The configuration of a filter of this type is shown in Fig. 6(a). The filter is of the "constant k" type if $L_1C_1 = L_2C_2$. We shall not say much about this filter as its properties are somewhat different from those of waveguide filters. The angular frequency for which $\beta = 0$ is $\omega_0 = 1/(L_1C_1)^{1/2} = 1/(L_2C_2)^{1/2}$ and $\omega_{cu} \cdot \omega_{cl} = \omega_0^2$, ω_{cu} and ω_{cl} being the upper and lower cut-offs. If $L_1C_1 \neq L_2C_2$ the filter shows two separate pass-bands which join when the resonances are made equal. Clearly, the lower part of the pass-band corresponds with backward-wave interaction, the upper part with forward waves.

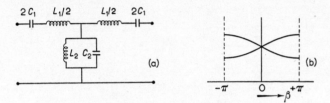

FIG. 6. (a) Simple bandpass filter section.
(b) Brillouin diagram for this section.

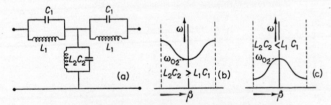

FIG. 7. (a) Bandpass filter of confluent pass-band type.
(b) Brillouin diagram when $L_2C_2 > L_1C_1$.
(c) Brillouin diagram when $L_2C_2 < L_1C_1$.

Fig. 7(a) shows a band-pass filter which does behave like waveguide structures. Here we can easily show that

$$\cos \beta = \frac{1 + (C_2L_1/C_1L_2)^{1/2}(\omega/\omega_{02} - \omega_{02}/\omega)}{2(\omega/\omega_{01} - \omega_{01}/\omega)} \qquad (14)$$

and $\beta = 0$ when $\qquad \omega = \omega_{02} = \dfrac{1}{(C_2L_2)^{1/2}} \qquad (15)$

When we consider the condition for $\beta = \pi$ we find there are two cases to be evaluated, $L_1C_1 > L_2C_2$ and $L_1C_1 < L_2C_2$. ($L_1C_1 = L_2C_2$ obviously yields no propagation.)

Case 1. $L_2C_2 > L_1C_1$

Here ω_{02} is the lower limit to the pass-band. The upper limit, $\omega_{cu} = \omega_{02}([1 + 4L_2/L_1]/[1 + 4C_1/C_2])^{1/2}$ The $\omega \sim \beta$ diagram is shown in Fig. 7(b).

Case 2. $L_1C_1 > L_2C_2$

ω_{02} is now the upper limit to the pass-band and $\omega_{cl} = \omega_{02}([1 + 4L_2/L_1]/[1 + 4C_1/C_2])^{1/2}$ once more. The behaviour of β is shown in Fig. 7(c).

Here, Fig. 7(b) shows the behaviour of a forward-wave structure and Fig. 7(c) that of a backward-wave one. An ordinary cylindrical waveguide exhibits roughly the behaviour of Fig. 7(b) if the upper cut-off is extended to infinite frequency. However, as we proved in Chapter 2, the phase velocity only diminishes to c at infinite frequency.

For all the circuits discussed we note that the group velocity, $g = 0$, at the cut-off frequencies, whenever these are finite and different from zero. This is in accordance with physical intuition. Interested readers can find tabulated data for many other types of filter section in radio handbooks.[3]

Before leaving the discussion of lumped constant networks we must comment on a question which may well have occurred to the reader. This is, "why are l.p. filters with properties shown in Fig. 5(a) not useful in video amplifiers, working down to d.c.?" The answer, which will emerge later, is that the r.f. current on the electron beam is directly proportional to ω so that the processes used for space-charge wave amplification will not operate at very low frequencies. The lower limit naturally depends on the actual parameters of the tube under discussion.

3.3. SPECIAL RELATIONS FOR SLOW WAVES

In the study of slow waves it is possible to introduce essential simplifications in the form of the wave equations. This reduces the problem to that of finding solutions to Laplace's equation. This procedure is valid only in so far as the phase velocity of the waves is much less than c. The first part of this section deals with this reduction, while the rest of the section treats some other useful relations which, for instance, allow one to estimate impedances from measured values of group velocity.

---

[3] A good collection is given in *Reference Data for Radio Engineers*, 4th Ed. Federal Telephone and Radio Co., New York, 1956.

The z direction is taken as the direction of propagation of the wave and of the electron beam, except in azimuthal devices, e.g., magnetrons and M-type carcinotrons. We are therefore mainly concerned with structures in which the field component E_z exists and thus with TM modes. Let us suppose that we have such a structure represented in a rectangular system of co-ordinates and that it propagates a wave with phase velocity p, $p \ll c$. Then, the wave equation for E_z is (Eq. (60) Chapter 2)

$$\nabla_t^2 \,.\, E_z + (k^2 - \beta^2)E_z = 0 \tag{16}$$

and (Eq. (57) in Chapter 2)

$$\beta^2 = \frac{\omega^2}{p^2} = \frac{\omega^2}{c^2} - \frac{\omega_c^2}{c^2} = k^2 - k_c^2 \tag{17}$$

But, since $p \ll c$, $\beta^2 \gg k^2$ and $k^2 - \beta^2$ is negative.

Then $$\nabla_t^2 \,.\, E_z - (\beta^2 - k^2)E_z = 0 \tag{18}$$

If we suppose, for a moment, that $\partial^2 E_z/\partial y^2 = 0$, the solutions to Eq. (18) are of the form

$$E_z = (A \sinh\, \zeta x + \beta \cosh \zeta x) \exp j(\omega t - \beta z) \tag{19a}$$

where $$\zeta = (\beta^2 - k^2)^{1/2} \tag{20}$$

Up to this point we have preserved the notation of the last chapter, which is commonly used in books on waveguides. It is now convenient to change over our notation to the common usage on valves, in which case we replace ζ by γ and note that $k = \beta_0$. Thus

$$E_z = (A \sinh \gamma x + \beta \cosh \gamma x) \exp j(\omega t - \beta z) \tag{19b}$$

Similarly, in the cylindrical case, we have

$$E_z = (AI_0(\gamma r) + BK_0(\gamma r)) \exp j(\omega t - \beta z) \tag{21}$$

It will be observed that these fields are solutions of Laplace's equation, as stated.

It is important to remember that the functions sinh, cosh, I_0, K_0 which appear in Eqs. (19) and (21) have no zeros except at the origin or infinity. In mathematical language these functions do not form orthogonal sets and thus it is not possible to satisfy boundary conditions by the technique of Fourier expansions of the transverse fields. Instead, the boundary conditions are satisfied by Fourier expansions in the longitudinal direction. This process is termed the resolution of the fields into space-harmonics and is discussed in full in the next section. A consequence of this observation is that there are no nodes in any of the fields at constant z.

In general, we find that the actual boundary conditions can only be satisfied by combination of TE and TM waves, although the interactions with the latter are much more important for the electronics of the structure.

If we relax the restrictions that $\partial E_z/\partial y$, $\partial E_z/\partial\theta = 0$, then more complicated wave functions with nodal properties result. The study of such structures has not been carried very far except in the case of the helix, which may be considered as a member of this class.

We conclude this discussion by summarizing in Table I the expressions for the field components of slow waves. These are obtained by specializing the results of Section 2.3.1 in accordance with the notation of this section.

TABLE 1

Field components for slow waves

Co-ordinate system	T.M. waves	T.E. waves
Rectangular	$E_z = A_x \exp j(\omega t - \beta z)$	$H_z = A_x \exp j(\omega t + \beta z)$
$\dfrac{\partial}{\partial y} = 0$	$E_x = j\dfrac{\beta}{\gamma^2}\dfrac{\partial E_z}{\partial x}$	$H_x = j\dfrac{\beta}{\gamma^2}\dfrac{\partial H_z}{\partial x}$
	$H_y = j\dfrac{k}{Z_0\gamma^2}\dfrac{\partial E_z}{\partial x}$	$E_y = -j\dfrac{kZ_0}{\gamma^2}\dfrac{\partial H_z}{\partial x}$
Cylindrical polar	$E_z = A_r \exp j(\omega t - \beta z)$	$H_z = A_r \exp j(\omega t - \beta z)$
$\dfrac{\partial}{\partial\theta} = 0$	$E_r = j\dfrac{\beta}{\gamma^2}\cdot\dfrac{\partial E_z}{\partial r}$	$H_r = j\dfrac{\beta}{\gamma^2}\dfrac{\partial H_z}{\partial r}$
	$H_\theta = j\dfrac{k}{\gamma^2 Z_0}\dfrac{\partial E_z}{\partial r}$	$E_\theta = -j\dfrac{kZ_0}{\gamma^2}\dfrac{\partial H_z}{\partial r}$
Azimuthal polar $\dfrac{\partial}{\partial z} = 0$	$H_z = A \exp j(\omega t - \beta z)$ $\qquad E_r = -j\dfrac{Z_0}{k}\dfrac{1}{r}\dfrac{\partial H_z}{\partial\theta}$ $\qquad E_\theta = j\dfrac{Z_0}{k}\dfrac{\partial H_z}{\partial r}$	

In the above, $k = \omega/c = \omega\sqrt{(\epsilon_0\mu_0)}$, $Z_0 = \sqrt{(\mu_0/\epsilon_0)} = 377$ ohms. The slower the wave, the better the approximation $\beta \doteq \gamma$.

E

Next, we take up the discussion of the circuit in terms of group velocity and stored energy. If W is the energy stored per unit length of the line, P is the power flow and g the group velocity, then, by definition,

$$P = W \cdot g \qquad (22)$$

for the power fed into the line during one second is stored in the length g. Now, both g and the electric fields are quantities susceptible to precise measurement. Thus, if we express W in terms of the electric fields, Eq. (22) enables us to determine P. In turn the goodness of a circuit for use in conjunction with an electron beam depends on a coupling impedance, one definition† of which is

$$Z_c = \frac{E^2}{\beta^2 P} \qquad (23)$$

where E is the longitudinal field, usually at the centre of the beam Since

$$Z_c = \frac{E^2}{\beta^2 W g} \qquad (24)$$

Z_c can be determined from the electric fields and g. Approximate expressions for the stored energy can frequently be determined from simplified analyses of real structures. PIERCE[4] gives some examples in Appendix III of his book, one of which may be quoted as an illustration. In a cylindrical co-ordinate system we suppose that the E_r and E_z components to be known at $r = a$. Pierce shows the average stored electric energy to be

$$W_E = \left(\frac{1}{2}\right)\left(\frac{\epsilon}{2}\right) \int_{r=0}^{\infty} [(E_{r\max})^2 + (E_{z\max})^2] \cdot 2\pi r\, dr \qquad (25)$$

The total energy $W = W_E + W_M = 2W_E$
Putting in the field expressions in terms of the arbitrary constant A_r

$$W = A_r^2 \cdot \frac{\pi \epsilon a}{\gamma}\left[\frac{I_1(\gamma a)}{I_0(\gamma a)} + \frac{K_1(\gamma a)}{K_0(\gamma a)}\right] \qquad (26)$$

and

$$\frac{E^2}{\beta^2 P} = \frac{c}{g}\left[\frac{120}{\beta a(I_1/I_0 + K_1/K_0)}\right] \qquad (27)$$

a measurement of g can thus be used to obtain a value for the coupling impedance. Other examples are given in the same reference.

---

† This is the original form, due to PIERCE.[4] We later use the preferred form $E^2/2\beta^2 P$.

[4] PIERCE; *Traveling-Wave Tubes*, Chapter 2, p. 17. Van Nostrand, 1950.

3.4 SPACE-HARMONICS, SOMETIMES CALLED HARTREE HARMONICS

Fig. 8 shows a disk-loaded circular waveguide together with the notation used for this discussion. This structure combines mathematical simplicity with a certain degree of practical utility. We use it as a guinea-pig. Let us assume that we have found a solution to the wave equation which obeys the boundary conditions, e.g., $E(r, \theta, z_0)$ is such a solution at $z = z_0$. Then at $z = z_0 + mL$ the solution can only be a multiple of that at z.

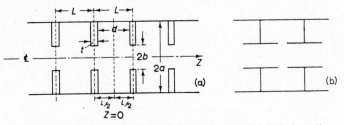

FIG. 8. Two versions of disk-loaded circular waveguide. This delay line is used in linear accelerators.

Thus $E(r, \theta, z_0 + L) = c_1 E(r, \theta, z_0)$

$$E(r, \theta, z_0 + 2L) = c_1 E(r, \theta, z_0 + L) = c_1^2 E(r, \theta, z_0) \text{ etc.,} \quad (28)$$

or $E(r, \theta, z_0 + mL) = c_1^m E(r, \theta, z_0)$

The analogy, which we have already suggested, between the sections of a lumped constant filter and the cells of a waveguide delay line, suggests that we put

$$c_1 = \exp(-j\phi_0) = \exp(-j\beta_0 L) \quad (29)$$

We note that this choice of c_1 has the property $|c_1| = 1$ which ensures that the geometric progression formed by summing the fields over an infinite chain of cells remains finite.

We now write down a Fourier expansion for the field, using the length L as the period of our functions. This must be done at a specific time t, i.e., we must write the Fourier expansion of

$$\exp j\omega t \, E(r, \theta, z) \quad (30)$$

But the time is related to distance along the structure by $\omega t = \beta_0 z$ so Eq. (30) becomes

$$\exp\left(j\beta_0 z\right) \mathbf{E}(r, \theta, z) = \sum_{n=-\infty}^{+\infty} A_n \exp\left(-j\frac{2\pi n}{L}z\right)$$

or

$$\mathbf{E}(r, \theta, z) = \sum A_n \exp\left\{-j\left(\beta_0 + \frac{2\pi n}{L}\right)z\right\} \quad (31)$$

$$= \sum_{-\infty}^{+\infty} A_n \exp\left(-j\beta_n z\right)$$

$$\beta_n = \beta_0 \pm \frac{2\pi n}{L}, \quad n = 0, 1, 2, \text{etc.} \quad (32)$$

This result is a consequence of Floquet's theorem.

Equation (31) shows that the field may be expanded as an infinite series of waves, all with the same frequency but with different phase velocities. Using Eq. (32) the phase velocities are given by

$$p_n = \frac{\omega}{\beta_0 \pm 2\pi n/L} \quad (33)$$

These waves, which serve to fulfil the spatial boundary condition, were first investigated by D. R. Hartree in his wartime investigations on magnetrons. They are sometimes called "Hartree Harmonics," the more usual term being space harmonics. German writers call them "Teilwellen", objecting to the word harmonic as all the frequencies are identical. This word might be translated into English as "partial waves", abbreviated to "partials". There is a case for the use of the latter term, if only on the score of brevity.

If we use Eq. (33) to determine the group velocity, we find

$$\frac{1}{g} = \frac{d\beta_n}{d\omega} = \frac{d\beta_0}{d\omega} \quad (34)$$

Since Eq. (34) does not depend on n all the partials have the same group velocity. However, p depends on n and, since $0 < \beta_0 L < \pi$, the largest phase velocity is p_0, i.e., ω/β_0. p_1 is at most $p_0/3$ while $p_0/2 < |p_{-1}| < p_0$, p_{-1} being obviously negative. In this way we can obtain interactions between electromagnetic waves and quite slow electron beams for, to obtain interaction, it is only necessary to make the electron velocity equal to the phase velocity of one of the partials. If this is done, all the partials, i.e., the complete wave-system, is amplified. However, the higher order partials decrease very rapidly with distance from the confining conductors and it is, at present,† usual to confine the range of operation of practical valves to p_0, p_1, p_{-1}.

It is useful at this point to make a summary of the quantities which we must know before we can calculate the interaction between a beam and a slow-wave structure. These are

(1) The coupling resistance $Z_c = E_z \cdot E_z^*/2\beta^2 P$.

(2) The power flow $P = \frac{1}{2}Re\iint_{\text{section}}(E \times H^*)_z \, dA$.

This is equal to the product of the stored energy per unit section length and the group velocity, i.e., $P = W \cdot g$

$$W = 2 \cdot \frac{\epsilon_0}{2} \frac{1}{L}\int_{Z_n}^{Z_n + L} dz \iint (E \times E^*) \, dA$$

The evaluation of the fields, from which these quantities are derived, is discussed in the rest of the chapter.

3.5. THE DISK-LOADED WAVEGUIDE

We now commence the study of actual slow-wave structures, which might be used in real valves. The simplest structure, from the theoretical viewpoint, which has any useful properties is the disk-loaded waveguide. This is extensively used in linear accelerators and the theory has therefore been studied by several investigators.[5,6,7] We here follow mainly the work of Walkinshaw. The notation used is shown in Fig. 8. The structure is divided into two regions, Region I $r \leqslant b$, where the fields are given by the slow-wave equations developed in Section 3.3. and Region II, $b < r < a$ where the fields are of radial transmission line type. The fields are matched by equating the E_z's at $r = b$ and by equating the H_θ's at the same radius. Practically, the last step is made approximately, by equating the mean H_θ in Region I to the first term of the series giving H_0 in Region II. This procedure results in an equation, often referred to as the dispersion equation, giving the radial propagation constant γ as a function of frequency. Knowing the explicit forms of the slow-wave fields the arbitrary constants for a given power flow are determined by use of the Poynting vector. Since we are interested

---

† If annular electron beams are developed so as to operate at even a small fraction of their limiting perveance, this situation would radically change.

[5] CHU and HANSEN; *J. Appl. Phys.*, 1947, **18**, 996.
[6] BRILLOUIN; *J. Appl. Phys.*, 1948, **19**, 1023.
[7] WALKINSHAW; *Proc. Phys. Soc.*, 1948, **61**, 246.

in interactions with charges moving in the z direction, we restrict ourselves to TM waves which exhibit an electric field in this direction.

Then we have, in Region I,

$$E_z = \sum_{-\infty}^{+\infty} A_n I_0(\gamma_n \cdot r) \exp j(\omega t - \beta_n z) \tag{35}$$

$$H_\theta = \sum_{-\infty}^{+\infty} A_n \frac{k_c}{Z_0 \gamma_n} I_1(\gamma_n \cdot r) \exp j(\omega t - \beta_n z) \tag{36}$$

We next determine the values of A_n by choosing some reasonable expression for E_z at $r = b$. Two choices are possible; these are

(1) $E_z = \text{constant} = E_0$ \hfill (37)

(2) $V_z = V_0 \sin^{-1}\left(\dfrac{2z}{d}\right), \qquad E_z = \left(\dfrac{E_0}{(1 - (2z/d)^2)^{1/2}}\right)$ \hfill (38)

The first of these would apply to the case when t is large and d is rather small, so that the radial transmission line is thin. The second is widely used in the theory of velocity modulation tube gaps and represents the field when such gaps have rather thin, sharp lips[8] as shown in Fig. 8(b). This is the expression used by Walkinshaw, who, however, points out that the dispersion relation is not critically dependent on the form of field assumed. We can retain both forms if we write

$$E_z = \frac{E_0}{\{1 - \delta(2z/d)^2\}^{1/2}}$$

where $\delta = 0$ or 1, according to the form we wish to assume. Then we have at $r = b$

$$E_{zI} = \begin{cases} \dfrac{E_0}{\{1 - \delta(2z/d)^2\}^{1/2}} & |z| \leqslant \dfrac{d}{2} \\[2mm] 0 & \dfrac{d}{2} \leqslant |z| \leqslant \dfrac{L}{2} \end{cases} \tag{39}$$

and by the usual integration to determine the Fourier coefficients

$$A_n I_0(\gamma_n b) = \frac{E_0}{L} \int_{-d/2}^{d/2} \frac{\exp j\beta_n z}{\{1 - \delta(2z/d)^2\}^{1/2}} \, dz \tag{40}$$

$$= \frac{E_0 d}{L} \begin{cases} \pi/2 \, J_0\,(\beta_n d/2), & \delta = 1 \\[2mm] \sin(\beta_n d/2)/\beta_n d/2, & \delta = 0 \end{cases} \tag{41}$$

[8] BECK; *Velocity Modulated Thermionic Tubes*, pp. 64–65, Cambridge University Press, 1948.

The similarity between Eq. (41) and the gap modulation co-efficients will be obvious to readers familiar with these quantities.

We now turn our attention to Region II. Here, the boundary conditions are $E_r = 0$, $z = \pm d/2$, $E_z = 0$ at $r = a$. The appropriate wave-functions are of somewhat more general type than any encountered in Chapter II, since the Bessel functions (Y_m) of the second kind are not excluded. A tabulation of the TE and TM fields is given by BECK.[9] For the present case, in which there is no θ variation, the expression for E_z which satisfies the above boundary conditions is

$$E_{zII} = \sum_{-\infty}^{+\infty} B_n \left[J_0(k'r) - \frac{J_0(k'a)}{Y_0(k'a)} Y_0(k'r) \right] \cos \frac{\pi n z}{d} \qquad (42)$$

where

$$k' = \left\{ k^2 - \left(\frac{\pi n}{d} \right)^2 \right\}^{1/2} \qquad (43)$$

Usually, only a single term of this series is used, so carrying out the determination of B_0, we have

$$B_0 \left[J_0(kb) - \frac{J_0(ka)}{Y_0(ka)} \cdot Y_0(kb) \right] = E_0 \begin{cases} \pi/2, \delta = 1 \\ 1, \quad \delta = 0 \end{cases} \qquad (44)$$

Finally, we approximately match the magnetic fields at $r = b$, putting

$$\frac{1}{d} \int_{-d/2}^{d/2} H_{\theta I} \, dz = H_{\theta II} = j \frac{B_0}{Z_0} \left(J_1(kb) - \frac{J_0(ka)}{Y_0(ka)} Y_1(kb) \right) \qquad (45)$$

Collecting the results, the dispersion relation becomes

$$\frac{1}{k} \left[\frac{J_1(kb) Y_0(ka) - Y_1(kb) J_0(ka)}{J_0(kb) Y_0(ka) - Y_0(kb) J_0(ka)} \right]$$
$$= \frac{db}{L} \sum_{-\infty}^{+\infty} \frac{I_1(\gamma_n b)}{\gamma_n b \cdot I_0(\gamma_n b)} \begin{cases} [\sin (\beta_n d/2)/(\beta_n d/2)] J_0(\beta_n d/2), & \delta = 1 \\ \sin^2 (\beta_n d/2)/(\beta_n d/2)^2, & \delta = 0 \end{cases} \qquad (46)$$

The L.H.S. of this rather formidable expression is easily plotted for any chosen ratio of a/b, the R.H.S. can be plotted as a function of b and the intersections determined.

By considering that only the $n = 0$ mode is important and integrating the power flow over the inner cross-section of the guide, Walkinshaw obtains the following result for the axial field at the guide centre

$$E_{z0} = \left\{ \frac{2 P Z_0 \gamma_0^2}{\pi b^2 k \beta [I_1^2(\gamma_0 b) - I_0(\gamma_0 b) I_2(\gamma_0 b)]} \right\}^{1/2} \qquad (47)$$

[9] BECK; loc. cit., pp. 29–30.

Fig. 9 reproduces his plot of Eq. (47). This figure illustrates one of the defects of this circuit for use in valves. The field on the axis is very small for low phase velocities ($p = 0.1 - 0.2c$) unless b/λ is made very small. This means that there is only a small area through which electron flow can take place.

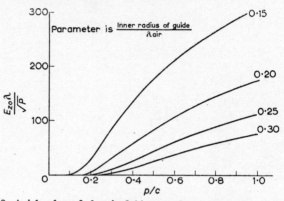

FIG. 9. Axial value of electric field strength as a function of relative wave velocity.

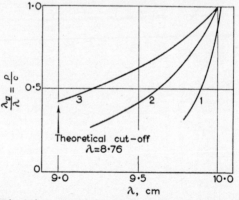

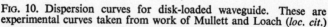

FIG. 10. Dispersion curves for disk-loaded waveguide. These are experimental curves taken from work of Mullett and Loach (loc. cit.)

Fig. 10 illustrates the major defect which renders this circuit of very little value. It shows a plot of the dispersion, expressed in the form $\lambda_g/\lambda = p/c$ as a function of λ. The curves relate to experimental results of MULLETT and LOACH,[10] which, however, may be

---

[10] MULLETT and LOACH; *Proc. Phys. Soc.*, 1948, **61**, 271.

taken to be in excellent agreement with the predictions of the Walkinshaw theory. The dimensions of the three guides studied are given on the figure, but all show very marked dispersion, i.e., p/c varies rapidly with λ or f. The least dispersive circuit is that for which a/λ is greatest. But Fig. 9 shows that the choice of dimensions which leads to minimum dispersion leads to unacceptably low values of coupling impedance and the circuit would only be useful for narrow-band amplification at relatively high voltages. This is unfortunate, because the structure is easy to make and capable of dissipating a good deal of power so that it would not matter if the beam interception were considerable.

A very similar structure, which can be handled by a parallel mathematical technique, is the disk-loaded coaxial line. Two variants of this are possible; that with the disks on the inner conductor and that with the outer loaded. The first of these has been studied in some detail by DEWEY et al.[11] Their results indicate that the dispersion can be minimized by reducing the spacing between the edges of the loading disks and the inside of the outer conductor. From the practical aspect this leads to a thin, annular electron beam, but such beams are theoretically able to carry large currents. Further discussion of this circuit is given by FIELD.[12]

Before discussing more practical types of slow-wave structure we wish to draw attention to the very illuminating discussion of lumped-circuit analogues given by PIERCE.[13] This gives a clear picture of what can be done by physical insight and very little mathematics.

3.6. INTERDIGITAL DELAY LINES

The simplest type of interdigital delay line is that shown in Fig. 2(c) with the fingers of the type shown in c_2. A line of this form could clearly be made by bending a parallel line in which the two conductors are strips instead of round wires. The TEM mode is supported by a system of this type, which has been exhaustively analysed since the time of Maxwell himself. The delay, here, is simply due to the fact that the wave has to cover a much greater distance than does the beam. If we denote the length of the fingers by h and the distance between fingers by L, the delay ratio is h/L. Strip transmission lines have been extensively reinvestigated since

[11] DEWEY, PARZEN and MARCHESE; *Proc. I.R.E.*, 1951, **39**, 153.
[12] FIELD; *Proc. I.R.E.*, 1949, **37**, 34.
[13] PIERCE; *Traveling-Wave Tubes.* Chapter 4, Van Nostrand, 1950.

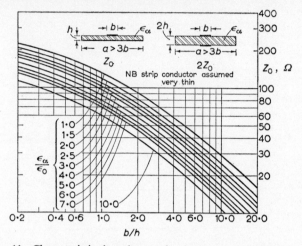

FIG. 11. Characteristic impedance of microstrip as a function of dielectric constant and strip width.

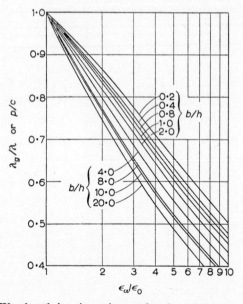

FIG. 12. Wavelength in microstrip as a function of dielectric constant and strip width.

the advent of the microstrip transmission system and a full account of this work is given by BLACK and HIGGINS.[14] DUKES[15] has confirmed the theoretical work by electrolytic trough plots. Dukes has prepared a plot of the "pseudo-TEM" solution for two types of line which is reproduced in Figs. 11 and 12. This shows that, for lines in vacuum, impedances of several hundred ohms are obtained when the breadth of the strips is roughly equal to the spacing between them. From the very simplest considerations it is clear that decreasing the width of the strip has much more effect on the capacitance per unit length than it does on the inductance and that Z_0 therefore increases. The fact that such relatively high values of Z_0 can be easily obtained is very encouraging from our point of view as it means that the electric fields associated with the system are strong and it thus gives promise of useful characteristics in interaction with the beam. Fig. 12 shows the corresponding phase velocity.

The interdigital line with fingers of the type indicated in c_1 can now be seen to be analogous to the second type of strip line, sketched on Fig. 11, that in which the breadth of one conductor only is reduced. The other is given the form of a ground plate. If the fingers now represent approximate quarter wavelength structures they may be alternately connected to either side of the ground plate without altering the performance of the circuit. This form of circuit has been treated by FLETCHER[16] and LEBLOND and MOURIER.[17] We here follow the treatment of Fletcher which proceeds in exactly the same manner as the last section. The form of circuit analysed and the notation are shown in Fig. 13. With the usual slow-wave assumptions we can write the TEM mode voltage as

$$V(x, y, z, t) = F(x, z) \exp(j\omega t)\left\{A \exp\left(-j.\frac{2\pi y}{\lambda}\right) + \beta \exp\left(j.\frac{2\pi y}{\lambda}\right)\right\}$$
(48)

with
$$\frac{\partial^2 F}{\partial x^2} + \frac{\partial^2 F}{\partial z^2} = 0$$
(49)

The voltage of the mth finger, that at $x = 0$, $z = mL$ is called V_m and the corresponding current, $I_m(y)$ which travels along this finger in the y direction. This current will later be found from the line

[14] BLACK and HIGGINS; *Trans. I.R.E.*, 1955, **MTT-3**, 93.
[15] DUKES; *Proc. I.E.E.*, 1956, **103**, 319.
[16] FLETCHER; *Proc. I.R.E.*, 1952, **40**, 951.
[17] LEBLOND and MOURIER; *Ann. Radioélec.*, 1954, **9**, 180; 1954, **9**, 311.

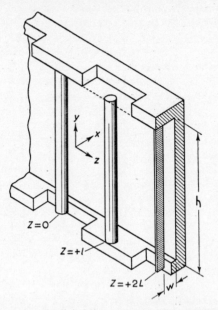

FIG. 13. Interdigital line, as analysed by Fletcher.

integral of H over the periphery of the finger. Since alternate fingers are connected to the base plate at $y \pm h/2$ the boundary conditions are of the form

$$V_{2n}\left(\frac{h}{2}\right) = V_{2n+1}\left(-\frac{h}{2}\right) = 0 \qquad (50)$$

$$I_{2n}\left(-\frac{h}{2}\right) = I_{2n+1}\left(\frac{h}{2}\right) = 0 \qquad (51)$$

These merely express the facts that the voltage is zero at a short circuit and the current zero at an open circuit. They also show that the period of the structure corresponds with $2L$, for the voltages and currents change by 2π over this distance. Writing $\Phi = 2\pi y/\lambda$, the most general solution for V_m is

$$V_m = (A_1 \cos \Phi + A_2 \sin \Phi) \exp \{-jm(\theta + \pi)\} + \\ + (A_3 \sin \Phi + A_4 \cos \Phi) \exp (-jm\theta) \qquad (52)$$

The characteristic impedance $Z_0(\theta)$ is defined as the ratio of V_m

to I_m for a single mode, propagating in the $+y$ direction when the z variation is a single mode varying as $\exp(-jm\theta)$. Then

$$I_m = \frac{j}{Z_0(\theta + \pi)} (-A_1 \sin \Phi + A_2 \cos \Phi) \exp \{-jm(\theta + \pi)\} +$$

$$+ \frac{j}{Z_0(\theta)} (A_3 \cos \Phi - A_4 \sin \Phi) \exp(-jm\theta) \quad (53)$$

The boundary conditions (50) put into (52) give

$$\left. \begin{aligned} A_1 &= -A_3 \tan(\Phi_0/2) \\ A_2 &= -A_4 \cot(\Phi_0/2) \end{aligned} \right\} \quad (54)$$

where
$$\Phi_0 = \frac{2\pi h}{\lambda} \quad (55)$$

These results, and the boundary conditions Eq. (51) are next put into Eq. (53) and solved for A_1 and A_2.

There are two sets of waves.

(1) $\quad A_2 = 0, \quad Z_0(\theta + \pi) = Z_0(\theta) \tan^2(\Phi_0/2) \quad (56)$

(2) $\quad A_1 = 0, \quad Z_0(\theta + \pi) = Z_0(\theta) \cot^2(\Phi_0/2) \quad (57)$

But, as the following reasoning shows, these are identical. Z_0 is the same for waves in the $-y$ direction as in the $+y$ direction, and therefore the same for $+\theta$ as for $-\theta$. Moreover, adding $2n\pi$ to θ does not alter the description of the mode.

Thus, $\quad Z_0(\theta) = Z_0(-\theta) = Z_0(\theta + 2n\pi) \quad (58)$

$$Z_0(\theta + \pi) = Z_0(\theta - \pi) = Z_0(\pi - \theta) \quad (59)$$

If we consider Eq. (56) as an equation defining $f_1(\Phi_0)$ as a function of frequency and Eq. (57) similarly for $f_2(\Phi_0)$ we now see that $f_1(\Phi_0) = f_2(\Phi_0) + \pi$ and the current and voltage waves show that wave 2 for $\theta + \pi$ is identical with wave 1. We continue with wave 1 only.

From Eq. (59), if $\theta = \pi/2$, $Z_0(\theta + \pi) = Z_0(\theta)$ and Eq. (56) then shows that $\Phi_0 = \pi/2$, independent of the value of Z_0. Therefore, when the fingers are exactly one-quarter wavelength long, the phase constant $\theta = \pi/2$, which is just the result we obtain when a wave with the velocity of light travels up one finger and down the next. Since the pass-band extends from $\theta = 0$ to $\theta = \pi$ the value of frequency which makes the length of the fingers equal to $\lambda/4$ is, at least approximately, the mid-band frequency for the interdigital line.

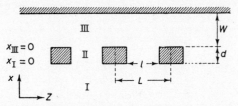

FIG. 14. Notation used for the fields on the fingers.

We next evaluate the characteristic impedance Z_0 for rectangular fingers as shown in Fig. 14. We need consider only one of the TEM waves which, by itself, need not satisfy any boundary condition in the $\pm y$ direction.

We take $V_m = A_0 \exp -j(\Phi + m\theta)$, $z = mL$.

I_m and $Z_0 = V_m/I_m$ are to be determined.

In the three regions shown on Fig. 14 we have

$$E_{zI} = \sum_{n=-\infty}^{+\infty} F_{nI} \exp |\theta + 2\pi n| \frac{x}{L} \exp(-j\Phi) \left\{\exp -j(\theta + 2\pi n)\frac{z}{L}\right\}$$
(60)

which goes to zero as x goes to $-\infty$.

$$E_{zIII} = \sum_{-\infty}^{+\infty} F_{nIII} \frac{\sinh(\theta + 2\pi n)([W-x]/L)}{\sinh(\theta + 2\pi n)W/L}$$
$$\times \exp(-j\Phi) \exp\left\{-j(\theta + 2\pi n)\frac{z}{L}\right\} \quad (61)$$

which goes to zero at $x = W$, if we now take the x origin at the other edge of the finger. Between the fingers the field is assumed to be uniform, which is physically reasonable for the geometry under discussion. Therefore

$$E_{zII} = \frac{V_{m+1} - V_m}{l} = E_0 \exp(-j\Phi) \exp -j(m + \tfrac{1}{2})\theta \quad (62)$$

for $(m + \tfrac{1}{2})L - l/2 < Z < (m + \tfrac{1}{2})L + l/2$, and zero elsewhere.

Here
$$E_0 = -\left|2j\frac{A_0}{2} \sin \frac{\theta}{2}\right| \quad (63)$$

For the electric field to be continuous across the boundaries

$$\sum F_{nI} \exp\left\{-j(\theta + 2\pi n)\frac{z}{L}\right\} = \sum F_{nIII} \exp\left\{-j(\theta + 2\pi n)\frac{z}{L}\right\}$$

$$= \begin{cases} E_0 \exp -j(m + \frac{1}{2})\theta, & (m + \frac{1}{2})L - \frac{l}{2} < z < (m + \frac{1}{2})L + \frac{l}{2} \\ 0, & mL - \frac{L-l}{2} < z < mL + \frac{L-l}{2} \end{cases} \quad (64)$$

If we multiply by $\exp j(\theta + 2\pi n)z/L$ and integrate over z from mL to $(m + 1)L$, we obtain

$$F_{nI} = F_{nIII} = F_n = (-1)^n \frac{l}{L} \frac{E_0 \sin (\theta + 2\pi n) l/2L}{(\theta + 2\pi n) l/2L} \quad (65)$$

which will be recognized as the familiar Fourier expansion of a rectangular wave-form. The rest of the field components can now be written down, using Maxwell's equations as given in Section 2.3.2. They are

$$H_{xI} = \sqrt{\frac{\epsilon_0}{\mu_0}} \sum F_n \exp |\theta + 2\pi n|\frac{x}{L}$$
$$\times \exp -j\Phi \exp\left\{-j(\theta + 2\pi n)\frac{z}{L}\right\} \quad (66)$$

$$E_{xI} = j\sum g_n F_n \exp |\theta + 2\pi n|\frac{x}{L} \exp -j\Phi \exp\left\{-j(\theta + 2\pi n)\frac{z}{L}\right\} \quad (67)$$

$$H_{zI} = -j\sqrt{\frac{\epsilon_0}{\mu_0}} \sum g_n F_n \exp |\theta + 2\pi n|\frac{x}{L}$$
$$\times \exp -j\Phi \exp\left\{-j(\theta + 2\pi n)\frac{z}{L}\right\} \quad (68)$$

$$H_{xII} = \sqrt{\frac{\epsilon_0}{\mu_0}} E_0 \exp -j\Phi \exp -j(m + \frac{1}{2})\theta,$$
$$(m + \frac{1}{2})L - \frac{l}{2} < z < (m + \frac{1}{2})L + \frac{l}{2} \quad (69)$$

$$H_{xIII} = \sqrt{\frac{\epsilon_0}{\mu_0}} \sum F_n \frac{\sinh (\theta + 2\pi n)(W - x)/L}{\sinh (\theta + 2\pi n)W/L}$$
$$\times \exp -j\Phi \exp\left\{-j(\theta + 2\pi n)\frac{z}{L}\right\} \quad (70)$$

$$E_{x\text{III}} = -j \sum F_n \frac{\cosh (\theta + 2\pi n)(W - x)/L}{\sinh (\theta + 2\pi n)W/L}$$

$$\times \exp -j\Phi \exp \left\{-j(\theta + 2\pi n)\frac{z}{L}\right\} \quad (71)$$

$$H_{z\text{III}} = j\sqrt{\frac{\epsilon_0}{\mu_0}} \sum F_n \frac{\cosh (\theta + 2\pi n)(W - x)/L}{\sinh (\theta + 2\pi n)W/L}$$

$$\times \exp -j\Phi \exp \left\{-j(\theta + 2\pi n)\frac{z}{L}\right\} \quad (72)$$

where $g_n = +1$ for $n \geqslant 0$, -1 for $n < 0$.

The current flowing in the fingers is found from the integration of the tangential magnetic field over a surface of the finger.

$$I_m = d[H_{x\text{II}(m + \frac{1}{2})} - H_{x\text{II}(m - \frac{1}{2})}] +$$

$$+ \int_{mL - (L - l)/2}^{mL + (L - l)/2} (H_{z\text{I}} - H_{z\text{III}})_{x=0} \cdot dz \quad (73)$$

When the values of H are inserted and the integration carried out, we find

$$\frac{1}{Z_0(\theta)} = 2\sqrt{\frac{\epsilon_0}{\mu_0}} \sin \frac{\theta}{2} \left\{ \frac{2d}{l} \sin \frac{\theta}{2} + \frac{L - l}{L} \sum_{-\infty}^{+\infty} \left[1 + \left| \coth (\theta + 2\pi n)\frac{W}{L} \right| \right] \right.$$

$$\left. \times \left[\frac{\sin (\theta + 2\pi n)l/2L}{(\theta + 2\pi n)l/2L} \right] \cdot \left[\frac{\sin (\theta + 2\pi n)(L - l)/2L}{(\theta + 2\pi n)(L - l)/2L} \right] \right\} \quad (74)$$

Equation (74) is summed for a range of values of θ between 0 and π and the results are used to solve Eq. (56) for Φ_0 or, more precisely, for $h/\lambda(hf/c)$. A plot of θ versus hf/c can then be prepared.

We next discuss the phase velocity of the waves. From Eqs. (52), (54) and (56)

$$E_z \sim V_{m+1} - V_m = -2A_1 \exp \left(-j\frac{\theta}{2}\right)$$

$$\times \left[\cos \frac{\theta}{2} \cos \Phi_0 \exp -jm(\theta + \pi) - j \sin \frac{\theta}{2} \sin \Phi_0 \exp -jm\theta \right] \quad (75)$$

Thus, E_z has two components with different phase constants. The component with phase θ varies as $\sin \Phi_0$ and thus has a zero at the centre of the fingers which makes it unsuitable for interaction with a broad flat beam. The other component varies as $\cos \Phi_0$, which is not serious for small Φ_0. Thus, it is better to use the $\theta + \pi$ phase and work with small θ corresponding with small Φ_0. The phase velocity is then, by definition

$$p_{\theta+\pi} = \frac{\omega L}{\theta + \pi} = \frac{cL}{h} \frac{\Phi_0}{\theta + \pi} \qquad (76)$$

The velocity for $\theta = \pi/2$ is $cL/3h$ and this may be regarded as a normalizing parameter. Fletcher shows that W/L can be chosen so as to make p constant over a considerable band of frequencies obtaining $\Delta p = \pm 1\%$ for $\Delta f = \pm 16\%$. His plot is shown in Fig. 15. The circuit is therefore useful as a fairly broad-band forward-wave amplifier.

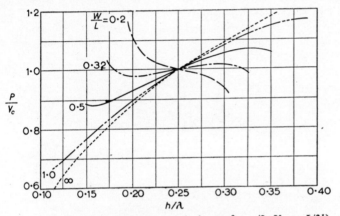

FIG. 15. Phase velocity (relative to velocity at $\theta = \pi/2$, $V_0 = cL/3h$) as a function of frequency. $d/l = 0.25$. $l/L = 0.4$.

The impedance parameter is discussed using the concepts of stored energy and group velocity. We have

$$Z_c = \frac{E \cdot E^*}{2\beta^2 \cdot g \cdot W_s} \qquad (77)$$

and

$$g = \frac{d\omega}{d\beta} = \frac{cL}{h} \cdot \frac{d\Phi_0}{d\theta} \qquad (78)$$

The stored energy per finger for a single TEM wave, $A_0 \exp -j\Phi$

F

is the product of the power flowing in the y direction multiplied by h/c. Therefore

$$W_s = \frac{1}{2} \frac{h}{cL} \frac{A_0{}^2}{Z_0(\theta)} \tag{79}$$

or, as we have to have two components to satisfy the boundary conditions, in the case under discussion

$$W_s = \frac{1}{4} \frac{h}{cL} \left[\frac{A_1{}^2}{Z_0(\theta + \pi)} + \frac{A_3{}^2}{Z_0(\theta)} \right] \tag{80}$$

But it is seen from Eqs. (41) and (43) that these are equal, and the stored energy at constant voltage is proportional to $\sqrt{\mu_0/\epsilon_0}$ $(Z_0(\theta)\sin^2 \Phi_0/2)^{-1}$, which turns out to be constant independent of frequency, but increases as W/L decreases.

For comparison purposes Fletcher determines the average field acting on a rectangular beam, using the $\theta + \pi$ harmonic. For this

$$E = \frac{2A_1}{L} \cos \frac{\theta}{2} \frac{\cos \Phi}{\cos \Phi_0/2} \frac{\sin (\theta + \pi)l/2L}{(\theta + \pi)l/2L} \tag{81}$$

and

$$Z_c = \frac{2}{\theta + \pi} \cdot \frac{p}{g} \cdot \cos^2 \frac{\theta}{2} \tan^2 \frac{I_0}{2}(I_0 + \sin I_0)$$
$$\times \left[\frac{\sin (\theta + \pi)l/2L}{(\theta + \pi)l/2L} \right]^2 Z_0(\theta) \tag{82}$$

This is shown in Fig. 16. It is seen that for fixed h and W/L the coupling impedance decreases with increasing frequency.† Z_c can be increased at any frequency by decreasing W/L but consideration of p as a function of f shows that at some value of W/L the bandwidth is optimum. For lower values of W/L increase in Z_c is at the expense of decreased bandwidth. The circuit compares quite favourably with the flattened helix but less well with the ordinary circular helix.

In the form of interdigital line described above, the connexions to the ground plate, which give rise to boundary conditions of the forms given in Eqs. (50) and (51) ensure that the line behaves as a band-pass network. The simple, meandering form of interdigital line, of course, does no such thing as it is clearly capable of transmission down to d.c. since there is no connexion between the two

---

† For further computations see WALLING; *Onde Élect.* 1957, **37**, 136.

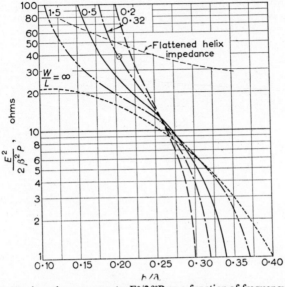

FIG. 16. The impedance parameter $E^2/2\beta^2P$ as a function of frequency for an interdigital circuit with rectangular fingers ($d/l=0.25$, $lL=0.4$). The dashed curve is that for a flat helix which has the same interaction surface as the interdigital circuit.

conductors. We now discuss such lines. The phase shift between fingers is

$$\theta_n = \frac{2\pi}{\lambda}(L+h) + (2n-1)\pi \qquad (83)$$

which reduces to the correct value $-\pi$ when $n=0$ and $\lambda \to \infty$. The phase velocity is

$$p_n = \frac{\omega}{\beta_n} = \frac{\omega L}{\theta_n} = \frac{C}{(1+h/L) + \lambda/2L(2n-1)} \qquad (84)$$

therefore

$$\frac{c}{p_n} = \left(1 + \frac{h}{L}\right) + \frac{\lambda}{2L}(2n-1) \qquad (85)$$

The group velocity is defined through

$$\frac{1}{g} = \frac{d\beta_n}{d\omega} = \frac{1}{L}\frac{d\theta_n}{d\omega} = \frac{1}{c}\left(1 + \frac{h}{L}\right) \qquad (86)$$

therefore

$$g = \frac{c}{1+h/L} \qquad (87)$$

The group velocity is independent of n, as it should be. For the fundamental, $n = 0$, Eqs. (84) and (87) show that p is negative and g positive for $\lambda/2 > (L + h)$. This is the requirement for a backward-wave oscillator and the circuit may be, and is, used for this purpose.

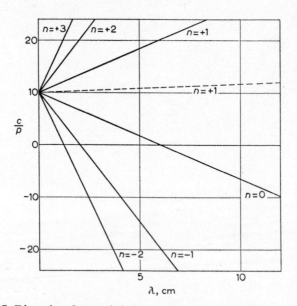

FIG. 17. Dispersion characteristic for meander line, $h/L = 9\cdot0$, $h = 2\cdot7$ cm.

Fig. 17 shows a plot of the dispersion characteristic Eq. (72) for $h/L = 9\cdot0$, $h = 2\cdot7$ cm. This shows that the $n = 0$ mode and all the backward space-harmonics ($n < 0$) show backward-wave behaviour when λ increases above some particular value depending on the mode. All the forward space-harmonics are very slow, but the circuit is not suitable for broadband travelling-wave amplification because $p \neq g$, except at the initial point. The dotted line is the first forward space-harmonic when the dimensions h and L are both multiplied by the factor 10. Even here the dispersion is marked.

The calculation of the coupling resistance is very straightforward if we assume that the fingers are thick in comparison with the hole diameter. We may then assume that the electric field is zero inside the hole through the finger (through which the beam passes) and constant between the fingers. The amplitude of the electric field is easily determined for any known power flow, because the characteristic impedance can be taken from Fig. 11 and

$$P = \frac{A^2 l^2}{2Z_0} \tag{88}$$

for uniform electric field, where $A =$ amplitude of the electric field. By Fourier's method

$$E_{2n} = \frac{A}{L} \int_{-l/2}^{+l/2} \exp(j\beta_n z)\, \mathrm{d}z \tag{89}$$

$$= \frac{A \sin(\beta_n l/2)}{\beta_n L/2} \tag{90}$$

therefore
$$Z_{cn} = \frac{E_{zn} \cdot E_{zn}{}^*}{2\beta_n{}^2 \cdot P} = Z_0 \frac{\sin^2(\beta_n l/2)}{\beta_n{}^2 L^2 (\beta_n l/2)^2} \tag{91}$$

It must be remembered that Z_0 is a function of l so the variation of Eq. (76) with l is more complicated than would be suggested by the explicit functions of l appearing in Eq. (78). It is interesting to discuss the variation of Eq. (78) with n as this has a bearing on the excitation of unwanted oscillations. The practical problem is that when the valve is set up to oscillate at some particular voltage, for example, that corresponding with $c/p = -10$ for the $n = 0$ mode, and the beam current is increased, oscillations may be observed at $\lambda = 4$ cm as well as the desired value $\lambda = 12$ cm. Taking the numerical values from Fig. 17 and $l = 0.1$ cm, these yield $\beta_0 = 2\pi/3$, $\beta_{-1} = 2\pi$, therefore

$$\frac{Z_{c0}}{Z_{c(-1)}} = 81 \frac{\sin^2(\beta_0 l/2)}{\sin^2(\beta_{-1} l/2)} \doteqdot 10 \tag{92}$$

There is thus a large factor between the two coupling impedances. In practice, the difference in starting currents is even greater than is implied in Eq. (92) because the fields in the space-harmonic modes extend to an increasingly smaller distance from the conductors and the weakening of the coupling when averaged over the beam is much more important for the higher space-harmonics. It is worth noting, before we leave the subject, that the frequencies with identical values of phase velocity are, from Eq. (92) related by

$$f_n = (1 - 2n)f_0 \tag{93}$$

Interdigital lines of this type may have their propagation characteristics modified to some extent by the addition of lumped or distributed loading, a technique which is well known in conjunction with the helix. PASCHKE[18] gives a discussion of some of the effects obtained by loading, which may be useful in producing a wide-band amplifier circuit.

3.7. THE HELICAL DELAY LINE

Because of its great practical importance the helix has been exhaustively treated by many authors using many different techniques. An excellent review of this work has been given by SEN-SIPER.[19] The best approach seems to be to begin with the sheath model, first applied by OLLENDORF[20] and used for T.W.T. theory by Schelkunoff and PIERCE.[21] Here, the actual helix is replaced by a sheath which is assumed to conduct only in the ψ direction, ψ being the angle of pitch of the helix. We may imagine this situation existing in a sheath with an infinitely thin helical cut made in it. The next stage is to consider a helix made of thin tape. The boundary conditions used are that the electric field at the edge of the tape should be perpendicular to the tape edge and the surface current density should be zero at the centre of the gap between two tapes. The current may only flow in the direction of the tape and the electric field in the axial direction goes to zero at the tape centre. This model has been extensively investigated by SENSIPER.[24] The final stage is to make the transition to a round wire helix, but this case appears only to have been fully treated in the limit of fine wires with narrow spacings.

From work of TIEN[22] it appears that the sheath helix model predicts impedances which are higher than those observed, by a factor of about two. A factor of this order will certainly lead to observable errors in the calculated gain, but errors of the order of 10–20% may easily be masked by lack of precise knowledge of the beam diameter and the spacing between the helix and the edge electrons of the beam. It therefore seems necessary to utilize the tape helix model but is probably not necessary to go over to the complete fine wire model. We start our study of the helix with the sheath model.

[18] PASCHKE; *A.E.Ü.*, 1956, **10**, 195.
[19] SENSIPER; *Proc. I.R.E.*, 1955, **43**, 149. This includes a very complete bibliography for the helix.
[20] OLLENDORF; *Die Grundlagen der Hochfrequenztechnik*. Springer, 1926.
[21] PIERCE; *Proc. I.R.E.*, 1947, **35**, 111.
[22] TIEN; *Proc. I.R.E.*, 1953, **41**, 1617.

3.7.1. The sheath helix

PIERCE (*loc. cit.*) deals with this in the case where it is assumed that there is no radial variation in the electric or magnetic fields. BECK[23] gives the same results working from the Hertzian vectors. SENSIPER[24] deals fully with the general case, where azimuthal variations are allowed. He derives the following determinantal equation which gives the radial propagation constant γ in terms of the geometrical parameters of the helix. It is

$$\frac{I_n'(\gamma a)K_n'(\gamma a)}{I_n(\gamma a)K_n(\gamma a)} = \frac{-(\gamma^2 a^2 + n\beta a \cot \psi)^2}{k^2 a^2 \cdot \gamma^2 a^2 \cdot \cot^2 \psi} \tag{94}$$

Here
$$\gamma^2 = \beta^2 - k^2$$

$$a = \text{internal diameter of the helix}$$

and the wave functions have been chosen of the form

$$\pi_z^{i,e} = A_n^{i,e} \begin{cases} I_n(\gamma r) \\ K_n(\gamma r) \end{cases} \exp -j(\beta z + n\theta)$$

i and e standing for internal and external respectively. I_n functions apply internally, K_n externally, because only in this way can the wave functions be made to behave correctly at zero and infinity. Equation (94) reduces to the well-known result when $n = 0$ (BECK, *loc. cit.* Eqs. 14–40)

$$(\gamma a)^2 \frac{I_0(\gamma a)K_0(\gamma a)}{I_1(\gamma a)K_1(\gamma a)} = (ka \cot \psi)^2 \tag{95}$$

since $I'_0 = I_1$, $K'_0 = -K_1$.

As usual, we are mainly interested in slow waves $\beta^2 \gg k^2$, so that $\gamma^2 \doteq \beta^2$, but Eq. (94) in fact shows that except for isolated cases, only slow waves can occur on the helix. Fig. 18 shows solutions of Eq. (81) for $n = 0$ and $+1$, derived by Sensiper. Fig. 19 shows the $n = 0$ curve in more detail, as given by Beck. These curves are $\omega - \beta$ or Brillouin diagrams with modified scales so that the considerations dealt with earlier in the chapter apply. In particular, since a straight line through the origin is nearly tangential to the $n = 0$ curve, the phase and group velocities are nearly equal over a broad band of frequencies which explains the success of the helix as a broad-band circuit element. It will also be observed on Fig. 18 that for $n = 1$ a region exists where the phase and group

[23] BECK; *Thermionic Valves*, Section 14.3, Cambridge University Press, 1953.
[24] SENSIPER; *M.I.T. Research Lab. of Electronics Tech. Rpt. No.* 194, 1951.

velocities are in opposite directions so that backward-wave oscillations are possible on this model. It may be thought peculiar that the $\omega \sim \beta$ plot is not symmetrical about the ω axis. Actually

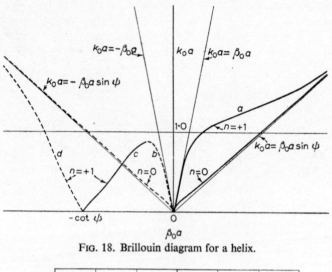

FIG. 18. Brillouin diagram for a helix.

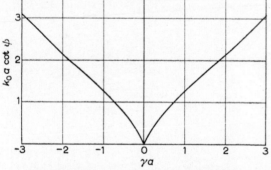

FIG. 19. Brillouin diagram for sheath helix.

the symmetry can be restored by plotting the $n = -1$ mode, so that a real propagation problem has to be solved by including the modes $n = 0$, $n = \pm 1$, ± 2 up to $\pm q$, the highest mode required.

Knowing the electric and magnetic fields it is a relatively simple piece of algebra to integrate Poynting's vector over the whole space, inside and outside the helix, thus obtaining an expression which eliminates the constant A_n. If we define the coupling impedance using the value of the electric field evaluated on the axis $E_z(0)$ we find

$$Z_c = \frac{120\gamma^4}{\beta^3 \cdot k} \frac{1}{(\gamma a)^2} \left\{ F_1(\gamma a) \right\}^{-1} \tag{96}$$

where

$$F_1(\gamma a) = \left\{ \left[1 + \frac{I_0 K_1}{I_1 K_0} \right] \left[I_1^2 - I_0 I_2 \right] + \frac{I_0^2}{K_0^2} \left[1 + \frac{I_1 K_0}{I_0 K_1} \right] \left[K_0 K_2 - K_1^2 \right] \right\} \tag{97}$$

and all the Bessel functions have the same argument γa. Physically Z_c is the coupling impedance which would apply to a thin pencil beam travelling along the axis of the tube. Normally, γ is very nearly equal to β so Eq. (83) can be simplified. Equation (83) leads to values of Z_c of a few hundred ohms or, taking a commonly used helix radius $\gamma a = 1 \cdot 5$ and a phase velocity of $c/10 (\doteqdot 2 \cdot 5$ kV), the

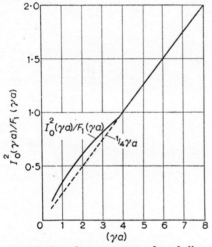

Fig. 20. Impedance parameter for a helix.

actual value is $\doteqdot 270 \,\Omega$. Fig. 20 shows a plot of $F_1(\gamma a) \sim \gamma a$. These results give the required information for the tube design. However, as has been stated earlier, they are known to give results which are too large by a factor of about two[25] so we must look for a more refined model, the tape helix.

---

[25] CUTLER; Proc. I.R.E., 1948, 36, 230.

3.7.2. The tape helix

SENSIPER[19],[24] has treated in great detail two special cases of the tape helix. These are known as the narrow gap and the narrow tape cases. In the narrow gap approximation the gap is considered to be small in comparison with the tape width and in the second case, the tape is considered to be narrow compared with the gap. In real valves tape and gap widths are usually nearly equal. The most striking difference between the tape and sheath models is that the symmetry properties of the tape model require the field solutions to take on typical space-harmonic form and therefore to present pass and stop bands just like all the other structures we have treated. It is interesting to recall that the existence of a stop-band in the vicinity of $ka = 1$, was observed in measurements[26] before its existence was understood.

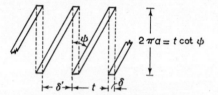

$$2\pi a = t \cot \psi$$

FIG. 21. Notation for tape helix.

The notation for the tape helix is given in Fig. 21. The space between turns is δ' and the tape width is δ so we shall either be concerned with $\delta'/\delta \ll 1$ or $\delta/\delta' \ll 1$. The symmetry properties of the structure are the following:—

1. If the helix is translated along the z axis by a distance mt where m is any integer and t is the pitch of the helix, the fields can only change by a constant factor since the new helix position coincides with part of the old.

2. If the helix is translated along the z axis by a distance $l < t$, it can be brought into coincidence with its old position by relation through an angle $2\pi l/t$.

The first of these, as usual, means we have to use wave functions including $\exp(-j\beta_m z)$

where
$$\beta_m = \beta_0 + \frac{2m\pi}{t} \tag{98}$$

[26] WATKINS and SIEGMAN; *J. Appl. Phys.*, 1953, **24**, 917.

Proceeding as before we find the appropriate functions are I_n, $K_n(\eta_m r/a) \exp j(n\theta - \beta_m z)$ where

$$\eta_m = (\beta_m^2 a^2 - k_0^2 a^2)^{1/2} \tag{99}$$

Inserting the value of β_m from Eq. (98) and eliminating t we find an alternative expression for η_m, viz.,

$$\eta_m = [m^2 \cot^2 \psi + 2m\beta a \cot \psi + \beta_0^2 a^2 - k_0^2 a^2]^{1/2} \tag{100}$$

As before, we have to use I_n inside the helix as $K_n(0) \to \infty$ and K_n outside as $I_n(\infty) \to \infty$. If we use the superscripts i and e to denote external and internal solutions, we can satisfy the boundary conditions at $r = a$ with a sum of space-harmonic modes.

$$\pi_z^{i,e} = \sum_{m,n} A_{mn}{}^{i,e} \frac{I_n}{K_n} (\eta_m r/a) \exp j(n\theta - \beta_m z) \tag{101}$$

We can now make use of the second symmetry condition.
Let $z' = z - l$, $\theta' = \theta - 2\pi l/t$.
These values are put into Eq. (101) to give

$$\pi_z^{i,e} = \exp -j(\beta_0 l + \beta_0 z') \sum_{m,n} A_{m,n}{}^{i,e} \frac{I_n}{K_n} (\eta_m r/a)$$
$$\times \exp j\left(n\theta' - (m - n)\frac{2\pi l}{t} - m\frac{2\pi}{t} z'\right) \tag{102}$$

Equations (101) and (102) must lead to identical results for all l, from the second condition of symmetry. This can only be true if $m = n$, i.e., if $m \neq n$,

$$A_{m,n}{}^{i,e} = 0$$

Therefore

$$\pi_z^{i,e} = \exp -j\beta_0 z \sum_m A_m{}^{i,e} \frac{I_n}{K_n} (\eta_m r/a) \exp -jm\left(\frac{2\pi z}{t} - \theta\right) \tag{103}$$

with a precisely similar expression $\pi_z^{*i,e}$ for the magnetic part of the potential. Explicitly

$$\pi_z^{*i,e} = \exp -j\beta_0 z \sum_m \beta_m{}^{i,e} \frac{I_n}{K_n} (\eta_m r/a) \exp -jm\left(\frac{2\pi z}{t} - \theta\right) \tag{104}$$

Using Eqs. (103) and (104) we could write down the fields in terms of the current on the tape, which constitutes a discontinuity of known value in the magnetic field at $r = a$. This involves a good deal of algebra and is relegated to Appendix III.

3.7.2.1. *The Forbidden Regions*

We are able to discuss the mode behaviour of the tape helix with the results already given. We first note that the wave functions used (K_n) outside the helix are the only ones which give rise to a possible solution to the physical problem set. Thus, for a real solution to the problem η_m must be real and positive. The forbidden regions are then simply regions in which no real, positive value of η_m is possible. Since k_0 is real and positive, we see from Eq. (99) that the condition on η_m is obeyed when

$$|\beta_m| > k_0 \tag{105}$$

Two possibilities have now to be examined, β_0 may be either positive or negative. In the first case Eq. (105) is satisfied if $|\beta_0| > k_0$ for m either zero or positive. If, however, m is negative, Eq. (100) shows that it is necessary to have

$$|\beta_0 a - |m| \cot \psi| > k_0 a \tag{106}$$

This can be expressed in another form as

$$|m| + \frac{k_0 a}{\cot \psi} < \frac{\beta_0 a}{\cot \psi} < |m| - \frac{k_0 a}{\cot \psi}, \quad |m| \geqslant 1, \quad \beta_0 > k_0 \tag{107}$$

Turning now to negative values of β_0, the inequality Eq. (105) is satisfied for m zero or negative, but for m positive a condition similar to Eq. (107) has to be obeyed. The final result for either plus or minus is

$$|m| + \frac{k_0 a}{\cot \psi} < \frac{|\beta_0| a}{\cot \psi} < |m| - \frac{k_0 a}{\cot \psi}, \quad |m| \geqslant 1, \quad |\beta_0| > k_0 \tag{108}$$

Let us now prepare a plot of $k_0 a/\cot \psi \sim |\beta_0| a/\cot \psi$ considering m as a parameter. For $m = 0$, we obtain a pair of straight lines through the origin of co-ordinates, at an angle of 45°. For $m = 1$, we obtain a similar pair of lines through the point $\beta_0 a/\cot \psi = 1$, and so on for each integer. This gives the diagram shown in Fig. 22, which shows that the lines intersect at the common vertex $\frac{1}{2}$. Propagation is allowed in the unshaded regions, the triangles, and is not allowed outside them. The fact that propagation with

$ka > \frac{1}{2} \cot \psi$ is always impossible is easily shown to mean that

$$t < \frac{\lambda}{2} \qquad (109)$$

This restriction is not an important one in existing valves.

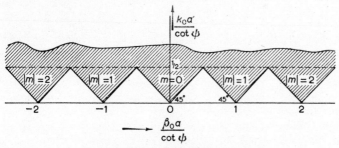

FIG. 22. Tape helix forbidden zones.

It should be emphasized that we have not yet calculated the actual dispersion curve of the tape helix, we have merely shown that there are large regions in which no propagation is possible. For the physical reasons for this, the reader should refer to a paper by PIERCE and TIEN[27] which gives a detailed explanation of the actual behaviour, with frequency, of the modes in terms of the coupling between the slow waves, with phase velocities of around c along the conductor and fast waveguide modes with velocities in excess of c along the axis.

3.7.3. Tape helix determinantal equation

In the tape theory both the electric fields and the current density have to obey the correct boundary conditions at the helix. That is, the current density must be zero in the gaps and constant over the tape while the tangential electric fields must be zero on the tapes and finite in the gap. In other words, the actual total fields and currents are built from Fourier expansions in terms of the space-harmonics. When this process is carried through, we find that β_0 is determined through the following, complicated determinantal equation

$$\sum_m \left\{ \left(\beta_0{}^2 a^2 - k_0{}^2 a^2 + k_0{}^2 a^2 \frac{m^2 \cot^2 \psi}{\eta m^2} \right) I_m(\eta_m) K_m(\eta_m) + \right.$$
$$\left. + k_0{}^2 a^2 \cot^2 \psi \, I'_m(\eta_m) K'_m(\eta_m) \right\} D_m \doteq 0 \qquad (110)$$

[27] PIERCE and TIEN; *Proc. I.R.E.*, 1954, **42**, 1389.

Here D_m is a quantity which depends on the precise nature of the assumptions made as to the gap field (or the current density) but for present purposes may be taken as $(\sin m\pi\delta/t)/(m\pi\delta/t)$,† δ = tape width (narrow tape). We have spoken of Eq. (110) as a determinantal equation for β_0, obviously it will give all the β's but it is much simpler having β_0, to use $\beta_m a = \beta_0 a + m \cot \psi$, from Eq. (98).

For the narrow gap case Eq. (110) is modified by dividing the mth term by $\eta_m^2 I_m(\eta_m) K_m(\eta_m) I'_m(\eta_m) K'_m(\eta_m)$ and summing over the resultant terms. D_m is replaced by D'_m which is the same function but with δ' (gap width) replacing δ.

Sensiper[19,24] solves Eq. (110) for β_0 with given values of $k_0 a$, $\cot \psi$ and δ by using approximate expressions for the products of the Bessel functions and procedures to improve the convergence of the series and states that solutions may be readily obtained for a wide range of parameters. Figs. 23 and 24 show his results, in two different forms, for a particular case. Before discussing these results, it is useful to give Sensiper's approximate analysis of Eq. (110). If none of the η_m's is near zero, it is permissible to put

$$I'_m K'_m = -\left(\frac{m^2 + \eta_m^2}{\eta_m^2}\right) I_m K_m \qquad (111)$$

Then, from Eq. (110)

$$\beta_0 a = k_0 a (1 + \cot^2 \psi)^{1/2} \qquad (112)$$

or

$$\beta_m a = k_0 a (1 + \cot^2 \psi)^{1/2} + m \cot \psi \qquad (113)$$

On the other hand, if one of the η_m's is near zero, for example if $\eta_q = 0$, then it can be shown that only the qth term of Eq. (97) is important and

$$\frac{\eta_q^2(\beta_0^2 a^2 - k_0^2 a^2) + k_0^2 a^2 q^2 \cot^2 \psi}{n_q^2 k_0^2 a^2 \cot^2 \psi} = \frac{-I'_q(\eta_q) K'_q(\eta_q)}{I_q(\eta_q) K_q(\eta_q)} \qquad (114)$$

Equations (112) and (114) are both forms of the determinantal equation for the sheath helix, Eq. (94), so we deduce the important result that we can use the propagation diagrams for the sheath helix, if we merely insert the forbidden regions which we have already determined.

---

† As usual, for thin tapes $J_0[(m\pi/t)\delta]$ gives a somewhat better result.

PIERCE and TIEN[27] carry the discussion somewhat further. They use Eq. (111), valid for $\eta_m > 0$, $|m| \geqslant 1$, in conjunction with (110) and (113) to obtain the following approximation

$$\eta_m^2(\eta_0^2 - k_0^2 a^2 \cot^2 \psi) = 0$$

so that either $\quad \eta_m = 0, \quad m = \pm 1, \pm 2, \pm 3$, etc.

or $\quad\quad\quad\quad\quad\quad \eta_0 = k_0 a \cot \psi$

The first choice, from Eq. (99) gives

$$\beta_m a = k_0 a, \quad m = \pm 1, \pm 2, \pm 3 \quad\quad\quad (115)$$

while the second gives

$$\beta_0^2 a^2 = k_0^2 a^2 (1 + \cot^2 \psi)$$

or $\quad\quad\quad\quad\quad\quad \beta_0 a \doteq k_0 a \cot \psi \quad\quad\quad\quad\quad (116)$

Therefore the helix propagates one slow wave, given by Eq. (116) and a double infinite sum of fast modes given by Eq. (115). The fast waves have an axial phase velocity equal to c, the velocity of light, and it is the coupling between these various waves which gives rise to the propagation characteristics of the helix.

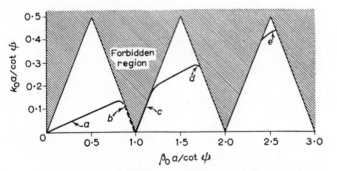

FIG. 23. Solutions of tape helix determinantal equation for $\psi = 10°$, $\pi\delta/t = 0.1$.

The approximate analysis gives excellent results for the propagation constants except for regions which are in the immediate vicinity of the forbidden zones, for instance the region b indicated in Fig. 23. We now discuss the more exact results shown in this figure and in Fig. 24. Let us discuss what happens if we start at zero frequency and gradually increase ω (i.e., k_0). At low frequencies,

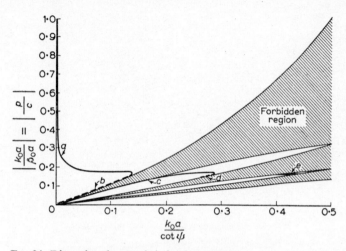

FIG. 24. Dispersion characteristic for the tape helix $\psi = 10°$, $\pi\delta/t = 0.1$.

$k_0a < 0.12 \cot \psi$, propagation is possible with three values of β_0 corresponding with the intersections of the chosen value of $k_0a/\cot \psi$ with branches a, b and c. The first of these β_0a is a forward wave (p and g in same direction), the second β_0b is a backward wave and the third is again forward. At $k_0a \doteq 0.12 \cot \psi$, g drops to zero for the first two waves, and only the third can propagate, which it does until $k_0a \doteq 0.3 \cot \psi$ where, in turn, its group velocity drops to zero and no propagation is possible. At $k_0a = 0.4 \cot \psi$ propagation is again allowed on branch e. Fig. 24 shows the same data plotted in a manner which gives the ratio p/c as a function of ω. It should be stressed that not only can several modes of oscillation exist simultaneously, but also each mode must be built up from a complete set of space harmonics in order to satisfy the boundary conditions.

The phase velocities are in the following ratio

$$\frac{p_m}{c} = \frac{k_0a}{\beta_m a} = \frac{k_0a \tan \psi}{m + \beta_0a \tan \psi} \tag{117}$$

Considering branch (a) alone, we see that while the space-harmonics with m positive have positive phase velocities, those with m

negative have negative p and can therefore be used for backward-wave interaction. On branch (b) on the other hand, the fundamental

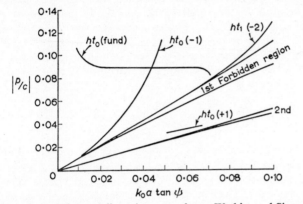

FIG. 25. Experimental dispersion curve due to Watkins and Siegman.

is a backward wave. Fig. 25 shows an experimental plot, due to WATKINS and SIEGMAN[28] of the observed phase velocities on a particular helix. The agreement with the theoretical predictions is seen to be good.

3.7.4. The power flow

Once the field expressions are known, the average axial power flow can be calculated by forming Poynting's vector for the space-harmonic components of each mode separately. This procedure is allowed because of the orthogonality of the θ components which causes cross products to vanish. It turns out that the space-harmonics account for quite a large proportion of the total power, so that the useful impedance is reduced, since the electron beam is only in synchronism with one of the harmonics (unless it is oscillating).

The most far-reaching calculations on this point are those of TIEN[29] who extends Sensiper's work to cover the case of a tape helix supported inside a dielectric cylinder. The electric field is concentrated in the dielectric and a further reduction in the impedance parameter is the result. Tien defines the reduction factor F, by which the sheath impedance must be multiplied to obtain the

[28] WATKINS and SIEGMAN; *J. Appl. Phys.*, 1953, **24**, 917.
[29] TIEN; *Proc. I.R.E.*, 1953, **41**, 1617.

tape impedance, as made up of two parts, $F = F_1 \times F_2$, where F_1 is due to the differences between the sheath and tape models and F_2 expresses the effect of the dielectric loading. This division is useful because F_2 turns out to be practically independent of the value of $k_0 a$. F_1 decreases as $k_0 a$ increases. The magnitude of the dielectric loading is measured by comparing the actual tape helix with dielectric support with a theoretical sheath helix in free space which has the same radius and is adjusted to give the same value of β_0 by altering cot ψ. Thus

$$\text{D.L.F. (dielectric loading factor)} = \frac{\cot \psi_t}{\cot \psi_s} \tag{118}$$

where the suffices refer to tape and sheath respectively. Equation (118) thus enables the D.L.F. to be measured for the more complicated support arrangements used in practical valves, where the dielectric is cut back from the helix as much as possible, so as to reduce the loading. On the basis of what has been said above, it is only necessary to make a measurement at one frequency.

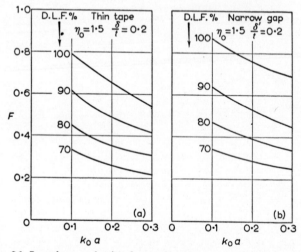

Fig. 26. Impedance reduction factors for thin tape and for narrow gap.

Since the calculations on power flow involve a great deal of heavy algebra, the work is relegated to Appendix 3. Tien's results are given in Figs. 26 and 27, both for the narrow tape and narrow gap cases. The practical conclusion to be drawn from these figures is that the D.L.F. should be made as large as possible, by the means already mentioned and the value of k_0a should be kept as small as possible. Calculations on the current distribution indicate that the space-harmonic components are minimized and the impedance maximized when $\delta/t \doteqdot \frac{1}{2}$.

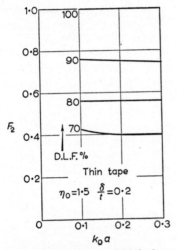

FIG. 27. The part of the reduction factor which is due to dielectric loading.

3.7.5. The helix as a backward-wave structure

In addition to its use as a slow-wave structure in forward-wave amplifiers, the helix has been fairly extensively used as a backward-wave structure. Several possibilities for such use exist but the more important is the use of the -1 space-harmonic of the ordinary slow forward fundamental mode and the fundamental mode of the region (b) in Fig. 23. Somewhat better values of coupling impedance can be obtained by the use of a bifilar or two-start helix. A good analysis of both single and two-start helices is due to WATKINS and ASH,[30] while TIEN[31] has also treated the bifilar helix in detail. Both these papers start from Sensiper's analysis but Watkins and Ash use conformal transformation methods to obtain a much more precise knowledge of the exact current distribution, since it might well be the case that the simple distributions used by Sensiper and Tien do not yield sufficiently accurate results for the space-harmonic impedances even though they are known to be useful for the funda-

[30] WATKINS and ASH; *J. Appl. Phys.*, 1954, **25**, 782.
[31] TIEN; *Proc. I.R.E.*, 1954, **42**, 1137.

mental. In point of fact, the simple distributions give results for the
-1 space harmonic in very good agreement with the more accurate
analysis and the work of Watkins and Ash can be considered as
confirming the validity of the simpler approach. Fig. 28 shows the
phase velocities of the $m = 0, \pm 1, \pm 2$ space-harmonics and Fig.
29 the impedance both as functions of $k_0 a$, as given by Watkins and
Ash. It will be observed that the coupling impedance for the -1
space-harmonic is considerably lower than the fundamental impedance. This is to be expected since the fundamental component
accounts for most of the power transmission. In fact for the small
values of $k_0 a$ used for forward-wave amplification (0·1–0·2) the
space-harmonic impedance is only a few per cent of the fundamental
impedance and it only increases with rather marked increases in
$k_0 a$. Thus, values of $k_0 a$ of 0·3–0·5 are used in B.W.O.s. It must
be remembered that not only is the coupling impedance lowered,
but also the space-harmonic fields are confined much more closely
to the immediate vicinity of the conductors than are the fundamental fields, since $\eta_m > \eta_0$, in general. For these reasons B.W.O.s
are often made with annular beams so that the convection current
is concentrated in the useful part of the field.

The behaviour of the bifilar helix at low values of $k_0 a$, is somewhat different from that of the single tape helix. This is because
an extra mode is present, which is the analogue of a TEM mode of
a two-wire transmission line. At a plane of constant z, the following
two possibilities may be distinguished.

1. The r.f. currents on the two tapes are equal and in-phase.

2. The r.f. currents are equal and in anti-phase.

In the first case odd space-harmonic components are all zero,
i.e., $A_m = 0, m = \pm 1, \pm 3, \pm 5$, while in the second even space-
harmonics are zero. The second case is clearly the TEM mode
and it persists, without dispersion, down to zero frequency. The
coupling impedance is therefore maintained to lower values of
frequency.

In passing, we should note that similar behaviour is to be expected
from helices with either inner or outer conductors as these also
transmit a TEM mode. BRYANT[32] has dealt with these systems in
the sheath helix approximation.

Returning now to the bifilar helix, TIEN[31] shows that the forbidden
regions in this case repeat at intervals of $2 \cot \psi$ instead of $\cot \psi$.
The TEM ends at $k_0 a \doteq 0.7$ where it meets the forbidden region.

[32] BRYANT; *Elec. Commun.*, 1954, **31**, 50.

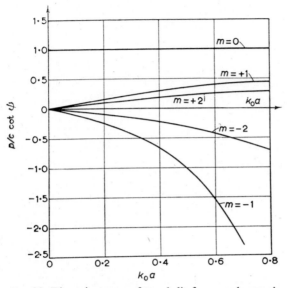

FIG. 28. Dispersion curve of tape helix for space-harmonics.

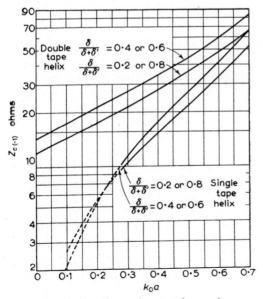

FIG. 29. Impedances for space-harmonics.

Fig. 30 shows the $\omega \sim \beta$ plot for cases (1) and (2). The reader should study this in conjunction with Figs. 22 and 23 to appreciate the differences fully.

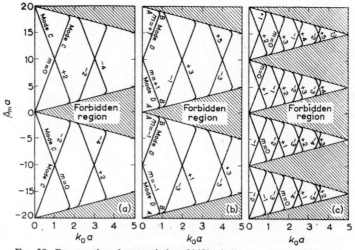

Fig. 30. Propagating characteristics of bifilar helix. $\cot \psi = 10$ (a) case 1 (b) case 2 (c) single-wire helix.

3.7.6.　Modified helix structures

Several variants of the basic helix structure exhibiting useful properties are known to exist, besides those which have already been mentioned. One of these is the contra-wound (or cross-wound) helix in which two wire or tape helices are wound in opposite directions. Often, this structure is simulated by the rod and ring structure of Fig. 31 in which the r.f. currents are easily seen to be

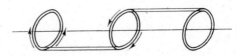

Fig. 31. Ring and bar type of contra-wound helix structure.

flowing in opposite orientations in adjacent rings. The contra-wound helix has been discussed by CHODOROW and CHU.[33] The

---

[33] CHODOROW and CHU; *J. Appl. Phys.*, 1955, **26**, 33.

modes of such a structure may be considered to arise from the superposition of the fields due to two single conductor helices carrying currents in opposite angular directions. The superposition may be with either fields in phase or in anti-phase and these are termed the symmetric and anti-symmetric modes. In the anti-symmetric mode it is clear that the fields are strong near the helix and weak on the axis, and the reverse for the symmetric mode. The symmetric mode turns out to be interesting for use in forward amplifiers using solid beams, for it has a large coupling impedance which does not depend critically on the beam location. The coupling impedance is large because the (useless) TE component of the fundamental mode is suppressed, all the energy going into the TM mode. Nor is this the only advantage, for the coupling impedance of the -1 space-harmonic is much lower than for a single helix. For these reasons the circuit is valuable in medium high voltage pulsed T.W.A.s which would tend to exhibit backward oscillations if a single helix were employed. In a practical case, considering a helix design for a valve working at around 10 kV, Chodorow and Chu find that Z_{c0} is doubled and $Z_{c-1} \div 20$ by the use of a contra-wound helix as compared with a single helix.

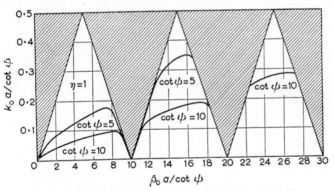

FIG. 32. Solution of determinantal equation for twin helix.

The theory has been established by the use of variational methods, about which something is said in Appendix 4. The Brillouin diagram is shown in Fig. 32, from which it will be observed that the circuit is considerably more dispersive than the other helix structures, so that the advantages detailed above are gained at the expense of bandwidth. This situation will appear normal to valve engineers.

For a careful experimental study of these structures see BIRDSALL and EVERHART.[34]

3.8. THE KARP STRUCTURE

This structure was illustrated in Figs. 2c and 2d. It is a useful structure both for very high frequency B.W.O.s and T.W.A.s largely because of its good mechanical properties and ability to dissipate fairly large powers. The theory has never been described in detail, but partial treatments have been given by PIERCE[35] and by LEBLOND and MOURIER.[17] Here we shall only give a brief description of the general behaviour of the circuit. Consider for the moment the array of wires, each one-half wavelength long, separated from the ridged guide. Such an array cannot propagate a slow wave because the modes are simply the set of frequencies for which the wire length $l = n\lambda/2$. Analysis shows this to be due to the fact that the electric and magnetic couplings between adjacent wires are equal and opposite. Now consider the situation when the ridge is present. The ridge strongly perturbs the electric field in the region around the centre of the wires and this perturbation unbalances the couplings, which in turn means that the new system can propagate slow waves in certain frequency bands. The upper limit of the first pass band is the frequency for which $l = \lambda/2$ while the lower limit is the cut-off frequency of the ridged guide, i.e. (Fig. 2c) $l_1 = \lambda_1/2$. The Karp circuit is thus inherently rather a narrow band device. Pierce's calculations, admittedly optimistic, show that the coupling impedance *for the forward-wave fundamental* of the Karp structure is high, being between 500–1,000 Ω. His theory is not of a form capable of giving information on the space-harmonics, but one would be safe in predicting a useful value of backward-wave impedance.

FIG. 33. " Anti-Karp " structure.

Pierce also discusses a structure which is similar to Karp's form, but behaves differently. This is the structure of Fig. 33, which is

[34] BIRDSALL and EVERHART; *P.G.E.D.*, 1956, *ED.3*, 190.
[35] PIERCE; *Trans. I.R.E., Electron Devices*, 1955, *ED.2*, **13**.

often called the anti-Karp circuit. Hence, the magnetic field has been perturbed, rather than the electric field. If this circuit is driven at the frequency for which $l = \lambda/2$ and the wires are removed, there is no propagation, for the guide is cut-off in these circumstances. When the wires are present, slow-waves are possible for values of λ somewhat less than $2l$. This circuit has a backward-wave fundamental, the phase constant is large and negative at $\lambda = 2l$, and becomes less negative as λ diminishes. Pierce obtains a curve of coupling impedance which drops from about 3 kΩ near cut-off to 500 Ω at $\omega/\omega_c \doteq 1\cdot3$. Experimental results on the anti-Karp structure have not yet been reported but measurements on a valve with the ridge structure have been reported by KARP.[36]

3.9. STRUCTURES DERIVED FROM LUMPED CIRCUIT EQUIVALENTS

The reader will by now have realized that, while it is very simple to devise possible slow-wave circuits, it is much more difficult to produce an even tolerably accurate theoretical estimate of their performance. One way round this difficulty has been rather widely used; this is the procedure of substituting cavity circuit elements for lumped circuit elements in circuits which are known to have desirable properties. We have already laid the basis for the substitution in our initial description of lumped constant circuits from the slow-wave viewpoint. PIERCE[4] gives a fairly detailed discussion of the disk-loaded waveguide along these lines. Before starting to discuss some examples it is useful to show in what circumstances one is likely to need such circuits. The helix, in one or other of the forms already described, is the most versatile slow-wave structure known to us, but it has several deficiencies as a circuit for high-powered, and therefore high voltage, valves. First, it is ill-adapted for use with high input powers, unless the helix itself can be liquid-cooled by passing coolant through a tubular conductor. Secondly, as the power increases, it becomes more prone to unwanted backward-wave oscillation. The contra-wound helix goes a considerable distance towards eliminating this defect, but at the cost of elaboration and further increase in the coupling problem. Another way of reducing the backward-wave interaction is to increase the helix diameter in relation to the beam diameter, depending on the rapid spatial diminution of the harmonics. Obviously, this solution only leads to a best compromise between

---

[36] KARP; *Proc. I.R.E.*, 1955, **43**, 41.

essentially conflicting requirements. On the other hand, the main disadvantage of many other types of circuit is often found to be an excessively low coupling impedance at low voltages. Pierce's parameter $C = (I_0 Z_c / 4 V_0)^{1/3}$ is fundamental in the design of T.W.A.s and the like. It is clear that if $I_0 \propto p V_0^{3/2}$, then, by working at sufficiently high voltage, any deficiency in Z_c can be set off by increasing current. Moreover, at higher voltages, the averaged Z_c taken over the region occupied by the beam may itself be significantly greater. We must therefore remember that circuits which are useless for low and medium powered valves may well be extremely useful in the high-powered valves which are so important today. More succintly, with voltages of over 100 kV one can work wonders.

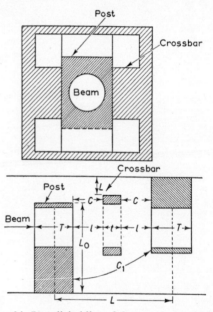

Fig. 34. Interdigital line of the type due to Hines.

The main developments along these lines are associated with Stanford University and some of the work is described by CRAIG.[37] From the examples discussed therein, we choose two as illustrations of the points made above. The first is due to Hines, of the Bell Laboratories, and is illustrated in Fig. 34. Posts are attached to

[37] CRAIG; *Technical Report No. 36, Electronics Research Laboratory and Microwave Laboratory.* Stanford University. November, 1954.

opposite sides of a waveguide, which is broken up into a number of tightly coupled cavities by means of the crossbar. The posts in the cavities act as coaxial resonators. A hole for the beam is bored as shown in the diagrams. An equivalent circuit, based on the circuit elements identified in Fig. 34, is shown in Fig. 35. This equivalent circuit can be reduced to a ladder network by normal circuit transformations and the cut-offs are then found to be determined by

$$\omega_l^2 = \frac{1}{2L_0(C + 2C_1)} \tag{119}$$

$$\omega_u^2 = \frac{1}{2C(L_0 + L_1)} \tag{120}$$

where l means lower, u upper. Detailed experimental investigation of this circuit showed that, when the dimensions were adjusted for operation at 100 kV, the bandwidth was around 5% and the impedance low. For less extreme voltages, however, it is more promising as the bandwidth is greater and unwanted energy storage can also be reduced. The relation between the power flow, stored energy and group velocity was given in Section 4 of this chapter.

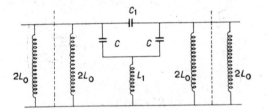

FIG. 35. Equivalent circuit for the line of Fig. 34.

A more important structure, due to Chodorow, is the clover-leaf structure. This is one of an important class of structures in which magnetic coupling between adjacent cavities is arranged to be in opposite directions on either side of an inductive slot. This can be represented as a negative mutual inductance and circuits employing this feature turn out to exhibit useful values of bandwidth and impedance. The clover-leaf structure is shown in Fig. 36. The basic unit is a pair of cylindrical cavities separated by a wall, in which, in the version shown in Fig. 36, eight radial slots and a central beam aperture are pierced. Each cavity is provided with four sector-shaped fingers located between alternate pairs of slots, so that the centre lines of the fingers make an angle of 90° with one another. The fingers in the two cavities are rotated at 45° with respect to one another. The projection of the fingers of the first cavity through into the second thus clears the fingers of the latter. The directions of the magnetic fields are then as shown on the diagram, very nearly opposite to one another. For a given internal diameter of the cylinder, a reasonable degree of adjustment of the centre frequency is achieved by altering the precise dimensions of the fingers. It will be seen that the function of the fingers is to force the magnetic field to be parallel to the radial slots and to increase its magnitude in their vicinity, so that the coupling is made as strong as possible. If the coupling looks like a negative mutual inductance, the circuit inductances will be reduced and the minimum frequency increased. The electric coupling through the central hole tends to increase the maximum frequency so that the net effect is a relatively (30%) broadband circuit.

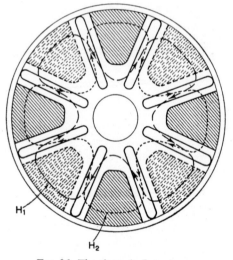

FIG. 36. The clover-leaf structure.

It is obviously very difficult to calculate the fields and power flow in a structure of this type, where the boundary is of a complicated shape. On the other hand it is quite easy to measure† the fields by perturbation methods. Theoretical methods, mentioned in

---

† See Appendix 5.

Section 3.3, can then be used to deduce the space-harmonic fields as functions of, for example, the radius. Suppose that the field along the tunnel wall of a clover-leaf cavity or system of individual cavities is measured by perturbation technique. Then, from Floquet's theorem, Eq. (25), we have

$$E(z) = \sum_{-\infty}^{+\infty} A_n \exp\left(-j\beta_n z\right) \qquad (121)$$

and by Fourier's theorem

$$A_n = \frac{1}{L} \int_{-L/2}^{+L/2} E(z) \exp\left(j\beta_n z\right) dz \qquad (122)$$

Where L is the length of the cavity. Typically E_z might be of the form

$$
\begin{cases}
E_z = E, & -\dfrac{l}{2} < z < \dfrac{l}{2} \\[2mm]
\quad = 0 & -\dfrac{L}{2} < z < -\dfrac{l}{2} \\[2mm]
\quad = 0 & \dfrac{l}{2} < z < \dfrac{L}{2}
\end{cases}
$$

in which case
$$A_n = \frac{V}{L} \frac{\sin\left(\beta_n l/2\right)}{\beta_n l/2} \qquad (123)$$

where V is the "voltage" El. Then, from the general theory of slow waves, the component A_n measured at r has the value

$$A_n(r) = \frac{V}{L} \frac{\sin\left(\beta_n l/2\right)}{\beta_n l/2} \cdot \frac{I_0(\gamma_n r)}{I_0(\gamma_n a)} \qquad (124)$$

where $\gamma_n{}^2 = \beta_n{}^2 - k_0{}^2 = \beta_n{}^2$,

a = radius of central aperture.

We wish to know how strongly the field will interact with an electron beam travelling synchronously with one of the space-harmonics, β_n. This is clearly given by Eq. (124) and we can define a generalized gap coupling coefficient by

$$M_n = \frac{\sin\left(\beta_n l/2\right)}{\beta_n l/2} \cdot \frac{I_0(\gamma_n r)}{I_0(\gamma_n a)} \qquad (125)$$

We have already discussed another typical form of E_z, observed with thin edges. This leads to

$$M_n = J_0\left(\frac{\beta_n l}{2}\right) \frac{I_0(\gamma_n r)}{I_0(\gamma_n a)} \tag{126}$$

Clearly, the technique is not restricted to forms of E_z which are expressible as analytical forms. The operation of Eq. (122) can be carried through by graphical or numerical means. This leads to numerical values for the coupling factor at the gap edge, which can be extended over the gap as in Eqs. (124) and (126).

The formulation of the results in terms of gap coupling factor is appropriate for the study of periodic field devices, e.g., klystrons and easitrons. For travelling-wave devices it is more appropriate to use

$$Z_{cn} = \frac{E_{zn} . E_{zn}{}^*}{2\beta_n{}^2 . P} = \frac{E_{zn} . E_{zn}{}^*}{2\beta_n{}^2 . g . W}$$

E_z being given by Eqs. (121) and (123). To illustrate the procedure let us follow PIERCE[4] in discussing the disk-loaded waveguide of Fig. 8(a). The energy stored in one section is $W_1 = CV^2/2$, and, as $C \propto 1/d$, we can write this as $W_1 = W_0 V^2/d$. The energy stored per unit length of line is then just $W = W_0 V^2/Ld$. But $E_n = V M_n/L$ or $V^2 = L^2 E_n{}^2/M_n{}^2$. Then, if we normalize to unit field $E_n = 1$ and $W = W_0 L/M_n{}^2 d$, or $W/W_0 = 1/M_n{}^2 . L/d = 1/M_n{}^2 . \theta_L/\theta_g$, where $\theta_L = \beta_n L$ = transit angle through section. $\theta_g = \beta_n d$ = transit angle through field.

If θ_L is very small, e.g., at very high electron velocities, then $\theta_L/\theta_g \to 1$, $M_n \to 1$ and $W \to W_0$ so that W_0 represents a limiting value of the stored energy. To obtain a high coupling impedance, W should be as small as possible. The minimum can be found by differentiation. If the M_n of Eq. (125) is used, W has a minimum for $\theta_g = 3\pi/4$. If $\theta_L \leqslant 3\pi/4$ radians, θ_g and θ_L should be made equal and the coupling impedance varies as $[(\sin \theta_g/2)/(\theta_g/2)]^2$ while if $\theta_L > 3\pi/4$, θ_g ought to be fixed at $3\pi/4$. The reduction factor is then $[1\cdot 45/\theta_L]$. Similar considerations can be applied to more complicated structures, such as that of Fig. 34, which is left as an exercise to the reader.

4

SPACE-CHARGE WAVE THEORY

IN THIS chapter we shall consider the electron beam in isolation from the circuit. We study first the space-charge waves which can propagate in infinite beams, next we introduce the effects of changing to a cylindrical geometry and the inclusion of metallic conductors surrounding the beam. Effects due to non-infinite magnetic fields are then surveyed as are questions of power flow. This prepares the ground for Chapter 5 in which we consider the interaction between beams and circuits. The reader should master the theory of d.c. focusing, given in Appendix 6 before reading further.

4.1. NOTATION

It has been somewhat difficult to decide on the notation for this chapter, in particular it is difficult to decide whether the beam current should be taken in the conventional direction or in the direction of electron motion, and whether the electronic charge should carry its own sign or not. Some writers adhere to one convention and some to the other. It was finally decided to consider that the electronic charge should be taken as $-e$ and an electron current, moving to the right, written as $-I_0$. An electronic space-charge is $-\rho_0$, a positive ion space-charge ρ_0. This convention leads to some irritating minus signs but has the overriding advantage that the resulting equations can be matched to field equations, written in standard form, without any special enquiry into the signs. When polar co-ordinates are used, a right-handed system is assumed. We then write d.c. beam current $= I_0$

$$\eta = |e/m|$$
$$\text{beam area} = \Sigma$$
$$\text{d.c. beam} \begin{cases} \text{potential} = V_0 \\ \text{velocity} = u_0, \ u_0 = \sqrt{(2\eta V_0)} \end{cases}$$
$$\text{d.c. charge density} = \rho_0 = I_0/\Sigma u_0$$
$$\text{a.c. charge density} = \rho_1$$
$$\text{a.c. velocity} = u_1$$
$$\text{a.c. current density} = J_1$$

ρ_1, u_1 and J_1 all have wave functions $\exp j(\omega t - \beta z)$† so that

$$\frac{\partial}{\partial t} \equiv j\omega, \qquad \frac{\partial}{\partial z} \equiv -j\beta$$

4.2. SPACE-CHARGE WAVES IN AN UNBOUNDED BEAM OF VERY LARGE CROSS-SECTION

We may picture this case as in Fig. 1 where we show a very large planar cathode placed close to a perfect, electron-permeable grid which is held at a positive potential V_0. Beyond the grid is a distant anode held at the grid potential. The whole device is immersed in a z-directed d.c. magnetic field which is infinitely strong, so that no transverse electron motion is possible. The average (negative) charge density is compensated by an equal charge density of positive ions so that the d.c. potential is uniform throughout the beam.

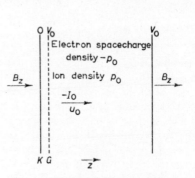

FIG. 1. Notation for electron flows.

Because of their much greater mass, the positive ions are considered not to move under the influence of r.f. fields. Under these, highly idealized, conditions, all electrons travel in straight lines between cathode and anode and the d.c. potential is everywhere V_0 in the grid anode space so that the velocity is everywhere u_0. We first use Maxwell's equations to form a general wave equation for the propagation of space-charge waves and then apply it to this system. Maxwell's equations are given in standard vector form by Eq. (1), Chapter 2. Putting in the indicated operations and separating out

---

† The use of $j\beta$ instead of Γ will be justified in the sequel.

the a.c. part we obtain

$$\nabla \times \mathbf{E} = j\omega \mathbf{B} \tag{1}$$

$$\nabla \cdot \mathbf{B} = 0 \tag{2}$$

$$\nabla \cdot \mathbf{E} = \rho_1/\epsilon_0 \tag{3}$$

$$\nabla \times \mathbf{B} = jk\omega \mathbf{E} + J_1 \tag{4}$$

Here, $k = \omega/c$ as usual.

We also require the a.c. part of the force, i.e.,

$$\frac{du_1}{dt} = \frac{\partial u_1}{\partial t} + u_0 \frac{\partial u_1}{\partial z} = -\eta E_z$$

or

$$j(\omega - \beta u_0)u_1 = -\eta E_z \tag{5}$$

and the continuity equation

$$\frac{\partial J_1}{\partial z} + \frac{\partial \rho_1}{\partial t} = 0$$

or

$$J_1 = \frac{\omega \rho_1}{\beta} \tag{6}$$

Lastly, we use the small-signal assumption, that cross products of a.c. quantities can be neglected.

Thus $(-J_0 + J_1) = (-\rho_0 + \rho_1)(u_0 + u_1)$ becomes

$$J_1 \doteq -\rho_0 u_1 + u_0 \rho_1 \tag{7}$$

The wave equation is derived by taking the curl of Eq. (1), using the vector relation

$$\text{curl curl} = \text{grad div} - \nabla^2$$

and substituting the expression for $\nabla \times \mathbf{B}$. The result is

$$\nabla^2 \mathbf{E} + k^2 \mathbf{E} = \frac{\nabla \rho_1}{\epsilon_0} + j\omega \mu_0 J_1$$

But $\nabla^2 \mathbf{E} = \partial^2 \mathbf{E}/\partial x^2 + \partial_2 \mathbf{E}/\partial y^2 - \beta^2 \mathbf{E}$ and if we now consider only the z component $\nabla \rho_1 = -j\beta \rho_1$ or

$$\frac{\partial^2 E_z}{\partial x^2} + \frac{\partial^2 E_z}{\partial y^2} - (\beta^2 - k^2) = -\frac{j\beta \rho_1}{\epsilon_0} + j\omega \mu_0 J_1 \tag{8}$$

H

Manipulating Eqs. (5), (6) and (7) we obtain

$$u_1 = j\eta \frac{E_z}{(\omega - \beta u_0)} \tag{9}$$

$$J_1 = -\frac{\omega \rho_0 u_1}{(\omega - \beta u_0)} \tag{10}$$

or

$$J_1 = -j \frac{\omega \rho_0 \eta}{(\omega - \beta u_0)^2} E_z \tag{11}$$

But $\rho_0 = I_0/u_0 \Sigma$

$$\therefore \qquad J_1 = -j \frac{\omega \eta I_0}{u_0 \Sigma (\omega - \beta u_0)^2} E_z \tag{12}$$

But the electron plasma frequency is defined through

$$\omega_p{}^2 = \eta \frac{I_0}{\epsilon_0 u_0 \Sigma}$$

so finally

$$J_1 = -j\omega \epsilon_0 \frac{\omega_p{}^2}{(\omega - \beta u_0)^2} E_z \tag{13}$$

If we now insert Eqs. (6) and (13) into Eq. (8) we find

$$\frac{\partial^2 E_z}{\partial x^2} + \frac{\partial^2 E_z}{\partial y^2} - (\beta^2 - k^2)\left(1 - \frac{\omega_p{}^2}{(\omega - \beta u_0)^2}\right) E_z = 0 \tag{14}$$

Equation (14) is the required wave equation.

For the rectilinear system in an infinite magnetic field, the assumptions made in the introductory paragraph ensure that all the electrons in any plane of constant z have the same instantaneous velocity. Thus

$$\frac{\partial^2 E_z}{\partial x^2} = 0 = \frac{\partial^2 E_z}{\partial y^2}$$

and

$$(\beta^2 - k^2)\left(1 - \frac{\omega_p{}^2}{(\omega - \beta u_0)^2}\right) E_z = 0 \tag{15}$$

The roots, by inspection, are

$$\beta_{1,2} = \pm jk \tag{16}$$

$$\beta_{3,4} = \left(\frac{\omega \pm \omega_p}{u_0}\right) \tag{17}$$

The first two waves propagate with the velocity of light since $k = \omega/c$, and are essentially waves which would be observed in the absence of the beam. The remaining two have phase velocities just above and below the beam velocity. The values are

$$p_{3,4} = \frac{u_0}{1 \pm \omega_p/\omega} \qquad (18)$$

and it can easily be shown that $\omega_p/\omega < 1$, in all normal beams. The group velocities are the same and both equal u_0. Thus, in any phenomenon which involves the transmission of energy along the beam the velocity of energy flow is equal to the electron velocity u_0.

A more intuitive deduction of Eq. (17) is due to PIERCE.[1] This is worth quoting as it links the preceding work with the idea of the Maxwellian total current. For the case where there are no transverse fields and no transverse displacement current, the total a.c. is, by definition ($i_1 = J_1\Sigma$, etc.)

$$I_{t_1} = i_1 + j\omega\epsilon_0\Sigma E_z$$

or, putting in the value of i,

$$I_{t_1} = j\omega\epsilon_0\left(1 - \frac{\omega_p{}^2}{(\omega - \beta u_0)^2}\right)\Sigma E_z$$

Now div $I_{t_1} = 0$, but both components are functions of z. Thus, if there is to be no current normal to the z direction I_{t_1} can only be zero. Thus β must be given by Eq. (17). When the beam is finite, as in the next section, I_{t_1} is not zero because a transverse electric field is set up. In this case the effective plasma frequency will be reduced, and the convection current is several times the displacement current.

4.3. THE CYLINDRICAL BEAM IN A CYLINDRICAL TUNNEL

The cylindrical beam, radius b, is now confined in a metallic tunnel of radius a. The magnetic field is still infinite and we again assume a positive ion space charge so that we can limit ourselves to a truly cylindrical beam.

---

[1] PIERCE; *B.S.T.J.*, 1954, **33**, 1343.

We now seek a solution of the wave equation which makes E_z finite on the axis of the system, zero at the metallic wall and which obeys the standard boundary conditions at $r = b$. From the symmetry of the problem, the fields can have no θ variation.

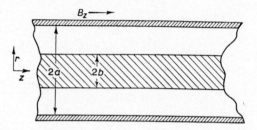

FIG. 2. A cylindrical beam in a hollow, cylindrical tunnel.

The solutions to the cylindrical wave equation

$$\frac{1}{r}\frac{\partial}{\partial r}\left(r\frac{\partial E_z}{\partial r}\right) + \gamma r^2 \cdot E_z = 0 \tag{19}$$

where

$$\gamma r^2 = (\beta^2 - k^2)\left(\frac{\omega_p^2}{(\omega - \beta u_0)^2} - 1\right) \tag{20}$$

are different inside and outside the beam.

Inside the beam

$$E_{zI} = A J_0(\gamma_r r) \tag{21}$$

since $Y_0(0) \rightarrow -\infty$.

Outside the beam, there is no current ($\omega_p^2 = 0$) so the solution is

$$E_{zII} = C I_0(\gamma_0 r) + D K_0(\gamma_0 r) \tag{22}$$

$$\gamma_0^2 = +(\beta^2 - k^2) \tag{23}$$

If the solution is at all like the solution of the last section $\beta \doteq \omega/u_0$ and therefore $k^2(= \omega^2/c^2)$ is negligible in comparison with β^2 and $\gamma_0 \doteq \omega/u_0$.

We now use the boundary conditions to express all the constants in terms of A.

Since $E_z = 0$ at $r = A$

$$\frac{D}{C} = -\frac{I_0(\gamma_0 a)}{K_0(\gamma_0 a)} \tag{24}$$

The radial and tangential components of the electric field are continuous at $r = b$, or the same result comes from continuity of E_r and H_θ.

Then,

$$\frac{A}{C} = \frac{1}{J_0(\gamma r b)}\left[I_0(\gamma_0 b) - \frac{I_0(\gamma_0 a)}{K_0(\gamma_0 a)}K_0(\gamma_0 b)\right]$$

$$= \frac{-\gamma_0 b}{\gamma_r b J_1(\gamma r b)}\left[I_1(\gamma_0 b) + \frac{I_0(\gamma_0 a)}{K_0(\gamma_0 a)}K_1(\gamma_0 b)\right] \quad (25)$$

therefore

$$-\frac{(\gamma_r b)J_1(\gamma_r b)}{J_0(\gamma_r b)} = \gamma_0 b\left[\frac{I_1(\gamma_0 b)K_0(\gamma_0 a) + I_0(\gamma_0 a)K_1(\gamma_0 b)}{I_0(\gamma_0 b)K_0(\gamma_0 a) - I_0(\gamma_0 a)K_0(\gamma_0 b)}\right] \quad (26)$$

This result was originally derived by RAMO.[2]

In the special case $a = b$, i.e., the beam fills the tunnel, we find that we merely have to satisfy

$$J_0(\gamma_r b) = 0$$

or

$$\gamma_r = \frac{2 \cdot 405}{b}, \quad \frac{5 \cdot 520}{b}, \quad \frac{8 \cdot 654}{b}, \text{ etc.} \quad (27)$$

The method of solving Eq. (26) is to compute the R.H.S. as a function of $\gamma_0 b \doteq \beta_e b = \omega b/u_0$ for a chosen value of a/b. The intersections with the various branches of the L.H.S. are then determined graphically. There are, of course, an infinite number of solutions, just as in Eq. (27).

Having determined γ_r as a function of γ_0 we can proceed by putting

$$\beta_{3,4} = \left(\frac{\omega \pm F\omega_p}{u_0}\right) \quad (28)$$

into Eq. (20), still neglecting k^2, we get

$$\gamma_r^2 = \left(\frac{\omega \pm F\omega_p}{u_0}\right)^2\left(1 + \frac{1}{F^2}\right) \quad (29)$$

or, if $F\omega_p \ll \omega$,

$$F^2 = \frac{1}{1 + (\gamma_r b/\gamma_0 b)^2} = \frac{1}{1 + (\gamma_r b/\beta_e b)^2} \quad (30)$$

---

[2] RAMO; *Phys. Rev.*, 1939, **56**, 276.

where we have written $\beta_e = \omega/u_0$. But, $\omega b/u_0$ is the normalized beam radius B (equal to the radius measured as a transit angle). B rarely exceeds 1 in normal valves, so Eq. (26) shows that, at any rate for the beam filling the tunnel $F_1 < 1$ and higher order values of F, denoted in general by F_n, are all less than F_1. The condition $\omega_p^2 \ll \omega^2$ is therefore much more stringent than $F_1^2\omega_p^2 \ll \omega^2$.

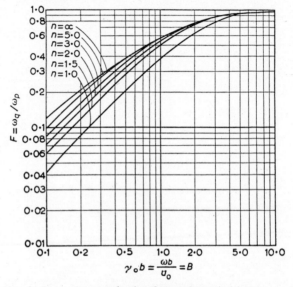

FIG. 3. Space-charge reduction factors for cylindrical beams in cylindrical tunnels.

Fig. 3† shows a plot of F_1 as a function of B, for various values of $n = a/b$, as a parameter. F_1 lies between 0 and 1 and, at any fixed value of B, increases as A increases. Investigation shows that this means a shorter space-charge wavelength, or, in other words, the debunching effects are more marked. Conversely, thin beams closely confined in narrow tunnels exhibit minimum debunching.

The reader may have wondered why we assumed that γ_r^2, as given by Eq. (20), is positive. If γ_r^2 were negative, the fields in the beam would be of the form $AI_0(\gamma_r . r)$. In the case of the beam filling the tunnel this would lead to the boundary condition $I_0(\gamma_r . b) = 0$, which is impossible, since I_0 increases monotonically

---

† These data were kindly computed for me by Mr. G. P. de Mengel of the Patent Dept., Standard Telephones & Cables, Ltd.

from unity. It can be shown in the general case that no solutions of this form are possible. Thus, γ_r^2 must be positive and $F^2 < 1$.

WEBSTER,[3] in his classic paper gave a theory of debunching in klystrons, which led to the value predicted in Section 4.2. Fig. 3 shows that his results would very seriously over-estimate the debunching in ordinary valve structures, which are of the geometrical form now under discussion.

4.4. THE SUPERPOSITION OF SPACE-CHARGE WAVES TO MATCH INITIAL CONDITIONS

This section is necessary for the appreciation of the use of space-charge wave concepts but is here in the nature of a digression, as the full treatment including all the modes is given in the next chapter.

We assume, with nearly all earlier writers, that only the first space-charge mode is excited so that we have only to consider waves with propagation constants $\beta_1 = (\omega + F_1\omega_p)/u_0$, $\beta_2 = (\omega - F_1\omega_p)/u_0$. It is now more convenient to use the d.c. and a.c. currents *per unit length of beam* instead of the densities.

We wish to satisfy the following initial condition at entry to a drift tube: $i_1 = i_{10}$, $u_1 = u_{10}$. The plane of origin is taken as $z = t = 0$. Then at the origin

$$u_{11} + u_{12} = u_{10}$$

$$i_{11} + i_{12} = i_{10}$$

Using Eqs. (9) and (12) and the values of β_1, β_2 we get

$$u_{10} = \frac{j\eta}{F_1\omega_p}(-E_{z1} + E_{z2}) \tag{31}$$

$$i_{10} = \frac{-j\eta}{u_0 F_1{}^2 \omega_p{}^2}(E_{z1} + E_{z2}) \tag{32}$$

The explicit relation for the E_z wave is

$$E_z = E_{z1}\exp j(\omega t - \beta_1 z) + E_{z2}\exp j(\omega t - \beta_2 z)$$

$$= \left\{ E_{z1}\exp\left(-j\frac{F_1\omega_p z}{u_0}\right) + E_{z2}\exp\left(j\frac{F_1\omega_p z}{u_0}\right) \right\} \exp j\left(\omega t - \frac{\omega z}{u_0}\right)$$

$$= \{(E_{z1} + E_{z2})\cos Z_1 + j(-E_{z1} + E_{z2})\sin Z_1\}\exp j\left(\omega t - \frac{\omega z}{u_0}\right)$$

where $Z_1 = F_1\omega_p z/u_0$.

---

[3] WEBSTER; *J. Appl. Phys.*, 1939, **10**, 501.

Then

$$E_z = \frac{F_1 \omega_p}{\eta}\left\{j\frac{u_0 F_1 \omega_p i_{10}}{I_0 \omega} \cos Z_1 + u_{10} \sin Z_1\right\} \exp j\left(\omega t - \frac{\omega z}{u_0}\right) \quad (33)$$

from Eqs. (31) and (32).

Then, directly from Eq. (12)

$$i_1 = \left\{i_{10} \cos Z_1 - j\frac{\omega I_0}{u_0 F_1 \omega_p} u_{10} \sin Z_1\right\} \exp j\left(\omega t - \frac{\omega z}{u_0}\right) \quad (34)$$

and a little manipulation gives

$$u_1 = \left\{u_{10} \cos Z_1 - j\frac{u_0 F_1 \omega_p}{\omega I_0} i_{10} \sin Z_1\right\} \exp j\left(\omega t - \frac{\omega z}{u_0}\right) \quad (35)$$

It must be remembered that since E_z is a function of r, e.g., in the beam $E_z = AJ_0(\gamma_r \cdot r)$, i_1 and u_1 are also functions of r, through the initial values u_{10} and i_{10}.

Consider now, for the moment, the buncher gap of a klystron in which, except for the (very small) noise currents $i_{10} = 0$. Suppressing the phase factor

$$u_1 = u_{10} \cos Z_1$$

$$i_1 = -ju_{10} \frac{\omega I_0}{u_0 F_1 \omega_p} \sin Z_1$$

But, gap theory[4] gives

$$u_{10} = \frac{\eta M V_1}{u_0} \,^\dagger \qquad \text{and} \qquad u_0{}^2 = 2\eta V_0$$

The quantity V_1/V_0 is called the depth of modulation and written α. Introducing this notation, and putting $\omega z/u_0 = Z$

$$u_1 = \frac{u_0 \alpha M}{2} \cos Z_1 \quad (36)$$

$$i_1 = -j\frac{I_0 \alpha M}{2} \cdot Z \cdot \frac{\sin Z_1}{Z_1} \quad (37)$$

---

[4] BECK; *Thermionic Valves*, Appendix 2, Cambridge University Press, 1953.

† Previously I have used the symbol β for the gap modulation coefficient. Owing to the use of this symbol as the phase constant in wave theory I have, rather reluctantly, decided to follow PIERCE in calling it M.

Equation (37) shows that the r.f. beam current lags 90° behind the voltage which produced it and that it reaches its maximum value when

$$\sin Z_1 = 1, \quad \text{or} \quad z = \frac{\pi u_0}{2F_1 \omega_p} \qquad (38)$$

The space-charge wavelength is $2\pi(u_0/F_1\omega_p)$ and is inversely proportional to F_1. No advantage is to be gained by lengthening a klystron beyond the value given by Eq. (38) unless for some practical reason we wish to make z an odd multiple of Eq. (38). (These remarks cease to apply when we consider the higher order modes.) We now know the r.f. current in our klystron beam. The current induced in an output resonator is given by $Mi_1(z)$ and the gain can easily be found if the resonator parameters are known.

To conclude this section we ought to draw the reader's attention to an inconsistency in Eqs. (36) and (37) which, however, are commonly used. We should, logically, take $\rho_{10} = 0$ instead of $i_{10} = 0$, for $i_{10} = -\rho_0 u_{10} + \rho_{10} u_0$ and if u_{10} is finite so is i_{10}. If we do this, we find the correction term depends on $F_1\omega_p/\omega$ which is $\ll 1$. In view of the smallness of the correction we have not departed from the usual convention.

4.5. SPACE-CHARGE REDUCTION FACTORS FOR OTHER GEOMETRIES

Still keeping to the infinite magnetic field we now take up the question of evaluating the reduction factor F in other geometrical arrangements. This has been extensively studied by BRANCH and

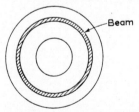

FIG. 4. An annular beam in a coaxial line.

MIHRAN.[5] The most general case is that of an annular beam in the region between coaxial conductors (Fig. 4). This is not commonly

[5] BRANCH and MIHRAN; *I.R.E. Prof. Group Electron Devices*, 1955, ED–2, 3.

used in valves but the slightly less involved case of an annular beam in a hollow tunnel (Fig. 5) is important. We divide the space into

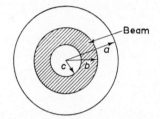

FIG. 5. Annular beam in a cylindrical tunnel.

three regions, those, I and III, where there is no charge and the beam region II. The fields in these regions are

$$E_{zI} = AI_0(\gamma_0 r) \tag{39}$$

$$E_{zII} = BJ_0(\gamma_r . r) + CY_0(\gamma_r . r) \tag{40}$$

$$E_{zIII} = DI_0(\gamma_0 r) + EK_0(\gamma_0 r) \tag{41}$$

The boundary conditions are, $E_{zIII} = 0$ at $r = a$.

$$\frac{H_{\theta III}}{E_{zIII}} = \frac{H_{\theta II}}{E_{zII}} \qquad \text{at } r = b$$

and $\qquad \dfrac{H_{\theta II}}{E_{zII}} = \dfrac{H_{\theta I}}{E_{zI}} \qquad \text{at } r = c$

Table I in Chapter 3 shows that $H_\theta \propto \partial E_z/\partial r$ so, for example

$$H_{\theta II} \propto -\gamma_r\{BJ_1(\gamma_r . r) + CY_1(\gamma_r . r)\} \tag{42}$$

The boundary conditions at c and b are used to obtain two different equations for C/B, and this quantity being eliminated, we obtain

$$\frac{Y_1(\gamma_r b) + \gamma_0/\gamma_r[Y_0(\gamma_r b)/\text{btnh }(a-b)]}{Y_1(\gamma_r c) + \gamma_0/\gamma_r[I_1(\gamma_0 c)/I_0(\gamma_0 c)]Y_0(\gamma_r c)}$$
$$= \frac{J_1(\gamma_r b) + \gamma_0/\gamma_r[J_0(\gamma_r b)/\text{btnh }(a-b)]}{J_1(\gamma_r c) + \gamma_0/\gamma_r[I_1(\gamma_0 c)/I_0(\gamma_0 c)]J_0(\gamma_r c)} \tag{43}$$

where btnh $(a - b)$ (Bessel hyperbolic tangent) is written for

$$\text{btnh}\,(\gamma_0 a - \gamma_0 b) = \frac{I_0(\gamma_0 b)K_0(\gamma_0 a) - K_0(\gamma_0 b)I_0(\gamma_0 a)}{I_1(\gamma_0 b)K_0(\gamma_0 a) + K_1(\gamma_0 b)I_0(\gamma_0 a)} \tag{44}$$

Finally,

$$\frac{\gamma_0^2}{\gamma_r^2} + \frac{\gamma_0}{\gamma_r}\left[\frac{I_0(\gamma_0 c)}{I_1(\gamma_0 c)}\frac{1}{\text{btnh}\,(\gamma_r b - \gamma_r c)} - \frac{\text{btnh}\,(\gamma_0 a - \gamma_0 b)}{\text{btn}\,(\gamma_r c - \gamma_r b)}\right] -$$

$$- \frac{I_0(\gamma_0 c)}{I_1(\gamma_0 c)}\frac{\text{bsn}\,(\gamma_r b - \gamma_r c)}{\text{bsn}\,(\gamma_r b - \gamma_r c)}\text{btnh}\,(\gamma_0 a - \gamma_0 b) \tag{45}$$

The contractions employed and the resolution of this equation are discussed in Appendix 7. Fig. 6 shows results[5] for an annular beam,

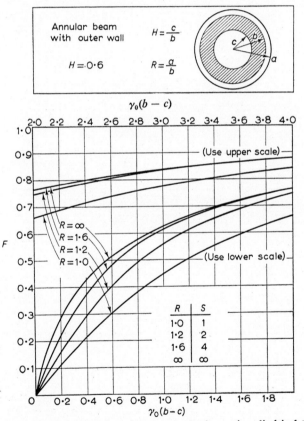

FIG. 6. Space-charge reduction factors for annular beams in cylindrical tunnels.

while Fig. 7 shows data for a planar beam taken from the same source. The planar results are deduced from the equivalent theory in rectangular co-ordinates, in which only trigonometrical and hyperbolic functions arise. The deduction of the relation between the transverse and longitudinal propagation constants is left as an exercise to the reader.

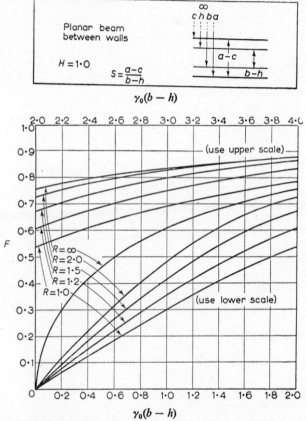

FIG. 7. Space-charge reduction factors for sheet beams between metal walls.

4.6. SPACE-CHARGE WAVES ON BRILLOUIN BEAMS

The theory of Brillouin beams is given in detail in Appendix 6. Brillouin focusing is a system in which the cathode is entirely shielded from the longitudinal magnetic focusing field. The electron beam enters this field suddenly, through a small hole. The sudden jump in B_z causes rotation of the whole beam about the axis as though it were a solid body, i.e., all electrons have the same angular velocity, which proves to be the Larmor frequency $\eta B_z/2$. Moreover, all the electrons have the same axial velocity u_0, but this is in general lower than the velocity equivalent of the wall potential, V_0. If the field is chosen correctly in relation to the beam diameter and beam current it is possible to achieve a balance between the outwards forces due to space-charge and centripetal acceleration and the inward magnetic force on the electrons. A stable cylindrical beam can thus be formed without the necessity of assuming the existence of a positive ion space charge. However, since the magnetic field is finite and depends on the beam parameters, local changes of current density in the beam will provoke transverse motions because the equilibrium condition is upset. Under the action of r.f. fields the beam assumes a scalloped shape (Fig. 8) and we wish to calculate the effect on the space-charge waves.

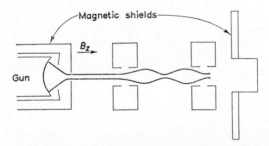

FIG. 8. Configuration of an electron beam perturbed by r.f. forces.

This problem has been treated by several authors. We here follow RIGROD and LEWIS[6] rather than LABUS and PÖSCHL[7] whose results differ considerably from those of RIGROD and LEWIS. The objections raised by the latter authors seem to me invalid.

We consider here only the case of a solid beam in a drift tube, for which we need only use the T.M. wave system. However, we require for more general cases the T.E. system also.

The necessary results are given in the table. These are derived from Eqs. (14) and (15) of Chapter 2, using wave functions $\exp j(\omega t - \beta z)$ and restricting ourselves to waves which are independent of θ in the

[6] RIGROD and LEWIS; B.S.T.J., 1954, 33, 399.
[7] LABUS and PÖSCHL; A.E.Ü., 1955, 9, 41.

T.M. case. Finally, because we are interested in slow waves, we ignore k^2 in comparison with β^2.

We now proceed to show that $(\omega\mu_0/\beta) J_r$ is negligible in comparison with $\partial E_z/\partial r$. In the infinite field case we have $J_z = (-j\omega\epsilon_0/F^2)E_z$ so the T.M. wave equation becomes

$$\frac{1}{r}\frac{\partial}{\partial r}\left(r\frac{\partial E_z}{\partial r}\right) + \beta^2\left(\frac{1}{F_B{}^2} - 1\right)E_z = \frac{\beta}{\omega\epsilon_0}\frac{1}{r}\frac{\partial}{\partial r}(rJ_r) \qquad (46)$$

where F_B is the reduction factor appropriate to the Brillouin case.

TABLE 1

Cylindrical, slow-waves in the presence of free charge

T.M. COMPONENTS
$\dfrac{1}{r}\dfrac{\partial}{\partial r}\left(r\dfrac{\partial E_z}{\partial r}\right) - \beta^2 E_z = -j\dfrac{\beta^2 J_z}{\omega\epsilon_0} + \dfrac{\beta}{\omega\epsilon_0}\dfrac{1}{r}\dfrac{\partial}{\partial r}(rJ_r)$
$E_r = \dfrac{j}{\beta}\dfrac{\partial E_z}{\partial r} - j\dfrac{\omega\mu_0 J_r}{\beta^2}$
$H_\theta = \dfrac{\omega\epsilon_0}{\beta}E_r - \dfrac{j}{\beta}J_r$

T.E. COMPONENTS
$\dfrac{1}{r}\dfrac{\partial}{\partial r}\left(r\dfrac{\partial H_z}{\partial r}\right) - \beta^2 H_z = -\dfrac{1}{r}\dfrac{\partial}{\partial r}(rJ_\theta)$
$H_r = \dfrac{j}{\beta}\left(\dfrac{\partial H_z}{\partial r} + J_\theta\right)$
$E_\theta = -\dfrac{\omega\mu_0}{\beta}H_r = -j\dfrac{\omega\mu_0}{\beta^2}\left(\dfrac{\partial H_z}{\partial r} + J_\theta\right)$

We now assume that F_B is not much different from F_∞. But F_∞ makes the R.H.S. of Eq. (46) zero and we conclude that when F_B is inserted the L.H.S. is only small, say Δ.

Then
$$J_r = \frac{\omega\epsilon_0 r}{2\beta}\Delta \qquad (47)$$

and $(\omega\mu_0)\beta/J_r$ is of order k^2/β^2 and is therefore to be neglected. The second equation of the table then becomes

$$E_r = \frac{j}{\beta}\frac{\partial E_z}{\partial r} \qquad (48)$$

Similar reasoning shows that we can neglect J_θ, compared with $\partial H_z/\partial r$. The calculations are in the following parts:

1. The calculation of the perturbations to the steady state motions caused by the r.f. forces.

2. The introduction of an r.f. surface current on a cylindrical beam which is equivalent to the actual beam with scalloped walls.

3. The matching of field equations to determine the space-charge reduction factor.

The necessary d.c. solution, extracted from Appendix 6 is

$$\dot{r} = 0, \qquad \dot{\theta}_0 = \omega_L = \frac{\eta B_z}{2}, \qquad \dot{z} = u_0$$

$$-\eta\frac{\partial V_0}{\partial r} = r\omega_L{}^2, \qquad \frac{\partial V_0}{\partial z} = 0 \quad \text{and} \quad \rho_0 = -2\frac{\epsilon_0\omega_L{}^2}{\eta}$$

The plasma frequency is related to ω_L by $\omega_p{}^2 = -\eta\rho_0/\epsilon_0 = 2\omega_L{}^2$.

The initial position of an electron was r_0, θ_0, z. At time t, its co-ordinates are $(r_0,\ \theta_0 + \omega_L t,\ z_0 + u_0 t)$. When a small a.c. field is present, we write ordinary small signal expressions for the perturbed co-ordinates.

$$r = r_0 + r_1(r_0)\exp j[\omega t - \beta(z_0 + u_0 t)] \tag{49}$$

$$\theta = \theta_0 + \omega_L t + \theta_1(r_0)\exp j[\omega t - \beta(z_0 + u_0 t)] \tag{50}$$

$$z = z_0 + u_0 t + z_1(r_0)\exp j[\omega t - \beta(z_0 + u_0 t)] \tag{51}$$

We thus emphasize that r_1, θ_1, z_1 are functions of the initial radial co-ordinate r_0. In the small signal theory it is accurate enough to take the values of the a.c. fields evaluated at the initial position of the electron. The a.c. values are now put into the force equations (5), (6) and (7) of Appendix 6. In this step we may disregard the effects due to a.c. magnetic fields, which are, as usual, negligible for non-relativistic velocities.

$$\ddot{r} - (r_0 + r_1)(\omega_L + \dot{\theta}_1)^2 = -\eta\left(-\frac{\partial V_0}{\partial r} + E_r + (r_0 + r_1)(\omega_L + \dot{\theta}_1)B_B\right) \tag{52}$$

$$(r_0 + r_1)\ddot{\theta}_1 + 2\dot{r}_1(\omega_L + \dot{\theta}_1) = \eta\dot{r}_1 B_B \tag{53}$$

$$\ddot{z}_1 = -\eta E_z \tag{54}$$

However, we must not forget that if the beam radius alters, the radial space-charge field must change to compensate through

$$\eta \frac{\partial V_0}{\partial r} = (r_0 + r_1)\omega_L{}^2 \tag{55}$$

Since $\partial/\partial t = j(\omega - \beta u_0)$ we find

$$r_1 = \frac{\eta E_r}{(\omega - \beta u_0)^2} \tag{56}$$

$$\theta_1 = 0 \tag{57}$$

$$z_1 = \frac{\eta E_z}{(\omega - \beta u_0)^2} \tag{58}$$

The components of the a.c. velocity v_1 at the spatial point (r, θ, z) are now

$$v_1 = j(\omega - \beta u_0)[r, r_1\theta_1, z_1] \tag{59}$$

The continuity equation is applied to find the a.c. space-charge density

$$\rho_1 = \frac{j\rho_0}{(\omega - \beta u_0)} \operatorname{div} V_1 \tag{60}$$

or, putting Eqs. (56)–(58) into Eq. (59)

$$\rho_1 = \frac{\eta\rho_0}{(\omega - \beta u_0)^2} \operatorname{div} E = \frac{\omega_p{}^2}{(\omega - \beta u_0)^2} \rho_1 \tag{61}$$

The second result comes from replacing div E from Eq. (3).
Equation (61) has two solutions

$$\omega_p{}^2 = (\omega - \beta u_0)^2 \tag{62}$$

$$\rho_1 = 0 \tag{63}$$

Equation (62) leads to $(\omega \pm \omega_p)/u_0$, i.e., to plasma waves as found in the infinite planar flow. Equation (46), however, shows that this solution leads to inconsistencies and it must be abandoned. Equation (63) on the other hand states that the a.c. convection current must be due mainly to changes in the beam radius. In fact we find

$$J_r = \frac{\omega_p{}^2 \epsilon_0}{\beta(\omega - \beta u_0)} \frac{\partial E_z}{\partial r} \tag{64}$$

$$J_\theta = 0 \tag{65}$$

$$J_z = \frac{-j\omega_p{}^2 \epsilon_0}{(\omega - \beta u_0)} E_z \tag{66}$$

Comparing Eq. (66) with Eq. (13) we see that $J_z = i_1(F_B \omega_p/\omega)$, i.e., $J_z \ll i_1$. Clearly, if we use Eq. (64) for J_r, then $(\omega \mu_0/\beta)J_r$ is actually very small and our earlier approximation is valid.

Equations (64) and (66) are now put into the wave equation and we get

$$\frac{1}{r} \frac{\partial}{\partial r}\left(r \frac{\partial E_z}{\partial r}\right) - \beta^2 E_z = 0 \tag{67}$$

which has the solution

$$E_z = A I_0(\beta r) \tag{68}$$

Equation (68) is chosen so as to be finite at $r = 0$.

For a beam of steady state radius b, the a.c. radius is

$$r(b) = b + r_1(b) \exp j(\omega t - \beta z)$$

The rippled beam can be replaced by a uniform beam with an a.c. surface charge density $\rho_0 r_1$ or a surface current density with components

$$G_z = \rho_0 r_1 u_0 \tag{69}$$

$$G_\theta = \rho_0 r_1 \omega_L b \tag{70}$$

Then, the total convection current density is

$$I_c = 2\pi\left[\int_0^b J_z \cdot r \, dr + b\rho_0 u_0 r_1(b)\right] \tag{71}$$

We determine E_r from Eq. (48) using Eq. (68) for E_z. The value is put into Eq. (65) to give the explicit value for $r_1(b)$.

$$r_1(b) = -j \frac{\omega_p{}^2 \epsilon_0 A}{\rho_0(\omega - \beta u_0)^2} I_1(\beta b) \tag{72}$$

I

Equation (71) then becomes

$$I_c = \frac{-j\omega\epsilon_0 \cdot 2\pi b \cdot A I_1(\beta b)}{F_B{}^2 \cdot \beta} \qquad (73)$$

where $F_B{}^2 = (\omega - \beta u_0)^2/\omega_p{}^2$ as usual.

We next consider the matching problem.
Outside the beam we write

$$E_{z\text{II}} = B I_0(\beta r) + C K_0(\beta r) \qquad (74)$$

$$H_{\theta\text{II}} = \frac{j\omega\epsilon_0}{B} [B I_1(\beta r) - C K_1(\beta r)] \qquad (75)$$

At the wall $r = a$, $E_z = 0$, therefore $C/B = -I_0(\beta a)/K_0(\beta a)$. At the edge of the beam the admittance looking outwards is, as usual, $H_{\theta\text{II}}/E_{z\text{II}}$. Looking inwards, however, the magnetic field shows a jump, equal in value to the surface current density G_z. The boundary condition at b is therefore

$$\frac{H_{\theta\text{I}} + G_z}{E_{z\text{I}}} = \frac{H_{\theta\text{II}}}{E_{z\text{II}}}$$

or $\quad \dfrac{j\omega\epsilon_0}{\beta}\left(1 - \dfrac{1}{F_B{}^2}\right) \dfrac{I_1(\beta b)}{I_0(\beta b)} = \dfrac{j\omega\epsilon_0}{\beta}\left[\dfrac{I_1(\beta b) - C/B\,K_1(\beta b)}{I_0(\beta b) + C/B\,K_0(\beta b)}\right]$

Putting in the value of C/B and solving for $F_B{}^2$, using the Wronskian relation $I_0(\beta b)K_1(\beta b) + I_1(\beta b)K_0(\beta b) = 1/\beta b$, we find

$$F_B{}^2 = \beta b I_1(\beta b)\left[K_0(\beta b) - \frac{I_0(\beta b)K_0(\beta a)}{I_0(\beta a)}\right] \qquad (76)$$

Solutions of Eq. (76) for F_B recomputed from the data of Rigrod and Lewis are given in Fig. 9. The region of most practical interest is that for which $\beta b < 1\cdot 5$. We find that F_B is smaller than F_∞ or the debunching in a Brillouin beam is less than in a beam focused by an infinite field. This is to be expected, since the finite magnetic field allows transverse motion and some of the effects of space charge are offset by beam spreading. This means that, other things being equal, a Brillouin beam will give more gain than a "brute force" beam. Unfortunately other things are not equal and, as we see when we discuss matching, the large r.f. beam spreading

makes it difficult to use Brillouin beams in other than low level
devices. We also note that there is only one value of F_B for a given
value of a/b, since I_0 and K_0 are monotonic functions.

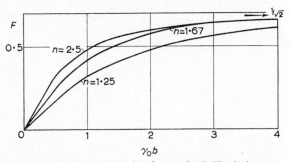

FIG. 9. Space-charge reduction factors for Brillouin beams.

4.7. SPACE-CHARGE WAVES ON CONFINED BEAMS

This question has been studied in unpublished work by PARZEN,[8]
and PIERCE[9] and in published work by BREWER.[10] It is a straightforward extension of the Brillouin case. The d.c. solution is given
in Appendix 6.

We perturb Eq. (10) putting $\theta = \theta_0 + \theta_1$, $r = r_0 + r_1$, to obtain,
now writing r_c for the radius at the cathode

$$\theta_1 = \frac{2r_1}{r_0} \cdot \frac{\omega_0 r_c^2}{r^2} \tag{77}$$

and, to save writing, put

$$\frac{\omega_0 r_c^2}{r^2} = \Omega \tag{78}$$

We next have to assume that the d.c. scalloping of the beam is
small, so that $\ddot{r} = 0$, $\dot{r}$ given by Eq. (11a), holds everywhere and is
not used merely for the equilibrium radius. From Eq. (11a)

$$E_{r0} = -\frac{\partial V_0}{\partial r} = r(\Omega^2 - \omega_L^2) \tag{79}$$

---

[8] PARZEN; *F.T.L. Technical Memorandum.*
[9] PIERCE; *Notes on space-charge waves.*
[10] BREWER; *Proc. Inst. Radio Engrs.*, N.Y., 1956, **44**, 896.

The perturbation of Eq. (11a) then yields

$$r_1 = \frac{\eta E_r}{F_c{}^2 \omega_p{}^2 - 4\Omega^2} \tag{80}$$

F_c stands for F-confined and we have used $(\omega - \beta u_0)^2 = F_c{}^2 \omega_p{}^2$ and the z equation becomes

$$z_1 = \frac{\eta E_z}{F_c{}^2 \omega_p{}^2} \tag{81}$$

We note that if $4\Omega^2 < F_c{}^2 \omega_p{}^2$ the a.c. spreading is greater than in the Brillouin case, but if $4\Omega^2 > 2F_c{}^2 \omega_p{}^2$ the spreading is less. We shall see that this is the usual case and the spreading is normally small, and in the opposite sense.

Equation (60) for ρ_1 still holds, so we write

$$\rho_1 = \frac{j\rho_0}{(\omega - \beta u_0)} \left[\frac{1}{r} \frac{\partial}{\partial r} (r u_{1r}) + \frac{\partial u_{1z}}{\partial z} \right] \tag{82}$$

We now form these velocities from Eqs. (80) and (81)

$$u_{1r} = jF_c \omega_p r_1 = \frac{j\eta F_c \omega_p}{F_c{}^2 \omega_p{}^2 - 4\Omega^2} E_r = \frac{-\eta F_c \omega_p}{\beta(F_c{}^2 \omega_p{}^2 - 4\Omega^2)} \frac{\partial E_z}{\partial r} \tag{83}$$

where we have used the relation between E_r and E_z to get the final result.

$$u_{1z} = \frac{-j\eta E_z}{F_c \omega_p}, \qquad \frac{\partial u_{1z}}{\partial z} = \frac{-\beta \eta E_z}{F_c \omega_p} \tag{84}$$

Putting these expressions into Eq. (82) we find

$$\rho_1 = j \frac{\epsilon_0 \omega_p{}^2}{\beta(F_c{}^2 \omega_p{}^2 - 4\Omega^2)} \frac{1}{r} \frac{\partial}{\partial r} \left(r \frac{\partial E_z}{\partial r} \right) - j \frac{\epsilon_0 \omega_p{}^2}{F_c{}^2 \omega_p{}^2} E_z \tag{85}$$

The components of the convection current density are:

$$J_{1r} = \rho_0 \cdot u_{1r} \tag{86}$$

$$J_{1\theta} = \rho_0 \cdot u_{1\theta} + \rho_1 u_0 \tag{87}$$

$$J_{1z} = \rho_0 \cdot u_{1z} + \rho_1 u_0 \tag{88}$$

Reference to the wave equation in the table shows that only the first and third are required. The explicit results are, remembering $\beta \doteq \omega/u_0$

$$\frac{\beta}{\omega\epsilon_0}\frac{1}{r}\frac{\partial}{\partial r}(rJ_r) = \frac{F_c\omega_p \cdot \omega_p^2}{\omega(F_c^2\omega_p^2 - 4\Omega^2)}\frac{1}{r}\frac{\partial}{\partial r}\left(r\frac{\partial E_z}{\partial r}\right) -$$

$$-\frac{j\beta^2}{\omega\epsilon_0}J_z = \frac{\beta^2\omega_p^2}{F_c^2\omega_p^2}\left(\frac{F_c\omega_p}{\omega} - 1\right)E_z + \frac{\omega_p^2}{(F_c^2\omega_p^2 - 4\Omega^2)}\frac{1}{r}\frac{\partial}{\partial r}\left(r\frac{\partial E_z}{\partial r}\right)$$

But, as in preceding work, we may neglect $F_c\omega_p/\omega$ in comparison with unity and the wave equation becomes

$$\frac{1}{r}\frac{\partial}{\partial r}\left(r\frac{\partial E_z}{\partial r}\right) - \gamma_c^2 E_z = 0 \tag{89}$$

where

$$\gamma_c^2 = \beta^2 \frac{(\omega_p^2/F_c^2\omega_p^2) - 1}{\omega_p^2/(F_c^2\omega_p^2 - 4\Omega^2) - 1} \tag{90}$$

To obtain the correct form of the solution to Eq. (89) we must decide whether γ_c^2 is positive or negative. The top line in Eq. (90) is fundamentally positive as $F_c < 1$ in all practical beams. The bottom line has a singularity at $F_c^2\omega_p^2 - 4\Omega^2 = \omega_p^2$ or $4\Omega^2 = \omega_p^2(F_c^2 - 1)$, which is an impossibility. The only cases which are physically realizable are therefore (a) $\Omega = 0$ (Brillouin flow) and (b) $4\Omega^2 > F_c^2\omega_p^2$ which makes the bottom bracket negative. The solutions to Eq. (89) then become

$$E_z = AI_0(\beta r), \qquad \Omega^2 = 0 \tag{91}$$

$$E_z = AJ_0(\gamma_c r), \qquad 4\Omega^2 > F_c^2\omega_p^2 \tag{92}$$

Equation (91) leads straight back to the results of Section 4.6. We can discuss the condition leading to Eq. (92) in more detail, by using the results of Appendix 6. We there show that, if α = ratio of flux cutting cathode to flux contained in the equilibrium beam diameter,

$$\alpha^2 = 1 - \frac{\omega_p^2}{2\omega_L^2} \tag{93}$$

If we now put the magnetic induction B_z actually used in the case under discussion equal to mB_B, $m > 1$

$$\alpha^2 = 1 - \frac{1}{m^2} \tag{94}$$

Then, using the definition of Ω in Eq. (78) we find

$$4\Omega^2 = 2(m^2 - 1)\omega_p{}^2 \tag{95}$$

giving the results in Table II.

TABLE 2

m	$\dfrac{4\Omega^2}{\omega_p{}^2}$	$\dfrac{\Omega}{\omega_p}$	$\dfrac{2(m^2-1)}{2(m^2-1)+1}$
1·00	0	0	0
1·25	1·13	0·53	0·53
1·50	2·50	0·79	0·71
1·75	4·13	1·02	0·80
2·00	6·00	1·23	0·86

In practical valves, $F_c{}^2$ should not exceed 0·25 so we see that $4\Omega^2/\omega_p{}^2 > 10F_c{}^2$ for m in excess of 1·5, i.e., for fields greater than 1·5 times the Brillouin value. Assuming that $4\Omega^2 \gg F_c{}^2\omega_p{}^2$ we can now obtain an approximate value for $F_c{}^2$ by casting Eqs. (89) and (90) into the same form as Eqs. (19) and (20). The result is

$$F_c{}^2 = F_\infty{}^2 \frac{2(m^2 - 1)}{2(m^2 - 1) + 1 - F_\infty{}^2} \tag{96}$$

This gives approximately the values in the last column of Table II. For the region in which it is valid, which is the region of most practical interest, the space-charge wavelength of a confined beam is less than 20% greater than the wavelength of a beam in an infinite magnetic field. We expect, on physical grounds, the difference to be in this sense. We reiterate that Eq. (92) gives an infinite series of space-charge modes. Equation (96) relates corresponding values in the two sets. While it is necessary to make the assumption $4\Omega^2 \gg F_c{}^2\omega_p{}^2$ to obtain a convenient analytical expression for $F_c{}^2$, it is easy to compute $F_c{}^2$ numerically by writing

$$\left(\frac{1}{F_c{}^2} - 1\right) = \left(1 - \frac{1}{F_c{}^2 - 4\Omega^2/\omega_p{}^2}\right)\left(\frac{1}{F_\infty{}^2} - 1\right) \tag{97}$$

Perhaps the quickest way to handle Eq. (97) is to put $F_c{}^2 = F_\infty{}^2$ on the R.H.S. and to solve by iteration.

In Brewer's work this lazy approach to the computation of F_c is not used. Instead, the procedure used to obtain Eq. (76) is repeated and the values of F_c computed directly from the resultant

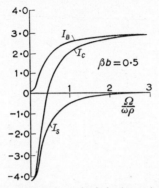

FIG. 10. The effect of field at the cathode in determining the surface and volume currents on confined beams.

equation. This elaboration is unnecessary as the values computed by the technique described above agree excellently with Brewer's calculations.

We now discuss the r.f. current. The expressions obtained below appear different from Brewer's because we use the $J_0(\gamma_c r)$ radial variations, with γ_c real instead of Brewer's $I_0(\gamma_c r)$ with imaginary γ_c. To determine the convection current density J_z we substitute for $(1/r)(\partial/\partial r)(r[\partial E_z/\partial r])$ from Eq. (89) into the immediately preceding equation for J_z. The result is

$$J_z = \frac{-j\omega\epsilon_0}{F_c{}^2}\left[1 - \frac{\gamma_c{}^2}{\beta^2}\frac{F_c{}^2\omega_p{}^2}{F_c{}^2\omega_p{}^2 - 4\Omega^2}\right]AJ_0(\gamma_c r) \tag{98}$$

The surface current density G_z in this case becomes

$$G_z = -\frac{\epsilon_0 u_0 \omega_p{}^2 E_r}{F_c{}^2\omega_p{}^2 - 4\Omega^2} = +j\frac{\epsilon_0 u_0 \omega_p{}^2\gamma_c AJ_1(\gamma_c r)}{\beta(F_c{}^2\omega_p{}^2 - 4\Omega^2)} \tag{99}$$

and the total conduction current

$$I_c = 2\pi\left[\int_0^b rJ_z \,.\, \mathrm{d}r + bG_z\right]$$

$$= -j\omega\epsilon_0 \,.\, 2\pi Ab^2 J_1(\gamma_c b)\frac{4\Omega^2/\omega_p{}^2 - (1 - F_c{}^2)}{F_c{}^2 \,.\, \beta Hb} \tag{100}$$

where $$H = \sqrt{\left(1 - F_c^2 + \frac{4\Omega^2}{\omega_p{}^2}\right)\left(\frac{1}{(F_c{}^2} - 1\right)\left(F_c{}^2 - \frac{4\Omega^2}{\omega_p{}^2}\right)} \qquad (101)$$

Brewer has plotted the reduced currents, given by Eq. (100) divided by $j\omega\epsilon_0$. $2\pi Ab^2$, as functions of Ω/ω_p for a case in which $\omega_p/\omega \doteqdot 0\cdot1$. One of these curves, that for $\beta b = 0\cdot5$, is shown in Fig. 10. For $\Omega = 0$, nearly all the current is in the surface scallops, the body of the beam contributing only the small $\rho_0 u_{1z}$ term. For small increases in Ω the surface current falls sharply while the body current rises fast, the total current passing through zero for a particular value of Ω/ω_p for which $4\Omega^2/\omega_p{}^2 + F_c{}^2 = 1$. For $\Omega > 2\omega_p$ substantially all the current is in the beam and only a few per cent on the surface. For bigger values of βb, the behaviour is qualitatively the same but the currents are reduced and the value of Ω/ω_p for negligible surface current decreases, being $\doteqdot 1$ for $\beta b = 1\cdot5$. Thus, for many confined beams the surface current is somewhat less than the value given in the infinite field case.

Values of F_c are shown in Fig. 11.

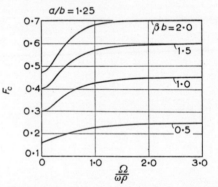

FIG. 11. Space-charge reduction factors for confined beams.

This concludes our work on the evaluation of the plasma frequency reduction factor in beams focused by longitudinal magnetic fields. We proceed to make use of some of the results derived.

4.8. THE TRANSMISSION-LINE ANALOGY

The analogy between a transmission line and an electron beam was first described by BLOOM and PETER[11] whose derivation gives

---

[11] BLOOM and PETER; R.C.A. Review, 1954, 15, 95.

the semblance of being restricted to the case of no transverse field, as they make use of the zero total current condition. In fact, there is no such restriction and we deduce the required results in a different way. We start with Eqs. (34) and (35) which give the r.f. current and velocity at a distance z from the input, in terms of the initial r.f. current and velocity. We introduce the kinetic voltage V_1 instead of the velocity u, by equating $(u_0 + u_1)^2 = 2\eta(V_0 + V_1)$ and neglecting $u_1{}^2$, according to the small-signal assumption, to get

$$V_1 = \frac{u_1 u_0}{\eta} \tag{102}$$

We also change the notation so that i_1, V_1 refers to the input conditions i_{10}, u_{10}, i_2, V_2 to the output conditions and introduce the contraction $Z_0 = -2V_0 F\omega_p/I_0\omega$.† Equations (34) and (35) then become

$$V_2 = V_1 \cos Z_1 + ji_1 Z_0 \sin Z_1$$

$$i_2 = jV_1 \frac{\sin Z_1}{Z_0} + i_1 \cos Z_1 \tag{103}$$

But Eqs. (103) are just those obtained for a lossless transmission line of length $l = Z_1/\beta$, when the direction of current flow is adjusted to agree with our convention. There seems no point in writing down the corresponding differential equations, since we shall use either Eq. (103) or the equivalent matrix equation

$$\begin{vmatrix} V_2 \\ i_2 \end{vmatrix} = \begin{vmatrix} \cos Z_1 & jZ_0 \sin Z_1 \\ j\dfrac{\sin Z_1}{Z_0} & -\cos Z_1 \end{vmatrix} \begin{vmatrix} V_1 \\ i_1 \end{vmatrix} \tag{104}$$

In English this matrix does not appear to have any special name in spite of its importance in circuit theory. Since the determinant of the matrix is unity, the inverse matrix is easily formed and we have

$$\begin{vmatrix} V_1 \\ i_1 \end{vmatrix} = \begin{vmatrix} \cos Z_1 & -jZ_0 \sin Z_1 \\ -j\dfrac{\sin Z_1}{Z_0} & \cos Z_1 \end{vmatrix} \begin{vmatrix} V_2 \\ i_2 \end{vmatrix} \tag{105}$$

This second matrix has a name in German, where it is called the "Kettenmatrix" or chain matrix.

---

† The minus sign here means that Z_0 is positive in the direction of the electron current. Z_0 is a characteristic impedance of the beam.

As an example of the use of these equations let us write down the output conditions at the end of a system composed of two transmission lines of different electrical lengths and characteristic impedances.

The expression is

$$
\begin{vmatrix} V_3 \\ i_3 \end{vmatrix} = \begin{vmatrix} \cos Z_2, & -jZ_{02} \sin Z_2 \\ -j\dfrac{\sin Z_2}{Z_{02}}, & \cos Z_2 \end{vmatrix} \begin{vmatrix} \cos Z_1, & -jZ_{01} \sin Z_1 \\ -j\dfrac{\sin Z_1}{Z_{01}}, & \cos Z_1 \end{vmatrix} \begin{vmatrix} V_1 \\ i_1 \end{vmatrix}
$$

where the suffix 2 refers to the line at the output end. Then

$$
\begin{vmatrix} V_3 \\ \\ i_3 \end{vmatrix} = \begin{vmatrix} \cos Z_2 \cos Z_1 - \dfrac{Z_{02}}{Z_{01}} \sin Z_2 \sin Z_1, \\ \qquad\qquad j(Z_{01} \cos Z_2 \sin Z_1 + Z_{02} \sin Z_2 \cos Z_1) \\ j\left(\dfrac{\sin Z_2}{Z_{02}} \cos Z_1 + \dfrac{\cos Z_2}{Z_{01}} \sin Z_1\right), \\ \qquad\qquad -\dfrac{Z_{01}}{Z_{02}} \sin Z_2 \sin Z_1 + \cos Z_2 \cos Z_1 \end{vmatrix} \begin{vmatrix} V_1 \\ \\ i_1 \end{vmatrix}
$$

$$\tag{106}$$

Some special cases are of interest; one is $V_1 = 0$, $Z_1 = Z_2 = \pi/2$, $Z_{01} \neq Z_{02}$. This corresponds to a change in beam impedance at a point where the current is instantaneously zero, a condition met in the velocity-jump amplifier of Chapter 1, Section 4. Here

$$
\begin{vmatrix} V_3 \\ i_3 \end{vmatrix} = \begin{vmatrix} -\dfrac{Z_{02}}{Z_{01}}, & 0 \\ 0, & -\dfrac{Z_{01}}{Z_{02}} \end{vmatrix} \begin{vmatrix} 0 \\ i_1 \end{vmatrix}
$$

Then

$$
i_3 = -\frac{Z_{01}}{Z_{02}} i_1 = \frac{V_{01}}{V_{02}} \cdot \frac{F_1 \omega_{p1}}{F_2 \omega_{p2}} \propto \left(\frac{V_{01}}{V_{02}}\right)^{3/4} \frac{F_1}{F_2} \tag{107}
$$

If $V_{01} > V_{02}$, reference back shows that $F_1 < F_2$ so the first term represents increased gain, the second loss of, however, a smaller amount.

A second case is that in which $i_1 = 0$, $z_1 = z_2 = \pi/2$, $Z_{01} \neq Z_{02}$. This is the space jump condition. Here $V_3 = -Z_{02}/Z_{01} \cdot V_1 = -F_2/F_1 \cdot V_1$ (for constant voltage). This means that there is gain if the drift tube is expanded after the first quarter space-charge wavelength. Plots of these conditions are shown in Figs. 12 and 13.

Bloom and Peter consider the application of these equations to a planar diode, following the space-charge wave analysis of SMULLIN.[12]

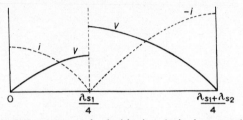

FIG. 12. R.F. currents and velocities in velocity-jump amplifiers.

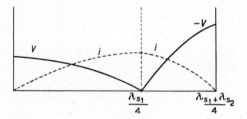

FIG. 13. R.F. currents and velocities in space-jump amplifiers.

They also tested a tapered transmission line proportioned so as to act as an analogue computer for a special diode. Standing-wave measurements on the analogue then served to determine the space-charge wavelengths in the diode. The method therefore provides an interesting approach to the determination of complicated space-charge structures.

On the other hand it should at this point be mentioned that there are some difficulties, conceptual and otherwise, in the use of the transmission line analogue which are not discussed by the above authors. A first point, which is made clear by Bloom and Peter, is that the analogue must be used by feeding power in at the collector end and adjusting matters so that the plane of excitation of the space-charge waves, i.e., input resonator gap or potential minimum in the diode case, is always a plane of open circuit, where V is finite and i zero. In the general case $i_1 = 0$ and the adjustment will be to

[12] SMULLIN; *J. Appl. Phys.*, 1951, **22**, 1496.

make the quantities assume their correct initial values at the frequency yielding a circuit wavelength equal to the space-charge wavelength.

Next, we must remember that, although the equivalent matrix of the space-charge wave system is that of a reciprocal network, there can in fact be no reciprocal action in the space-charge wave system, i.e., no waves at all can be observed to the left of the plane of excitation. Again, we have to return to the physics of the system to be able to write down correct boundary conditions. For instance, in the velocity jump amplifier, the kinetic voltage is continuous over the discontinuity, the a.c. velocity is not. If the kinetic velocity were not continuous the matrix multiplication used above would not give correct results for this amplifier. Yet it is not obvious without doing the calculation that the velocity discontinuity is removed. To my mind it is unfortunate that the mathematical structure does not bring out the differences more clearly and it is not much help to verbalize the problem by saying that quantities are transformed to a plane of reference travelling with the electrons.

The main application of the matrix method is in the formulation of noise problems, studied in Chapter 10.

4.9. POWER FLOW AND SPACE-CHARGE WAVES

Considerations of power flow seem first to have been applied to space-charge waves by Chu (unpublished), who set up expression for the kinetic power and demonstrated that it is negative for the slow space-charge wave. A general derivation can be based on Maxwell's equations in the vector form of Eq. (1) of Chapter 2. The equation for curl $\mathbf{H}$ is rewritten

$$\text{curl } \mathbf{H} = \rho\mathbf{u} + \sigma\mathbf{E} + \epsilon_0 \frac{\partial \mathbf{E}}{\partial t} \tag{108}$$

so that we explicitly recognize the presence of free charges with density ρ and surface currents on conductors ($\sigma\mathbf{E}$). Using this expression, Eq. (4) of Chapter 2 becomes

$$\text{div } \mathbf{S} = \text{div } (\mathbf{E} \times \mathbf{H}) = -\left[\tfrac{1}{2} \frac{\partial}{\partial t}(\epsilon_0\mathbf{E}^2 + \mu_0\mathbf{H}) + \sigma\mathbf{E}^2 + \rho(\mathbf{u} . \mathbf{E}) \right] \tag{109}$$

The Lorentz force law gives

$$\mathbf{E} = \frac{1}{\eta} \frac{d\mathbf{u}}{dt} - \mu_0(\mathbf{u} \times \mathbf{H})$$

but $\qquad \dfrac{d\mathbf{u}}{dt} = \dfrac{\partial \mathbf{u}}{\partial t} + (\mathbf{u} \cdot \nabla)\mathbf{u} = \dfrac{\partial \mathbf{u}}{\partial t} + \dfrac{1}{2}\nabla \mathbf{u}^2 - (\nabla \times \mathbf{u}) \times \mathbf{u}$

But $\qquad\qquad \nabla \mathbf{u}^2 = \nabla \cdot \mathbf{u}^2 + 2(\nabla \times \mathbf{u}) \times \mathbf{u}$

Therefore $\qquad\qquad \dfrac{d\mathbf{u}}{dt} = \dfrac{\partial \mathbf{u}}{\partial t} + \dfrac{1}{2}\nabla \cdot \mathbf{u}^2$ $\qquad\qquad$ (110)

and $\qquad \mathbf{E} = \dfrac{1}{\eta}\left[\dfrac{\partial \mathbf{u}}{\partial t} + \dfrac{1}{2}\nabla \cdot \mathbf{u}^2\right] - \mu_0(\mathbf{u} \times \mathbf{H})$

or $\qquad \rho\mathbf{u} \cdot \mathbf{E} = \dfrac{1}{2\eta}\left[\dfrac{\partial}{\partial t}(\rho\mathbf{u}^2) - \mathbf{u}^2 \cdot \dfrac{\partial \rho}{\partial t} + \rho\mathbf{u} \cdot \nabla \cdot \mathbf{u}^2\right]$ $\quad$ (111)

since $\mathbf{u} \cdot (\mathbf{u} \times \mathbf{H})$ is the triple scalar product, which is zero if two of the vectors are identical.

Now, from the continuity equation

$$\nabla \cdot (\rho\mathbf{u}) = -\dfrac{\partial \rho}{\partial t}$$

Equation (111) therefore becomes

$$\rho\mathbf{u} \cdot \mathbf{E} = \dfrac{1}{2\eta}\left[\dfrac{\partial}{\partial t}(\rho\mathbf{u}^2) + \mathbf{u}^2 \cdot \nabla \cdot (\rho\mathbf{u}) + \rho\mathbf{u} \cdot \nabla \cdot \mathbf{u}^2\right]$$
$$= \dfrac{1}{2\eta}\dfrac{\partial}{\partial t}(\rho\mathbf{u}^2) + \nabla \cdot \left(\dfrac{\mathbf{u}^2}{2\eta} \cdot \rho\mathbf{u}\right) \qquad (112)$$

Equation (109) can be transformed, using Eq. (112) to

$$\text{div}\left[\mathbf{E} \times \mathbf{H} + \left(\dfrac{\mathbf{u}^2}{2\eta} \cdot \rho\mathbf{u}\right)\right] = -\dfrac{1}{2}\dfrac{\partial}{\partial t}\left(\epsilon \mathbf{E_0}^2 + \mu_0\mathbf{H}^2 + \dfrac{\rho\mathbf{u}^2}{\eta}\right) - \sigma\mathbf{E}^2$$

But $\mathbf{u}^2/2\eta$ is the kinetic energy equivalent to a voltage V_1 and $\rho\mathbf{u}$ is the conduction current density.

Therefore

$$\text{div}\,[\mathbf{E} \times \mathbf{H} + V_1 \cdot \mathbf{J}] = -\dfrac{1}{2}\dfrac{\partial}{\partial t}\left(\epsilon_0\mathbf{E}^2 + \mu_0\mathbf{H}^2 + \dfrac{\rho\mathbf{u}^2}{\eta}\right) - \sigma\mathbf{E}^2$$
$$= -\dfrac{\partial W}{\partial t} - \sigma\mathbf{E}^2 \qquad (113)$$

We interpret Eq. (113) as meaning that the L.H.S. is a generalized Poynting vector, which has two parts, an electromagnetic part, as discussed in Chapter 2, and an electro-kinetic part $V_1 \cdot \mathbf{J_1}$. The divergence of this vector is equal to the time rate of change of energy in the system. Since $\sigma = 0$, everywhere except on the conductor surfaces, the last term is merely the Joule loss in the system, and in nearly all our work, is negligible.

LOUISELL and PIERCE[13] derive and discuss this result in its one-dimensional form. The average power flow density in the z direction is

$$P_z = \tfrac{1}{4}[(E \times H^* + E^* \times H)_z + (VJ^* + V^*J)] \qquad (114)$$

where all the values are peak values.

In the infinite planar case, dealt with in Section 1 of this chapter, there is no total current flow and H_z is zero. Thus, the total power is just $-\tfrac{1}{4}(VJ^* + V^*J)$.

When we consider flow in a narrow drift tube the displacement current is negligible in comparison with the convection current and there is an electromagnetic component in the power flow. Louisell and Pierce demonstrate that

$$\frac{P_{\text{e.m.}}}{P_{\text{kin}}} = \frac{F_c \omega_p}{\omega} \qquad (115)$$

This is a quantity which we have always neglected in comparison with unity. We thus conclude that for small space-charge (small ω_p) the electromagnetic component is negligible in all cases. When the space charge is large one would have to take up the problem of integrating Eq. (115) directly, over the system.

We must now refer to an apparent difficulty about Eq. (113). If we introduce linearized a.c. quantities of the usual form, $u = u_0 + u_1 \exp j(\omega t - \rho z)$, etc., we immediately see that the R.H.S. of Eq. (113) becomes $-j\omega/2(\mu_0 HH^* + \epsilon_0 EE^* + \rho_0 u_1 u_1^*/\eta) - \sigma EE^*$. Since σ is positive, this must represent a loss plus a purely reactive term. How, then, can the power gain arise? The answer is that space-charge wave theory is only strictly applicable between the output terminals of the input device and the input terminals of the output device. The input device imposes velocity and current modulations on the beam. This process requires power, which can certainly be computed by dynamical methods. Once this power has been given to the beam, however, the latter acts as a lossless transducer (unless $\sigma \neq 0$, a condition only met in the resistive wall amplifier). As the beam proceeds along the device there is no conversion of d.c. energy into r.f. energy, but simply conversion of velocity variation into density variation and vice versa. The conversion of d.c. into

---

[13] LOUISELL and PIERCE; *Proc. I.R.E.*, 1955, **43**, 425.

a.c. energy takes place in the output device itself, where, because small signal conditions generally do not apply, dynamical methods of calculation must be used. Let us apply these ideas to the simplest case, that of a two-cavity klystron amplifier. Here the beam reaching the first gap is unmodulated and only velocity modulation is set up in the input region. The effect of the drift tube is simply to operate on the initial v.m. with a space-charge matrix, which, if the length is correctly chosen, transforms v.m. into density modulation. The output device is not sensitive to velocity variations, but only to current variations and the relatively large a.c. current present on the beam produces large a.c. voltages on the output gap. These voltages slow down all the electrons in the gap in the negative half-cycle and d.c. energy is converted into a.c. Travelling-wave tube operation can be thought of in the same way but is basically more complicated because the output region is not sharply defined. Space-charge waves, therefore, never by themselves represent a power gain. The power gain arises from changes in the relative phase and instantaneous size of the voltage and current operating upon output regions with correctly chosen characteristics.

A further difficulty with linear theory has been discussed by WALKER.[14] It might be thought that the linear theory would not be capable of predicting the initial power transferred to the beam, because of the small signal assumption. Walker has calculated the stored kinetic energy and the power flow in space-charge waves retaining non-linear terms. He considered the special cases in which the initial a.c. field grew only in time, i.e., as $a(t)$ and grew only in space, i.e., as $a(z)$ and obtained a general result depending upon the power to which the a.c. velocity is raised in forming the quantity discussed. Denoting this power by n, for stored energy density $n = 2$ and for power flow $n = 3$, then $\langle u^n \rangle_2 / \langle u^n \rangle_1 = n - 1/n$ where 2 refers to $a(z)$ and 1 refers to $a(t)$. Thus, these quantities depend on the way in which the field is established at the beginning of the system. Moreover, he showed that space-charge wave theory was capable of giving the same results when correctly applied.

This last statement appears unlikely at first sight, since one might argue that calculations based on, for example, the square of a velocity, must be wildly in error because the neglected cross-product terms should be of the same order as the squares of a.c. terms explicitly appearing. But we observe that in practical input devices the a.c. velocity is large and the current small and, in general, both quantities are unlikely to be at their maximum values simultaneously,

---

[14] WALKER; *J. Appl. Phys.*, 1955, **25**, 615.

no matter how complicated the operations carried out on the beam. In other words the last term in the complete a.c. current $-\rho_0 u_1 + \rho_1 u_0 + \rho_1 u_1$ is small because of the phase difference between u_1 and ρ_1 independently of the values of $\hat{u}_1$ and $\hat{\rho}_1$. Whenever this is the case, the linear theory should give a correct answer to questions of power, etc. In doubtful cases recourse must be made to dynamics.

These questions of power and energy considerations have been stressed because misconceptions as to the considerations involved have led to errors in the past. For instance, the criticisms directed by PIDDINGTON[15,16] at the conventional theory of the double-beam space-charge amplifier seem to be founded on the expectation that the device ought to show an increase in a.c. power along the beam, whereas we know that this is not the case.

The essential idea of space-charge waves, a very simple one, is that of rearrangement of electron positions. Once an initial impulse has been given, the rearrangement carries on without any need for extra power to be given to the beam.

Let us now return to the power flow of the space-charge waves and consider each wave separately, instead of the standing wave superposition. The power densities are

$$P_1 = \tfrac{1}{4}(V_1 . J_1{}^* + V_1{}^* J_1)$$

$$P_2 = \tfrac{1}{4}(V_2 . J_2{}^* + V_2{}^* J_2)$$

We introduce the characteristic impedance Z_{01}, Z_{02} as in the last section, except that we use Eqs. (9) and (11) to define the voltage and current, with $\beta_1 u_0 = \omega + F\omega_p$, $\beta_2 u_0 = \omega - F\omega_p$ and find

$$Z_{01} = -\frac{V_1}{\Sigma J_1} = -\frac{2F\omega_p V_0}{I_0 \omega}$$

$$Z_{02} = -\frac{V_2}{\Sigma J_2} = \frac{2F\omega_p V_0}{I_0 \omega}$$

The first wave, which from Eq. (18) has the slow phase velocity $u_0(1 - F\omega_p/u_0)$ has a negative characteristic impedance and the power flow becomes

$$-\frac{|Z_{01}|}{2}[J_1 J_1{}^*] \tag{116}$$

[15] PIDDINGTON; *Phys. Rev.*, 1955, **101**, 14.
[16] PIDDINGTON; *Aust. J. Phys.*, 1956, **9**, 31.

This is obviously negative, so we say that this wave carries a negative power. Since the electron motion is only in the $+z$ direction there is no question of a positive power flow in the negative direction.

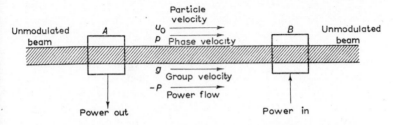

FIG. 14. Diagram illustrating power flow in space-charge wave systems.

PIERCE[17] illustrates this situation by Fig. 14. If device A sets up the slow space-charge wave only, it must remove power from the unmodulated beam. Negative power flows from A → B so that power must be fed into B to restore the beam to the original state. We again note that if the slow wave loses power, i.e., the power becomes more negative, then the amplitude must increase, while, for the fast wave, loss of power means decreased amplitude. Sometimes it is more convenient to consider the running waves separately, as in the resistive wall amplifier, but usually the standing wave treatment is more useful.

4.10. THE EXCITATION OF SPACE-CHARGE WAVES: ELEMENTARY THEORY

Space-charge waves can be excited in many ways. The density and current fluctuations inherent in any beam of electrons originating from a thermionic cathode excite space-charge waves which are therefore present on a so-called "unmodulated" beam. We normally agree to disregard these waves unless we are actually studying noise phenomena. Space-charge waves are also excited whenever a circuit interacts with an electron beam. In this section we wish to discuss, very briefly, the phenomena encountered in the simplest type interaction, viz., interaction at a short gap, where by short we mean such that the transit angle $\omega l/u_0$ is $<\pi/2$. Such gaps may be

---

[17] PIERCE; *B.S.T.J.*, 1954, 33, 1343.

K

furnished with grids or may be gridless. If grids are used, they are here assumed to be ideal electron permeable membranes.

4.10.1 Gridded gaps

Perhaps the most systematic approach to the behaviour of gridded gaps is through the use of the Llewellyn electronics equations, which enable the exit values of r.f. velocity and current to be deduced in the most general case, when the two grids, on either side of the gap, are different d.c. potentials and the d.c. space charge is sufficient to depress the space potential below the linear value. Here we do not attempt such generality, but rely on the fact that practical v.m. valves of today operate with grids at the same potential and with relatively high d.c. voltages so that the space-charge is insufficient to affect the space potential. The result of passing an unmodulated beam through such a gap is well known,[18] it is

$$u_{\text{exit}} = u_0 + u_{10} \exp j\omega t = u_0 + \frac{u_0 \alpha M}{2} \exp j\omega t \qquad (117)$$

where $\alpha = \dfrac{V_1}{V_0}$ = depth of modulation at the gap

$$M = \text{gap modulation factor,} \quad \frac{\sin L/2}{L/2} \qquad (118)$$

$$L = \text{d.c. gap transit angle,} \quad \frac{\omega l}{u_0} = \beta_e l$$

$$i_{\text{exit}} = I_0 + \alpha I_0 \left\{ \frac{1 - \cos L}{L^2} - \frac{\sin L}{2L} \right\} \exp j\omega t + j\alpha I_0$$

$$\times \left\{ \frac{\sin L}{L^2} - \frac{1 + \cos L}{2L} \right\} \exp j\omega t \qquad (119)$$

From Eq. (119) the power taken from the cavity by the beam is

$$P_b = \frac{V_1^2}{2R_0} \left[\frac{1 - \cos L}{L^2} - \frac{\sin L}{2L} \right] \qquad (120)$$

$$R_0 = \text{d.c. beam resistance} = V_0/I_0$$

The beam can be said to appear as a shunt admittance across the resonator, with components $G + jB$, equal to $G_0(= I_0/V_0)$ times the

---

[18] BECK; *Thermionic Valves*, p. 199, Cambridge University Press, 1953.

real and imaginary transit angle functions in Eq. (119). Equation (119) is deduced without linearized assumptions and is correct to $O(\alpha^2)$.

If we now inspect the transit angle function apearing in the real power Eq. (120), we find that it can be expressed as $2M \cdot M'$, where $M' = \beta_e \, \partial M / \partial \beta_e$. If we write $P_b = I_0 V_0 \eta_D$, where η_D is the diode efficiency of the gap,

$$\eta_D = \frac{\alpha^2}{4} MM' \qquad (121)$$

We shall find this form preserved in gaps without grids.

The technique for using these results with space-charge waves is to put the initial velocity and current in Eqs. (34) and (35) using

$$u_{10} = \frac{u_0 \alpha M}{2}, \qquad i_{10} = 0$$

We see from Eq. (119) that we have neglected a term in i_{10} equal to $I_0 \alpha \{(1 - \cos L/L^2) - \sin L/2L\}$. Reference to Fig. 7.3, of BECK[19] shows that for $L < \pi/2$ this term is $<0 \cdot 1\alpha I_0$. Since α is, by definition, small, e.g., $<0 \cdot 3$, this is negligible because $\hat{\imath}_1$ is certainly of the order of I_0. However, if we had put $\rho_{10} = 0$ we should have had a finite i_{10} which could take care of this term. The power loss at the gap has to be included in the power drawn from the driving generator, for if the input resonator is of high quality, the beam loading may represent most of the input loss. We thus lump the beam loss with the cavity loss. The shunt susceptance merely causes a slight detuning of the cavity.

4.10.2. Gaps with no grids

This case is dealt with fully elsewhere.[20] It can be shown that MV_1 is equal to the Fourier transform of the gap field, i.e.,

$$MV_1 = \int_{-\infty}^{+\infty} E_{(z)} \exp \left(j\beta_e z \right) \mathrm{d}z \qquad (122)$$

and the power loss is again $\alpha^2 MM'/4$.

For gaps in circular tunnels M takes on two values according to whether the lips of the gap are thick or thin. Usually they are thin and $M = J_0(L/2) \, I_0(\beta_e r)/I_0(\beta_e a)$, a = tunnel radius, r = radial coordinate of the electron considered. It is often convenient to denote

[19] BECK; *Thermionic Valves*, Appendix 2, Cambridge University Press, 1953.
[20] BECK; *Velocity Modulated Thermionic Valves*, p. 62 *et seq.*, Cambridge University Press, 1948.

transit angles (normalized distances) by capital letters, so

$$M = \frac{J_0(L/2)\, I_0(R)}{I_0(A)} \tag{123}$$

For thick lips
$$M = \frac{\sin L/2}{L/2} \cdot \frac{I_0(R)}{I_0(A)} \tag{124}$$

Various averages over the gap are required, for instance, the R.M.S. value of M is

$$J_0\!\left(\frac{L}{2}\right)\!\left(\frac{I_0{}^2(R) - I_1{}^2(R)}{I_0{}^2(R)}\right) \tag{125}$$

The R.M.S. value of M' is

$$\frac{M}{2}\left[\frac{L J_1(L/2)}{J_0(L/2)} - \frac{2 I_1{}^2(R)}{I_0{}^2(R) - I_1{}^2(R)} + \frac{2 R I_1(R)}{I_0(R)}\right] \tag{126}$$

Similar results are available for long slots.[21] The initial velocity modulation is obtained as before, using the appropriate value of M. It is obviously now a function of gap radius or width and in the circular case, varies from $J_0(L/2)$ at the edge of the gap to $J_0(L/2)/I_0(A)$ on the axis. This variation over the gap which, obviously, arises from the corresponding variation of the electric field, is the fundamental reason why the transverse dimensions of electron beams are limited. In the sequel we shall find that the maximum tolerable solid beam diameter is around $B = 1\cdot0$, so that, allowing for some scalloping, $A < 1\cdot5$, $I_0(A) < 1\cdot6$. The resultant variation in a.c. velocity is therefore by no means negligible.

4.11. SPACE-CHARGE WAVES IN ACCELERATING OR RETARDING FIELDS

We now take up the study of space-charge waves in regions where the d.c. potential is a function of z. Examples of such regions are the space-charge limited diode, regions where the d.c. voltage changes suddenly as in velocity jump amplifiers and the repeller region in reflex klystrons. We treat first the case in which no transverse variations of fields or velocities are allowed. This corresponds with the infinite plane diode analysis of Llewellyn.

---

[21] FREMLIN, PETRIE et al.; J. Inst. Elec. Engrs., 1946, **93**, Pt. IIIa, No. 5, 868.

The analysis is very slightly different from that in Section 2 of this chapter. We have to retain the operator $\partial/\partial z$ because the d.c. velocity u_0 depends on z. The force equation thus takes on the following modified form:

$$-\eta E_{\text{tot}} = \frac{du}{dt} = j\omega u_1 + u_0 \frac{du_1}{dz} + u_1 \frac{du_0}{dz} \qquad (127)$$

where we have written E_{tot} to show that imposed fields and space-charge fields are both included.

Equation (6) becomes

$$\frac{\partial J_1}{\partial z} = -j\omega \rho_1 \qquad (128)$$

By definition $\qquad J_1 = \rho_1 u_0 - \rho_0 u_1$

therefore $\qquad u_1 = j\frac{u_0{}^2}{J_0\omega} \frac{\partial J_1}{\partial z} - \frac{u_0 J_1}{J_0} \qquad (129)$

and $\quad \dfrac{du_1}{dz} = j\dfrac{u_0{}^2}{J_0\omega} \dfrac{\partial^2 J_1}{\partial z^2} + j\dfrac{2u_0}{J_0\omega} \dfrac{du_0}{dz} \cdot \dfrac{\partial J_1}{\partial z} - \dfrac{u_0}{J_0} \dfrac{\partial J_1}{\partial z} - \dfrac{J_1}{J_0} \dfrac{du_0}{dz} \quad (130)$

By integrating the divergence condition Eq. (3), we find

$$E_{\text{tot}} = j\frac{J_1}{\omega \epsilon_0} + E_z \qquad (131)$$

where $E_z = E \exp j\omega t$ is the applied field, if any. Equations (129), (130) and (131) are then put into Eq. (127) to obtain

$$J''_1 + J'_1\left(\frac{2j\omega}{u_0} + \frac{3}{u_0}\frac{du_0}{dz}\right) + J_1\left(\frac{\eta J_0}{\epsilon_0 u_0{}^3} + \frac{2j\omega}{u_0{}^2}\frac{du_0}{dz} - \frac{\omega^2}{u_0{}^2}\right) = j\frac{J_0\omega\eta}{u_0{}^3}E_z \qquad (132)$$

This equation was first obtained by SMULLIN,[22] who applied it to space-charge limited diodes and to general diodes. It was applied to gaps with a linear velocity variation by TIEN and FIELD[23] and to regions in which $u_0 = Kz^\alpha$ by MÜLLER.[24] The technique of solution is to observe that the homogenous equation equivalent to Eq. (129) is solved by $J_1 = P(z) \exp\left(-j\omega \int dz/u_0\right) = P(z) \exp(-j\omega\tau_z)$, by

[22] SMULLIN; *J. Appl. Phys.*, 1951, **22**, 1496.
[23] TIEN and FIELD; *Proc. Inst. Radio Engrs.*, N.Y., 1952, **40**, 688.
[24] MÜLLER; *A.E.Ü.*, 1955, **9**, 505.

elementary means. Physically, this involves a transformation to a plane of reference moving with the d.c. electron velocity at any plane z. The velocity u_1 is then given by

$$u_1 = j\frac{u_0^2}{J_0\omega}\frac{dP_{(z)}}{dz} \tag{133}$$

and, making the substitutions in Eq. (132),

$$\frac{d^2P_{(z)}}{dz^2} + \frac{3}{u_0}\frac{du_0}{dz}\frac{dP_{(z)}}{dz} + \frac{\eta J_0}{\epsilon_0 u_0^3}P_{(z)} = 0 \tag{134}$$

The solutions of Eq. (134) lead to Bessel function expressions and the general results are given in Appendix 8. Here we may quote the results of Tien and Field for $u_0 = Kz^{1/2}$. By analogy with the Llewellyn matrix, these authors write

$$\begin{vmatrix} J_2 \\ u_2 \end{vmatrix} = \begin{vmatrix} E & F \\ H & I \end{vmatrix} \begin{vmatrix} u_1 \\ J_1 \end{vmatrix} \tag{135}$$

where the potential increases in the $+z$ direction. Decreasing potential conditions are determined by inverting the matrix. The matrix elements are determined through a dimensionless parameter

$$X = 4\left(\frac{\eta J_0 z^{1/2}}{\epsilon_0 K^3}\right)^{1/2}. \tag{136}$$

s is the value of X measured at the origin.

$$E = \frac{\pi s^2}{2X}(Y_1(X)J_2(s) - J_1(X)Y_2(s)) \tag{137}$$

$$F = jG\frac{\pi s}{X}(Y_1(X)J_1(s) - J_1(X)Y_1(s)) \tag{138}$$

$$H = j\frac{\pi s^2}{4G}(Y_2(X)J_2(s) - J_2(X)Y_2(s)) \tag{139}$$

$$I = \frac{\pi s}{2}(J_2(X)Y_1(s) - Y_2(X)J_1(s)) \tag{140}$$

where $G = 2\omega J_0/K^2$, a characteristic admittance appropriate to this case. Plots of these functions are given in Fig. 15.† These show the general behaviour of the elements of the matrix earlier derived for field-free space, with differences due to stretching.

---

† The reader should not be perturbed by the fact that Eqs. (137) – (140) appear different from the forms given by Tien and Field. A Wronskian determinant has been used to simplify the relations given above.

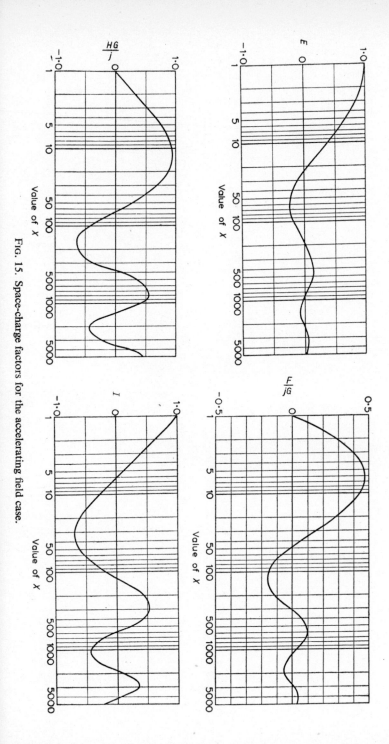

FIG. 15. Space–charge factors for the accelerating field case.

The extension to the case of a cylindrical beam has been treated by PARZEN.[25] Equation (132) is written in the form

$$J'' + J'\left(\frac{2j\omega}{u_0} + \frac{3}{u_0}\frac{du_0}{dz}\right) + J\left(\frac{2j\omega}{u_0{}^2}\frac{du_0}{dz} - \frac{\omega^2}{u_0{}^2}\right) = j\frac{J_0\omega\eta}{u_0{}^3}E_z \qquad (141)$$

where E_z is the component of the electric field in the direction of propagation, all transverse motions still being neglected, i.e., a very strong magnetic field is tacitly assumed. The wave equation gives

$$\nabla_t{}^2E + \frac{\partial^2 E_z}{\partial z} + k^2E = j\sqrt{\frac{\mu_0}{\epsilon_0}}\left(k^2J + \frac{\partial^2 J}{\partial z^2}\right) \qquad (142)$$

Solutions of the form below are introduced

$$E = E_1 \exp\left(-j\omega\tau_z\right)J_0(\gamma_r \cdot r)$$
$$J = J_1 \exp\left(-j\omega\tau_z\right)J_0(\gamma_r \cdot r)$$

Equation (134) then becomes

$$\frac{\partial^2 J_1}{\partial \tau^2} + \frac{3}{u_0}\frac{\partial u_0}{\partial \tau}\frac{\partial J_1}{\partial \tau} = j\frac{\eta J_0\omega}{u_0}E_z \qquad (143)$$

while Eq. (143) yields

$$u_0\frac{\partial^2 E_1}{\partial \tau^2} - \left(\frac{\partial u_0}{\partial \tau} + 2j\omega u_0\right)\frac{\partial E_1}{\partial \tau} + \left[(-\beta^2 - \gamma_r{}^2 + k^2)u_0{}^3 + j\omega\frac{\partial u_0}{\partial \tau}\right]E_1$$
$$= j\sqrt{\frac{\mu_0}{\epsilon_0}}\frac{1}{k}\left\{u_0\frac{\partial^2 J_1}{\partial \tau^2} - \left(\frac{\partial u_0}{\partial \tau} + 2j\omega u_0\right)\frac{\partial J_1}{\partial \tau} + \left[(-\beta^2 + k^2)u_0{}^3 + j\omega\frac{\partial u_0}{\partial \tau}\right]J_1\right.$$
$$(144)$$

Equation (144) is then simplified by the usual approximations, viz., $k^2 \ll \beta^2$, $\omega_p \ll \omega$ and $(1/\omega u_0)/(\partial u_0/\partial \tau) \ll 1$ which assumes that the d.c. velocity is changing only slowly in the region under discussion. The approximate equivalent of Eq. (144) is

$$E_1 = -j\sqrt{\frac{\mu_0}{\epsilon_0}} \cdot \frac{1}{k} \cdot \frac{J_1}{1 + \gamma_r{}^2/\beta^2}$$

$$= -j\sqrt{\frac{\mu_0}{\epsilon_0}} \cdot \frac{1}{k} \cdot F^2J_1 \qquad (145)$$

[25] PARZEN; *J. Appl. Phys.*, 1952, **23**, 215. Reprinted in *Elec. Commun.*, 1952, **29**, 238. See also *Elec. Commun.*, 1953, **30**, 134.

where F^2 is the appropriate plasma frequency reduction factor. Equation (145) is now substituted in Eq. (143) and gives

$$\frac{\partial^2 J_1}{\partial \tau^2} + \frac{3}{u_0} \frac{\partial u_0}{\partial \tau} \frac{\partial J_1}{\partial \tau} + \frac{\eta}{\epsilon_0} F^2 J_0 . J_1 = 0 \qquad (146)$$

Equation (146) may be considered as stating that the d.c. current density J_0, which would appear in the infinite field extent problem, here appears reduced by the factor F^2. At first sight, it may appear curious that the major alteration is in the effective d.c. current value, but it is obvious that a given d.c. density produces much less depression of the space potential when it passes through a cylindrical electrode of not too large a diameter than it does when passing through a system of very extensive planar grids. Since F^2 is likely to be a small number in practical cases, this effect is important.

Parzen demonstrates how to obtain solutions of the differential equations, by the WBK approximation method: these are applied to the problem of determining space-charge wavelengths in the gun region of travelling-wave tubes, where this knowledge is required to design for minimum noise figure.

4.12. SPACE-CHARGE WAVES IN CROSSED FIELDS

We now turn our attention to space-charge waves in an electron beam formed between two parallel plates at different potentials and constrained by the mutual action of this field and a magnetic field perpendicular both to the direction of motion and to the electric field. Guns of this type are briefly described in Appendix 6. Here we proceed by assuming that a rectilinear beam can, in

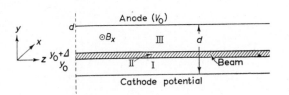

Fig. 16. Notation for crossed-field beam.

fact, be produced under these conditions and then considering the perturbations caused by a space-charge field. Fig. 16 shows the notation for this problem. The unperturbed velocity in the z

direction is supposed to be the same for all electrons and the value is

$$u_0 = \frac{V_0}{\mathrm{d}B_0} \tag{147}$$

No account is taken of the gross effect of space-charge in depressing the d.c. potential; we may, if we wish, suppose that the negative space charge is annulled by positive ions. The analysis is very similar to that of Sections 4.6 and 4.7. The unperturbed trajectories are, as shown in Appendix VI,

$$y = y_0$$
$$z = u_0 \tau \tag{148}$$

These are subjected to the usual perturbations, of the form $F(z)$ $\exp j(\omega t - \beta z)$ and the T.M. wave equations for Section 2.2.1 become

$$\frac{\partial E_z}{\partial y} + j\beta E y = -j\omega\mu_0 H_x - \tag{149}$$

$$-j\beta H_x = j\omega\epsilon_0 E_y - \rho_0 u_{1y} - \tag{150}$$

$$-\frac{\partial H_x}{\partial y} = j\omega\epsilon_0 E_z - \rho_0 u_{1z} + \rho_1 u_0 \tag{151}$$

with Poisson's equation,

$$\frac{\partial E_y}{\partial y} - j\beta E_z = \frac{\rho_1}{\epsilon_0} \tag{152}$$

The perturbation terms in the equation of motion are

$$y_1 + \omega_c \dot{z}_1 = -\eta(E_y + u_0 B_x) \exp j(\omega t - \beta z) \tag{153}$$

$$\ddot{z}_1 - \omega_c \dot{y}_1 = -\eta E_z \exp j(\omega t - \beta z) \tag{154}$$

Remembering that $\mathrm{d}/\mathrm{d}t = j(\omega - \beta u_0)$ we easily find

$$y_1 = \frac{-\eta}{\omega_c{}^2 - (\omega - \beta u_0)^2} \left[\frac{j\omega_c E_z}{(\omega - \beta u_0)} + E_y + u_0 B_x \right] \tag{155}$$

$$z_1 = \frac{\eta}{\omega_c{}^2 - (\omega - \beta u_0)^2} \left[\frac{j\omega_c E_y}{(\omega - \beta u_0)} - E_z + \frac{ju_0\omega_c B_x}{(\omega - \beta u_0)} \right] \tag{156}$$

$$u_{1y} = \frac{-\eta}{\omega_c{}^2 - (\omega - \beta u_0)^2} \left[-\omega_c E_z + j(\omega - \beta u_0)(E_y + u_0 B_x) \right] \tag{157}$$

$$u_{1z} = \frac{-\eta}{\omega_c{}^2 - (\omega - \beta u_0)^2} \left[\omega_c(E_y + u_0 B_x) + j(\omega - \beta u_0)E_z \right] \tag{158}$$

The continuity equation is

$$u_0 \frac{\partial \rho_1}{\partial y} - \rho_0 \left(\frac{\partial u_{1y}}{\partial y} + \frac{\partial u_{1z}}{\partial z} \right) = -j\omega\rho_1 \qquad (159)$$

If we form the bracket in Eq. (159), we find that the leading terms, those with ω_c as multiplier, vanish when we use Eq. (149). The remaining terms are multiplied by $(\omega - \beta u_0)$, which we know to be small and assume to be negligible compared with ω_c^2. The bracket is then zero, and we conclude that $\rho_1 = 0$. From Eq. (152)

$$\frac{\partial E_y}{\partial y} = j\beta E_z \qquad (160)$$

It is now easy to show from Eqs. (140), (150) and (151) that, if we neglect terms of order k^2

$$\frac{\partial^2 E_z}{\partial y^2} - \beta^2 E_z = 0 \qquad (161)$$

Thus, in the beam (region II)

$$E_z = A_2 e^{\beta y} - B_2 e^{-\beta y}$$

So far we have followed the treatment of WARNECKE et al.[26] We now depart from their treatment and stress the analogy with Rigrod and Lewis theory of the Brillouin beam, in which, we recall, ρ_1 was also zero. We proceed to match the beam admittance to the wave admittance at both the upper and lower edges of the beam, where, as before, the r.f. magnetic field is increased by the surface current density to compensate for the perturbation of the surface.

At the lower edge of the beam $y = y_0$, and the admittance looking outwards from the beam is

$$Y_1 = \frac{-j\omega\epsilon_0}{\beta} \frac{\cosh \beta y_0}{\sinh \beta y_0} = \frac{-j\omega\epsilon_0}{\beta} \coth \beta y_0 \qquad (162)$$

At the upper edge $y = y_0 + \Delta$.

$$Y_{III} = \frac{-j\omega\epsilon_0}{\beta} \left\{ \frac{\exp(-2\beta d) \exp[\beta(y_0 + \Delta)] + \exp[-\beta(y_0 + \Delta)]}{\exp(-2\beta d) \exp[\beta(y_0 + \Delta)] - \exp[-\beta(y_0 + \Delta)]} \right\}$$

$$= \frac{-j\omega\epsilon_0}{\beta} \coth \beta(y_0 + \Delta - d) \qquad (163)$$

---

[26] WARNECKE, DOEHLER and BOBOT; Ann. Radioélectricité, 1950, 5, 279.

The fields inside the beam are to be the same as they would be in the absence of the beam, but the magnetic field exhibits a discontinuity, equal to the magnitude of the surface current density G_z, at each edge. As before

$$G_z = \rho_0 u_0 y_1 \tag{164}$$

so we have to determine y_1 explicitly. Using Eq. (149) we show that, neglecting terms of order k^2, $E_{yII} = -j(A_2 e^{\beta y} + B_2 e^{-\beta y})$
Then

$$
\begin{aligned}
y_1 &= \frac{-j\eta}{(\omega - \beta u_0)[\omega_c^2 - (\omega - \beta u_0)^2]} \\
&\quad \times [A_2 e^{\beta y} \{\omega_c - (\omega - \beta u_0)\} - B_2 e^{-\beta y} \{\omega_c + (\omega - \beta u_0)\}] \\
&= \frac{-j\eta}{(\omega - \beta u_0)} \left[\frac{A_2 e^{\beta y}}{\omega_c + (\omega - \beta u_0)} - \frac{B_2 e^{-\beta y}}{\omega_c - (\omega - \beta u_0)} \right] \tag{165}
\end{aligned}
$$

$$\doteq \frac{-j\eta E_z}{(\omega - \beta u_0)\omega_c} \tag{166}$$

Thus, at the boundary between regions I and II we have

$$Y_I = \frac{H_x(y_0)}{E_z(y_0)} - \frac{j\eta\rho_0 u_0}{(\omega - \beta u_0)\omega_c} \tag{167}$$

and between regions II and III

$$Y_{III} = \frac{H_x(y_0 + \varDelta)}{E_z(y_0 + \varDelta)} - \frac{j\eta\rho_0 u_0}{(\omega - \beta u_0)\omega_c} \tag{168}$$

Writing these in full we find

$$\frac{A_2/B_2 \exp(\beta y_0) + \exp(-\beta y_0)}{A_2/B_2 \exp(\beta y_0) - \exp(-\beta y_0)} = \frac{\omega_p^2}{(\omega - \beta u_0)\omega_c} + \coth \beta y_0 \tag{169}$$

$$
\frac{A_2/B_2 \exp[\beta(y_0 + \varDelta)] + \exp[-\beta(y_0 + \varDelta)]}{A_2/B_2 \exp[\beta(y_0 + \varDelta)] - \exp[-\beta(y_0 + \varDelta)]}
$$
$$= \frac{\omega_p^2}{(\omega - \beta u_0)\omega_c} + \coth \beta(y_0 + \varDelta - d) \tag{170}$$

Solving for A_2/B_2, and equating the results we obtain

$$\left[\frac{1 + C + D}{1 - C - D} \right] = e^{-2\beta\varDelta} \left[\frac{1 + C + G}{1 - C - G} \right] \tag{171}$$

where $C = \omega_p^2/(\omega - \beta u_0)\omega_c$, $D = \coth \beta y_0$ and $G = \coth \beta(y_0 +$

$\varDelta - d$). We now solve Eq. (171) for C, obtaining a quadratic equation

$$C^2 + C(D + G) - E = 0 \qquad (172)$$

where $\qquad E = \left[\dfrac{e^{-\beta\varDelta}}{2 \sinh \beta\varDelta} + \coth \beta\varDelta(D - G) - GD \right] \qquad (173)$

This can be simplified to

$$E = \left[\frac{e^{-\beta\varDelta}}{2 \sinh \beta\varDelta} + D - G\left(\frac{1 - \coth^2 \beta\varDelta}{\coth \beta d - \coth \beta\varDelta} \right) \right] \qquad (174)$$

Purely analytical methods cannot take us much further but a little numerical investigation shows that for normal values, E is a large number and $D + G$ small. C is large, since it is to be of order $1/F$. Thus the roots of Eq. (172) are, very roughly,

$$C \doteqdot \pm \sqrt{E} \qquad (175)$$

and we finally obtain the required result

$$\omega - \beta u_0 \doteqdot \pm \frac{\omega_p^2}{\omega_c \sqrt{E}} \qquad (176)$$

This result is very similar to the results obtained for confined cylindrical beams, since F depends both on the magnetic field and on $E^{1/2}$, which, in the approximation handled here, is a purely geometrical quantity.

WARNECKE, DOEHLER and BOBOT,[26] although they do not consider the simplified problem dealt with above, do consider the propagation of space-charge waves in the case when no positive ions are assumed present. In this case the unperturbed velocity U_0 is a function of y, of the form $u_0(y) = u'_0 + \omega_p^2 y/\omega_c$, where u'_0 is a constant slightly different from u_0. Their analysis leads to a complex value of γ, i.e., to a solution with growing waves in the absence of the circuit. The effect has been made use of in a tube called the "Diocotron" and gain has been measured by GUÉNARD and HUBER.[27] However, the details of the measurements do not agree with theory and this tube must be classed as one whose operation is not fully understood.

4.13. VELOCITY DISTRIBUTION AND THE LIOUVILLE THEOREM

We now come to the problem of removing the most serious limitation of the theory as developed up to this point; the assumption

---

[27] GUÉNARD and HUBER; *Ann. Radioélectricité*, 1952, 7, 252.

that, at any plane $z = $ constant, the observed electron velocity is a single-valued function. Clearly, this assumption is never rigorously true for a real electron beam originating at a thermionic cathode since the Maxwellian distribution of the initial velocities characteristic of the cathode temperature makes the assumption false. However, the range of initial velocities is luckily small, for an oxide cathode of the order of the velocity equivalent of 0·3 eV, and when the beam has been accelerated to a mean velocity corresponding to several hundred volts, the velocity distribution is narrow in comparison with the mean velocity. This fact permits us to use the theory, as already deduced, in many cases. There are cases where the theory cannot apply, at least in detail. Among these are: noise phenomena in the immediate vicinity of the cathode, and dense beams in tunnels, where Appendix 6 shows that d.c. space-charge effects produce a depression of potential in the beam, which, on the axis, can easily amount to 5–10% of the wall potential. An even more difficult and important case is that of strongly velocity-modulated beams in which the effect of drifting is to cause a situation characterized by some electrons overtaking others so that the a.c. velocities, i.e, velocities relative to a reference electron, take on positive and negative values. The solution of such problems is, as yet, far from complete and this section should be regarded as a mere statement of possible lines of approach. The first of these is the use of Liouville's theorem from classical statistical mechanics. This approach has been applied by WATKINS[28],[29] and by YADAVALLI.[30]

Liouville's theorem[31] states that the total time derivative of the density function in phase space vanishes, or, in symbols

$$\frac{df}{dt} = 0 \tag{177}$$

Therefore
$$\frac{\partial f}{\partial t} + u\frac{\partial f}{\partial z} + \frac{\partial u}{\partial t} \cdot \frac{\partial f}{\partial u} = \frac{\partial f}{\partial t}\bigg|_c \tag{178}$$

Here $f = f(z, u, t) = e$ times the number of electrons in the space interval $z - (z + dz)$, and the velocity interval $u - (u + du)$, per unit beam cross-section. We have restricted ourselves to merely longitudinal motion. The term on the right-hand side is the so-called collision term representing the net change in the number of electrons in the given velocity interval due to electron–electron collisions.

[28] WATKINS; *J. Appl. Phys.*, 1952, **23**, 568.
[29] WATKINS and RYNN; *J. Appl. Phys.*, 1954, **25**, 1375.
[30] YADAVALLI; *Q. Appl. Maths.*, 1954, **12**, 105.
[31] LINDSAY; *Physical Statistics*, p. 114. Wiley, 1941.

Such collisions can either introduce new members into the specified velocity class or scatter old members out of it. The evaluation of this term is very difficult for particles obeying a Coulomb force law, because the forces cannot be assumed to be confined to the immediate vicinity of the electrons. The gross effect of the Coulomb force is taken into account as the smeared out space-charge potential (Poisson's Equation), but the collisions still give rise to this difficulty. Some calculations have been made by VLASOV[32] which are often cited as evidence that collisions can be neglected in normal electron beam problems. This is probably true everywhere except in the immediate vicinity of the potential minimum in front of the cathode. At any rate, to progress we assume that the R.H.S. is negligible.

The force law gives, for the case of no transverse magnetic field

$$\frac{\mathrm{d}u}{\mathrm{d}t} = -\eta E_{(z,t)} \tag{179}$$

and, by definition, the convection current density is

$$J_{(z,t)} = -\int_{-\infty}^{+\infty} uf(z, u, t)\,\mathrm{d}u \tag{180}$$

The Maxwellian total current density $J_{(t)}$ is independent of z and is given by

$$J_t = J_{(z,t)} + \epsilon_0 \frac{\partial E_{(z,t)}}{\partial t} \tag{181}$$

As usual, we now separate the quantities into d.c. and a.c. parts of the form $J_{(z,t)} = -J_0 + J_{1(z)} \exp(j\omega t)$ etc., and neglect products of a.c. quantities. We obtain

$$u\frac{\partial f_0}{\partial z} + \eta\frac{\partial V_0}{\partial z}\frac{\partial f_0}{\partial u} = 0 \tag{182}$$

$$j\omega f_1 + u\frac{\partial f_1}{\partial z} + \eta\frac{\partial V_0}{\partial z}\frac{\partial f_0}{\partial u} = \eta E_1\frac{\partial f_0}{\partial u} \tag{183}$$

$$J_1 = -\int_{-\infty}^{+\infty} uf_1\,\mathrm{d}u + j\omega\epsilon_0 E_1 \tag{184}$$

f_0 is a function of z and u, only. f_1 includes the understood variation in time, $\exp j\omega t$.

The second equation of the above triplet specifies the whole behaviour of the system. If V_0, f_0 and J_1 are known, f_1 can be

³² VLASOV; J. Phys. U.S.S.R., 1945, 9, 25.

determined from a single boundary condition, such as a knowledge of f_1 at the initial plane. WATKINS[28],[29] gives examples of the direct application of these results, using power series expansions. YADA-VILLI[30] carries the analysis through to the extent of deriving an integral equation. This is of considerable practical importance because it renders problems of this type susceptible to computer methods. The integral equation is derived as follows: f_0 is a function of v only, where $v^2 = u^2 - 2\eta V_0$. Then

$$u \, du = v \, dv + \eta \frac{\partial V_0}{\partial z} \, dz, \quad dz = dz$$

$$\frac{\partial}{\partial u} = \frac{u}{v} \frac{\partial}{\partial v}, \qquad \frac{\partial}{\partial z} = \frac{\partial}{\partial z} - \eta \frac{1}{v} \frac{\partial V_0}{\partial z} \frac{\partial}{\partial v}$$

Then, Eq. (183) becomes

$$j \frac{\omega}{u} f_1 + \frac{\partial f_1}{\partial z} = \eta \frac{E_1}{v} \frac{\partial f_0}{\partial v}$$

This can be integrated, by use of the integrating factor exp $(-j\omega \int dz/u)$ to

$$f_1(z, u) = f_1(o, v) \exp \left[-j\omega \int_0^z \frac{d\zeta}{u(\zeta, v)} \right] +$$
$$+ \eta \int_0^z \frac{1}{v} \frac{\partial f_0}{\partial v} E_1(\zeta) \exp \left[-j\omega \int_\zeta^z \frac{d\zeta}{u(\zeta, v)} \right] d\zeta \quad (185)$$

This integral equation can be solved for $f_1(z, u)$ if we know $u(z, v)$ $f_0(v)$, $E_1(z)$ and the single boundary condition $f_1(o, v)$. In the special cases where the a.c. total current density is zero,

$$E_1 = -j \frac{J_1}{\omega \epsilon_0} \tag{186}$$

and Eq. (185) gives for the a.c. conduction current density

$$J_{1c(z)} = \int_0^\infty v f_1(o, v) \exp \left[-j\omega \int_0^z \frac{d\zeta}{u(\zeta, v)} \right] dv -$$
$$- \frac{j\eta}{\omega \epsilon_0} \int_0^z J_1(\zeta) \, d\zeta \int_0^\infty \frac{\partial f_0}{\partial v} \exp \left[-j\omega \int_\zeta^z \frac{d\zeta}{u(\zeta, v)} \right] dv \tag{187}$$

This is an inhomogeneous integral equation of Volterra type which, in general, can only be solved by numerical integration.

When the beam is in a space free of d.c. fields, we find

$$f_1(z, v) = f_1(o, v) \exp\left(\frac{-j\omega z}{v}\right) + \frac{\eta}{v} \int_0^z \frac{\partial f_0}{\partial v} E_1(\zeta) \exp\left[\frac{-j\omega(z - \zeta)}{v}\right] d\zeta \tag{188}$$

$$J_1 c(z) = \int_0^\infty v f_1(o, v) \exp\left(\frac{-j\omega z}{v}\right) dv -$$
$$- \frac{j\eta}{\omega\epsilon_0} \int_0^z J_1(\zeta) \, d\zeta \int_0^\infty \frac{\partial f_0}{\partial v} \exp\left[\frac{-j\omega(z - \zeta)}{v}\right] dv \tag{189}$$

An integral equation which is the single velocity analogue of the last expression, was found long ago by PETRIE, STRACHEY and WALLIS† and by PIERCE and SHEPHERD.[34] It is, when the initial conditions are inserted,

$$J_{1c} = \left[J_1(o) + \frac{j\omega z}{u_0} \rho_0 u_1(o)\right] \exp\left(\frac{-j\omega z}{u_0}\right) +$$
$$+ \frac{jI_0}{2V_0} \int_{-\infty}^z E(\zeta) \frac{\omega}{u_0} (z - \zeta) \exp\frac{-j\omega}{u_0} (z - \zeta) \, d\zeta \tag{190}$$

Allowing for the differences of notation, this result follows from Eq. (189). Equation (190) can be derived as a Laplace transform of Eq. (132) when $du_0/dz = 0$ and J_0 is neglected.

Some further progress can be made by the use of the Laplace Transform.[35,36] The L transform of J_{ic} is

$$J(s) = \int_0^\infty J_1(z) e^{-sz} \, dz \tag{191}$$

and the inverse transform is

$$J_1(z) = -\frac{j}{2\pi} \int_{\gamma-j\infty}^{\gamma+j\infty} J(s) e^{sz} \, ds \tag{192}$$

where the contour is so chosen that the singularities of $J_1(z)$ lie in the region where $R_e(s) < \gamma$.

---

† Unpublished, but the final formulation in which the increase in energy only is used can be found in *J.I.E.E.*, 1946.[33]

[33] FREMLIN, PETRIE, STRACHEY and WALLIS; *J.I.E.E.*, 1946, **93**, Pt. IIIa, 825.

[34] PIERCE and SHEPHERD; *B.S.T.J.*, 1947, **26**, 460, App. 8.

[35] CHURCHILL; *Modern Operational Mathematics in Engineering*. McGraw-Hill, New York, 1944.

[36] CARSLAW and JAEGER; *Operational Methods in Applied Mathematics*, 1st Ed., Oxford University Press, 1941.

Using tables of L transforms and the properties of convolution or "Faltung" integrals, we find

$$J_1(s) = \left[\int_0^\infty \frac{v f_1(o, v)\, dv}{s + j(\omega/v)} \right] \left[1 + \frac{j\eta}{\omega \epsilon_0} \int_0^\infty \frac{\partial f_0}{\partial v} \frac{1}{s + j(\omega/v)}\, dv \right]^{-1}$$

(193)

Yadavalli discusses the application of this transform to the solution of several problems, including the drifting electron stream with small signal V.M. and the derivation of results similar to those of Llewellyn for an accelerated electron beam. We leave this question for the moment and digress to consider the connection between space-charge wave theory and plasma oscillations.

4.14. PLASMA OSCILLATIONS

It has long been known that longitudinal electric oscillations at fairly high frequencies are observed in ionized gases. The frequencies are sufficiently high for the motions of the ions to be ignored so these oscillations are correctly regarded as electronic phenomena. On the other hand, relatively little success has been achieved in relating the complicated behaviour of the observed oscillations with the boundary conditions, field distribution and velocity distributions encountered. The problem has several points of interest in relation to our work: first, we would like to be able to make practical use of organized plasma oscillations, second, the results would have a distinct bearing on the behaviour of electron beams with velocity distributions and third, our much more detailed knowledge of boundary conditions in purely electronic problems may assist in the further development of the plasma theory.

Existing plasma theory begins with the deduction of a dispersion equation which is alleged to give the necessary information as to the values of complex propagation constant and complex frequency which give rise to waves with exponential growth. In view of what has previously been said as to the possibility of gain in space-charge wave systems with purely reactive waves, we may have certain doubts as to whether exponential growth is a necessary condition for the setting up of plasma oscillations, but we leave this consideration for the moment. There are more fundamental difficulties concerned with the plasma dispersion equation itself. This has been derived in two different ways:—(a) The substitution method or "Ansatz" method, used recently by VLASOV[32] and by BOHM and GROSS[37] and

---

[37] BOHM and GROSS; *Phys. Rev.*, 1949, **75**, 1851, 1968; *Phys. Rev.* 1950, **79**, 992.

extended by FEINSTEIN and SEN.[38] This method basically assumes plane waves, in that an electric field variation $\exp j(\omega t - \gamma z)$ is assumed to create electron density variations also of the form $\exp j(\omega t - \gamma z)$. (b) The substitution method has been criticized by LANDAU,[39] TWISS[40] and, more recently by BERZ.[41] These authors show that the dispersion equation depends strongly on the initial conditions and the results of the substitution method are particular solutions rather than general solutions. These criticisms are valid, but we begin with the substitution analysis to exhibit the differences between the results obtained. The following assumptions are made.

1. There is no stationary electric field in the z direction and there are no transverse motions, i.e., a strong magnetic field is assumed. Interactions with the r.f. magnetic field are negligible.

2. The negative space charge is balanced by positive ion charge.

3. Collisions and ionic movements are neglected.

4. Small signal conditions obtain and $k^2 \ll \gamma^2$.

5. The charges can be assumed to give rise to a continuous smeared out field.†

6. The same distribution function is valid in every ross-section of the plasma. This assumption is the onewhich will be subsequently dropped.

We consider, with Feinstein and Sen, a distribution which exhibits a number n of discrete beams superposed on a continuous velocity distribution. This situation has applications in some types of electron tubes, such as Haeff's two-beam space-charge amplifier.

Let $D_0 =$ density of charges (number of electrons/unit volume) then

$$D_0 = \sum_{q=1}^{n} D_{0q} + \int_{-\infty}^{+\infty} f_0(u_0) \, du_0 \qquad (194)$$

The division into d.c. and a.c. parts is made as usual and we can write

$$\rho_1 = -e \sum D_{0q(1)} - e \int_{-\infty}^{+\infty} f_1(u) \, du_0 \qquad (195)$$

$$i_1 = -e \sum (D_{0q} \cdot u_{1q} + u_{0q} \cdot D_{0q1}) - e \int_{-\infty}^{+\infty} [f_0 \cdot u_1 + u_1 \cdot f_0] \, du_0 \qquad (196)$$

---

† This assumption had never been questioned until the work of ECKER.[42]

[38] FEINSTEIN and SEN; *Phys. Rev.*, 1951, **83**, 405.
[39] LANDAU; *J. Phys. U.S.S.R.*, 1946, **10**, 25.
[40] TWISS; *Phys. Rev.*, 1952, **88**, 1392.
[41] BERZ; *Proc. Phys. Soc. B.*, 1956, **69**, 939.
[42] ECKER; *Z. Phys.*, 1955, **140**, 274, 293.; *Z. Phys.*, 1956, **141**, 294.

From the plane wave assumption continuity follows for each velocity group $u_0 - u_0 + du_0$ and therefore

$$\rho_1 = +\frac{j}{\omega}\frac{\partial i_1}{\partial z} \tag{197}$$

is valid for each group. If the wave functions are of the assumed form we immediately obtain

$$(\omega - \gamma u_{0q}) \cdot D_{0q1} = \gamma D_{0q} \cdot u_{1q} \tag{198}$$

and

$$(\omega - \gamma u_0)f_1 = \gamma f_0 u_1 \tag{199}$$

Poisson's equation gives us the relation between E_1 and ρ_1 and the equation of motion that between E_1 and u_1, precisely as in our earlier derivations.

Then

$$j(\omega - \gamma u_0)u_1 = \eta E_1 \tag{200}$$

and

$$j(\omega - \gamma u_0)u_{1q} = \eta E_1 \tag{201}$$

with

$$E_1 = +\frac{j\rho_1}{\gamma \epsilon_0} \tag{202}$$

If we eliminate u_1 and u_{1q} using Eqs. (200) and (201) we can form the dispersion equation by equating our two expressions for ρ_1. We obtain

$$-\frac{e\eta}{\epsilon_0}\left[\sum_{q=1}^{n}\frac{D_{0q}}{(\omega - \gamma u_0)^2} + \int_{-\infty}^{+\infty}\frac{f_0(u_0)\,du_0}{(\omega - \gamma u_0)^2}\right] = 1 \tag{203}$$

As a check on this expression, consider what happens when there is just one beam with fixed velocity. The term $-\eta(eD_{01}/\epsilon_0)$ is then simply ω_p^2 and the dispersion equation is $(\omega - \gamma u_0)^2 = \omega_p^2$ as we should expect.

The more general problem is to deduce conditions under which the dispersion equation gives rise to complex values of γ. If we now limit ourselves to a continuous distribution between the velocity limits u_{01} and u_{02} it is clear that γ cannot have real solutions which make $(\omega - \gamma u_0)$ zero as the integral would become infinite at such values. Thus, real γ's in the range $\omega/u_{01} < \gamma < \omega/u_{02}$ are excluded. Further discussion of this equation is given by KENT[43] who shows that there can be one real zero in the range $-\infty < \gamma < \omega/u_{01}$ and another in the range $\omega/u_{02} < \gamma < \infty$.

[43] KENT; J. Appl. Phys., 1954, 25, 32.

The complex values are discussed under the assumptions that $f_0(u)$ and $f_{01}(u)$ are finite and continuous in the interval $u_{01} - u_{02}$ and vanish outside, while f_{01} has a single zero at u' in the interval. A partial integration can be carried out with these conditions by changing variable, giving

$$1 + \int_{1/u_{01}}^{1/u_{02}} \frac{g(\tau)\, d\tau}{(\tau - \gamma/\omega)} = 0 \tag{204}$$

where

$$g(\tau) = f_0'\left(\frac{1}{\tau}\right) \frac{e\eta}{\omega^2 \epsilon_0} \tag{205}$$

This can be separated into real and imaginary parts for $\gamma = (\alpha + j\beta)\omega$ and it can be shown that no complex propagation constants can exist. This proves that exponentially growing waves are impossible unless f_0' has more than one zero, as would be the case, for instance, in the two-beam tube. Exponential gain should not, therefore, be expected in the case of continuous velocity distributions, a finding which is not in agreement with experiment. We emphasize that this does not constitute a proof that a continuous system should not exhibit gain or oscillation, but only that it should not exhibit gain which increases exponentially along the beam.

Let us now strike out the plane wave assumption. The modified dispersion equation is deduced by Berz[41] in the manner used in Section 13 of this chapter. Owing to the first assumption made in the present treatment, $\partial V_0/\partial z = 0$ and Eq. (183) becomes

$$\frac{\partial f_1}{\partial t} + u_1 \frac{\partial f_1}{\partial z} - \eta E_1 \frac{\partial f_0}{\partial u} = 0 \tag{206}$$

Poisson's equation is

$$\frac{\partial E_1}{\partial z} = -\frac{1}{\epsilon_0} \int_{-\infty}^{+\infty} f_1(u, z, t)\, du \tag{207}$$

Now, E_1 is still assumed to be of the form $\exp j(\omega t - \gamma z)$ since any function can be expanded in a Fourier series of these wave functions, but f_1 is not assumed to be of this form. Berz proceeds with the case in which γ is assumed real, so that a complex value of ω leads to waves which are either amplified or damped with increasing time. The physical situation is that the build-up of oscillations in time is studied. The build-up with distance could be studied using the same technique. Then, γ real, $f_1 = f(u, t) \exp(-j\gamma z)$. Therefore

$$\frac{\partial f_1}{\partial t} - j\gamma u f_1 - \eta E_1 e^{j\omega t} \frac{\partial f_0}{\partial u} = 0 \qquad (208)$$

$$-j\gamma E_1 e^{j\omega t} = -\frac{1}{\epsilon_0} \int_{-\infty}^{+\infty} f_1(u, t) \, du \qquad (209)$$

As before, we use the integrating factor to obtain the first integral,

$$f_1(u, t) = \frac{-j\eta E_1 f'_0(u) e^{j\omega t}}{(\omega - \gamma u)} - j\eta C(u) e^{j\gamma u t} \qquad (210)$$

If this is put back into Eq. (209) and simplified, we find

$$\left(\frac{\omega_p}{\gamma}\right)^2 \left[-\int_{-\infty}^{+\infty} \frac{f'_0(u) \, du}{\omega/\gamma - u} + \frac{\gamma}{E_1} e^{-j\omega t} \int_{-\infty}^{+\infty} C(u) e^{j\gamma u t} \, du \right] = 1 \quad (211)$$

and to be self-consistent this has to be independent of t, while $C(u)$ is an arbitrary function of u, determined in practice by the initial conditions at $t = 0$. If

$$C(u) = \frac{E_1 C_0}{\omega/\gamma - u} \qquad (212)$$

where C_0 is a constant, then, by use of Jordans lemma and the calculus of residues, we find

(a) $I_m(\omega) > 0$ (damped waves)

$$\int_{-\infty}^{+\infty} \frac{e^{j\gamma u t}}{\omega/\gamma - u} = j \cdot 2\pi \, e^{j\omega t}$$

Therefore $\left(\frac{\omega_p}{\gamma}\right)^2 \left[\int_{-\infty}^{+\infty} \frac{f'_0(u) \, du}{u - \omega/\gamma} + j \cdot 2\pi\gamma C_0 \right] = 1 \qquad (213)$

(b) $I_m(\omega) < 0$ (amplified waves)

$$\int_{-\infty}^{+\infty} \frac{e^{j\gamma u t}}{\omega/\gamma - u} = 0$$

Therefore $\left(\frac{\omega_p}{\gamma}\right)^2 \left[\int_{-\infty}^{+\infty} \frac{f'_0(u) \, du}{u - \omega/\gamma} \right] = 1 \qquad (214)$

These results show that, whereas some new features are intro-duced into the dispersion equation for damped waves, the dis-persion equation for amplified waves will only give the required solutions for special forms of $f'_0(u)$. This follows because the last dispersion equation is identical with that found earlier if we use the planar assumption to put $f'_0 = \gamma(u - \omega/\gamma)$. The improved treatment does not, therefore, help us in understanding why valves with continuous velocity distributions operate.

4.15. SPACE-CHARGE WAVES IN RELATIVISTIC BEAMS

So far all our work has been based on the assumption that the electron velocity is only a small fraction of the velocity of light. As the electron velocity increases, relativistic effects must be considered. The first effect to be encountered is that the electronic mass departs from the rest mass m_0 and for voltages in excess of about 15 kV the relation $m_0 u_0^2 = 2 eV_0$ is invalid.
The relativistic mass is

$$m = m_0(1 - u_0^2/c^2)^{-1/2} \tag{215}$$

Fig. 17 gives a plot of u_0/c versus the accelerating voltage. Since pulsed klystrons are operated up to voltages of at least 400 kV, at

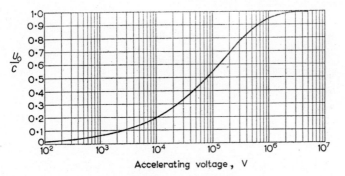

Fig. 17. Relativistic electron velocity.

which $u_0/c \doteqdot 0.83$, this effect must be considered. Secondly, the increased velocity means that the term in the Lorenz force law due to the magnetic field of the electron beam is no longer negligible, or explicitly, we have to use $\mathbf{E}_1 + (\mathbf{u}_1 \times \mathbf{B}_1)$ instead of merely $\mathbf{E}_1$ for the first order a.c. force component. Finally, and this is not due to relativity but merely to the increase in velocity, we may no longer let $\beta^2 - k^2 \to \beta^2$.

By repeating the procedure of Section 2 of this chapter, the reader can easily derive from Maxwell's equations the following results

$$\nabla_t^2 E_z - (\beta^2 - k^2)E_z = \frac{\nabla \rho_1}{\epsilon_0} + j\omega\mu_0 i_z \tag{216}$$

$$\nabla_t^2 \mathbf{B} - (\beta^2 - k^2)E_z = -\mu_0 \cdot \nabla \times \mathbf{i}_z \tag{217}$$

The force law is now

$$\frac{d}{dt}(m\mathbf{u}_1) = -e\left\{\mathbf{E}_1 + (\mathbf{u}_1 \times \mathbf{B}_1)\right\} \tag{218}$$

The operation d/dt still means times $j(\omega - \beta u_0)$. We put $\omega - \beta u_0 = \omega_s$. Equation (218) then gives for the z component

$$jm_0\omega_s R^3(\mathbf{l}_z \cdot \mathbf{u}) = -e\{\mathbf{l}_z[\mathbf{E}_1 + (\mathbf{u}_1 \times \mathbf{B}_1)]\} \tag{219}$$

where $\mathbf{l}_z$ is the unit vector in the z direction and $R = (1 - u_0^2/c^2)^{-1/2}$. For a detailed discussion of this relativistic force law the reader should consult PAGE and ADAMS.[44] For the infinite magnetic field Eq. (219) leads to

$$jm_0\omega_s R^3 u_1 = -eE_z \tag{220}$$

We may now proceed as before, using the continuity equation to obtain Eq. (10)

$$i_z = -\frac{\omega\rho_0 u_1}{\omega_s}$$

or, using Eq. (220)

$$i_z = -j\frac{\eta\rho_0\omega}{\omega_s^2 R^3} E_z \tag{221}$$

Here $\eta = e/m_0$, i.e., the normal value. The a.c. current is modified from Eq. (11) only by division by R^3. The current is therefore reduced much below the value given by non-relativistic theory.

If we introduce ω_p^2 as before, the analogue to Eq. (13) becomes

$$i_z = -j\omega\epsilon_0 \frac{\omega_p^2}{R^3\omega_s^2} \cdot E_z \tag{222}$$

and

$$\rho_1 = -j\beta\epsilon_0 \frac{\omega_p^2}{R^3\omega_s^2} \cdot E_z \tag{223}$$

---

[44] PAGE and ADAMS; *Electrodynamics*, Van Nostrand, 1940.

Putting these values into Eq. (216) we find

$$\nabla t^2 \cdot E_z + (\beta^2 - k^2)\left(\frac{\omega_p^2}{R^3\omega_s^2} - 1\right)E_z = 0 \qquad (224)$$

For the infinite planar beam, we now have

$$\omega_r^2 = (\omega - \beta u_0)^2 = \frac{\omega_p^2}{R^3}$$

or

$$\beta = \left(\frac{\omega}{u_0} \pm \frac{\omega_p}{u_0 R^{3/2}}\right) \qquad (225)$$

and the space-charge waves have phase velocities closer to u_0, than have the non-relativistic space-charge waves.

In the cylindrical case Eq. (224) transforms to

$$\frac{1}{r}\frac{\partial}{\partial r}\left(r\frac{\partial E_z}{\partial r}\right) + (\beta^2 - k^2)\left(\frac{\omega_p^2}{R^3\omega_s^2} - 1\right)E_z = 0 \qquad (226)$$

and

$$E_z = \sum_{n=0}^{\infty} A_n J_0(\gamma_r \cdot r)$$

Restricting ourselves to the case of a beam filling a tunnel of radius a, we find

$$\gamma_{rn}^2 = \left(\frac{\lambda_n}{a}\right)^2 = (\beta_n^2 - k^2)\left(\frac{\omega_p^2}{R^3\omega_{sn}^2} - 1\right) \qquad (227)$$

where λ_n is the nth root of $J_0(\lambda) = 0$. This equation is a quadratic in β_n, and is somewhat complicated by the fact that β_n^2 is no longer much greater than k^2.

If, guided by past experience, we start by neglecting k^2 and put $\omega_{sn} = F_n\omega_p/R^{3/2}$ we find that $F_n = \{1 + (\lambda_n/A)^2\}^{-1/2}$ as before. Since the correction is small, we can put $\beta_n = \beta_e$ in the first bracket of Eq. (227), leading to

$$F'_n = \left\{1 + \frac{\lambda_n}{(\beta_e^2 - k^2)a^2}\right\}^{-1/2} \qquad (228)$$

This shows that F_n is smaller than F_n, so that the neglected term is even smaller than we assumed. It can easily be demonstrated that a further stage of approximation gives a quite negligible correction. The space-charge waves, then, have β's given by

$$\beta_{3n}, \beta_{4n} = \frac{\omega}{u_0} \pm \frac{F'_n\omega_p}{u_0 R^{3/2}} \qquad (229)$$

F'_n being given by Eq. (228).

In our earlier discussion, we neglected the other pair of roots of Eq. (227). If we proceed by analogy from the infinite planar case, these should be the waves observed in the absence of the beam, i.e., evanescent waves in a cut-off tunnel. If we put $\beta = \pm j\gamma$ it is easy to show that

$$\beta_{1,2} \doteq \pm j\sqrt{(\gamma r^2 - k^2)} \tag{230}$$

We conclude then that the general behaviour of space-charge waves on electron beams at relativistic velocities is very similar to that at normal velocities. The phase velocities of the fast and slow waves are even closer to that of the unperturbed beam that was the case at lower velocities. The a.c. velocity and the a.c. current are reduced from their former values by division by R^3. On the other hand, the relation between the potential and the velocity is now

$$\eta V_0 = c^2(R - 1)$$

From the definition of R, it follows that

$$\eta V_0 = u_0{}^2 \frac{R^2}{R + 1} \tag{231}$$

For low voltages, the a.c. velocity gained in a V.M. gap is given by $u_1/u_0 = \eta(MV_1/u_0{}^2)$. Here, we shall have

$$\frac{u_1}{u_0} = \frac{\eta MV_1}{u_0{}^2 R^3} = \frac{MV_1}{V_0} \cdot \frac{1}{R(R + 1)} \tag{232}$$

where we have used Eq. (232). We see that a factor of $\frac{1}{2}$ is replaced by $1/[R(R + 1)]$, or, for the 400 kV cited, about $\frac{1}{3}$. While these differences are important enough to make considerable alterations in the detailed design of, for example, a high-voltage klystron, the general behaviour is not significantly modified.

5

MATCHING SPECIFIED INPUT CONDITIONS WITH SPACE-CHARGE WAVES

IN THE last chapter we have tacitly assumed that only a single space-charge wave, that with the smallest wavelength, is set up on the electron beam. A single wave would, in fact, give an exact solution for the infinite planar system in which there are no transverse fields in the beam. It also turns out to be correct for the Brillouin beam, for different reasons but, in general, the input conditions have to be satisfied by an infinite series of space-charge waves. In the same way an arbitrary displacement of a violin string has to be represented as an infinite series (Fourier series) of harmonic waves or to take a closer analogy, the temperature distribution on a circular rod with an arbitrary initial temperature gives rise to an infinite series of modes. The problem, as we shall soon see, is one of Fourier–Bessel expansions. However, to simplify the working, we use the technique of finite Hankel transforms first applied to this problem by BECK[1] in a paper on which this chapter is based. This method presents the necessary results in the form of pairs of transforms to which simple operations must be applied to obtain the desired results. For simplicity we begin with infinite magnetic fields and the beam filling the tunnel.

5.1. BEAM FILLING THE TUNNEL

This is the situation discussed in Section 4.3 with $\gamma_o a = \beta_e a = A$ made equal to B. The electric field in the beam, at points distant from the gap is then

$$E_z = \sum_{n=1}^{\infty} C_n J_0(\gamma_{rn} \cdot r) \tag{1}$$

where $\gamma_{rn} = 2 \cdot 405/b$, $5 \cdot 520/b$, $8 \cdot 654/b$, etc.

By "distant" we mean sufficiently far from the lips of the gap to ensure that all the evanescent waveguide modes established near

---

[1] BECK; *J. Electronics*, 1957, **2**, 489.

the gap have decayed to negligible values. For usual tunnels, this is not a stringent condition. The coefficients in Eq. (1) have now to be determined so that Eq. (1) correctly represents the fields set up in the beam by the action of the gap.

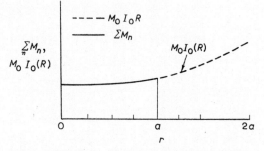

FIG. 1. Radial field variation assumed in the analysis.

We shall require to know the space-charge wavelength corresponding with the various radial modes. The generalization of Eq. (28) in Chapter 4 is

$$\beta_n = \frac{\omega \pm F_n \omega_p}{u_0} \tag{2}$$

where

$$F_n{}^2 = \frac{1}{1 + ([\gamma_{rn} \cdot b]/[\beta_e \cdot b])^2} \tag{3}$$

We observe that the F_n's decrease uniformly with increasing n, so that the phase constants of the higher order modes get progressively nearer to $\beta_e = \omega/u_0$ and the phase velocities get nearer to u_0. The a.c. velocity for each wave is given by

$$u_{1n} = \frac{j\eta E_z}{(\omega - \beta_n u_0)} \tag{4}$$

which shows that u and E_z both have the same functional dependence on r. Consider now that the beam was initially free from modulation so that the condition at the exit terminals of the gap is $u = u_{10}$, $i = 0$. Then, from our gap theory we have

$$u_{10} = \frac{\alpha u_0}{2} M = \frac{\alpha u_0}{2} \sum_{n=1}^{\infty} M_n \tag{5}$$

where the M_n are the coupling factors for the individual waves.

Putting Eq. (5) into the generalized form of Chapter 4, Eq. (35) we get

$$u_1 = \frac{\alpha u_0}{2} \sum_n M_n \, \cos \frac{F_n \omega_p z}{u_0} \exp j(\omega t - \beta_e z) \tag{6}$$

and

$$E_z = \frac{\alpha u_0}{2\eta} \sum_n F_n \omega_p M_n \sin \frac{F_n \omega_p z}{u_0} \exp j(\omega t - \beta_e z) \tag{7}$$

Equation (7) is, however, to be of the form of Eq. (1) so that $M_n \propto J_0(\gamma_{rn} \cdot r)$ and our problem will be solved if we use Eq. (5) and make

$$M = \sum_{n=1}^{\infty} C_n J_0(\gamma_r \cdot r) \tag{8}$$

In the particular problem under discussion the γ_r's are given by $J_0(\gamma_{rn} \cdot a) = 0$. Denote the roots of this equation by λ_n and Eq. (8) then becomes

$$M = \sum_{n=1}^{\infty} C_n J_0\left(\lambda_n \cdot \frac{r}{a}\right) \tag{9}$$

Two cases must be distinguished—gaps with and without grids.

Case 1. With grids

$$M = \frac{\sin(L/2)}{L/2} = \sum_{n=1}^{\infty} C_n J_0\left(\gamma_n \cdot \frac{r}{a}\right)$$

By a standard Fourier–Bessel expansion, we can represent M, $0 < r < a$ by

$$C_n = \frac{2M}{a^2 J_1^2(\lambda_n)} \int_0^a r J_0\left(\lambda_n \frac{r}{a}\right) dr = \frac{2M}{\lambda_n J_1(\lambda_n)}$$

or

$$M = \sum_{n=1}^{\infty} \frac{2M}{\lambda_n J_1(\lambda_n)} \cdot J_0\left(\lambda_n \frac{r}{a}\right) \tag{10}$$

i.e., $M_q = 2M/[\lambda_q \cdot J_1(\lambda_q)] \cdot J_0(\lambda_q r/a)$ is the gap coupling factor for the qth mode.

We shall also require the average value of M_q^2, taken over the gap. This quantity we denote by $\langle M_q^2 \rangle$

$$\langle M_q^2 \rangle = \left(\frac{2M}{\lambda_q J_1(\lambda_q)}\right)^2 \frac{2\pi}{\pi a^2} \int_0^a r J_0^2\left(\lambda_q \frac{r}{a}\right) dr$$

$$= \frac{4M^2}{\lambda_q^2} \tag{11}$$

Case 2.   Without grids

$$M = \frac{J_0(L/2)I_0(\beta_e r)}{I_0(A)}$$

so

$$C_n = \frac{J_0(L/2)}{I_0(A)} \cdot \frac{2}{a^2 J_1^2(\lambda_n)} \int_0^a r I_0(\beta_e r) J_0\left(\lambda_n \frac{r}{a}\right) \, \mathrm{d}r$$

$$= \frac{2\lambda_n}{A^2 + \lambda_n^2} \frac{J_0(L/2)}{J_1(\lambda_n)}$$

and

$$M_q = \frac{2J_0(L/2)\lambda_q}{(A^2 + \lambda_q^2)J_1(\lambda_q)} \cdot J_0\left(\lambda_q \frac{r}{a}\right)$$

$$\langle M_q^2 \rangle = \frac{4\lambda_q^2}{(A^2 + \lambda_q^2)^2} J_0^2(L/2) \ . \tag{12}$$

We have to be quite clear as to the meaning of these results. First, the series expansions given only represent M over the range $o < r < a$. At $r = a$, the sum of the series drops suddenly to zero (Fig. 1), in accordance with the boundary condition (beam filling the tunnel) $E_z = 0$, $r = a$. It can easily be shown, by direct integration, that the cross products $M_p \cdot M_q$ are identically zero with respect to the weight factor r. This is, of course, just a consequence of the fact that the Bessel functions constitute an orthogonal set appropriate to this problem.

Table 1 compares the overall average coupling factor with the average values for the first three modes. We observe the following facts:

TABLE 1

The overall gap factor and the first three components

	A	$\sum\limits_1^\infty \langle M_q^2 \rangle$	$\langle M_1^2 \rangle$	$\langle M_2^2 \rangle$	$\langle M_3^2 \rangle$
(a) Gridded Gaps	—	1·0	0·69	0·13	0·05
(b) Gridless Gaps	0·5	0·94	0·62	0·13	0·053
	1·0	0·80	0·51	0·12	0·052
	1·5	0·64	0·36	0·11	0·050
	2·0	0·51	0·24	0·10	0·048

All values have been normalized by dividing by M_e^2, the value at the gap edge.

1. The coupling factors fall off relatively slowly with increasing mode number.

2. The third, and higher order modes are practically independent of A.

3. The effect of the higher order modes is much more important in big diameter beams, because $\langle M_1{}^2 \rangle$ depends markedly on A. The single space-charge mode description is therefore inadequate for beams of normal diameter, which is rarely less than 0·5.

The series deduced above, combined with the various results deduced in the last chapter, allow us to write down the explicit results for all the a.c. quantities. The most important are the current and velocity, but the longitudinal field and the a.c. current density are also useful. The results are

$$u_z = \frac{\alpha u_0 J_0(L/2)}{2} \sum_1^\infty \frac{2\lambda_n J_0(\lambda_n r/a)}{(A^2 + \lambda_n{}^2)J_1(\lambda_n)} \cos\left(\frac{F_n \omega_p z}{u_0}\right) \exp j(\omega t - \beta_e z) \tag{13}$$

$$E_z = \frac{\alpha u_0 J_0(L/2) \cdot \omega_p}{2\eta} \sum_1^\infty \frac{2F_n \lambda_n J_0(\lambda_n r/a)}{(A^2 + \lambda_n{}^2)J_1(\lambda_n)} \sin\left(\frac{F_n \omega_p z}{u_0}\right) \exp(\omega t - \beta_e z) \tag{14}$$

$$i_z = \frac{-j\alpha J_0(L/2)I_0 \omega}{2\omega_p} \sum_1^\infty \frac{\lambda_n J_0(\lambda_n r/a)}{F_n(A^2 + \lambda_n{}^2)J_1(\lambda_n)}$$
$$\times \sin\left(\frac{F_n \omega_p z}{u_0}\right) \exp j(\omega t - \beta_e z) \tag{15}$$

$$\rho_z = \frac{-j\alpha J_0(L/2)I_0}{2\omega_p} \sum_1^\infty \frac{\beta_n \lambda_n J_0(\lambda_n r/a)}{F_n(A^2 + \lambda_n{}^2)J_1(\lambda_n)}$$
$$\times \sin\left(\frac{F_n \omega_p z}{u_0}\right) \exp j(\omega t - \beta_e z) \tag{16}$$

E_r and H_θ are derived, using the T.M. wave expressions in Table 1, of Chapter 4, and termwise differentiation of Eq. (14).

Let us now discuss the fields E_z set up in the beam. In the older terminology these are the debunching fields. From Eq. (14) we see that the field on the axis is given by

$$E_z = \text{constant} \sum_1^\infty \frac{2F_n \lambda_n}{(A^2 + \lambda_n{}^2)J_1(\lambda_n)} \sin\left(\frac{F_n \omega_p z}{u_0}\right)$$

Now, it is known that, when λ_q is the qth root of $J_0(\lambda) = 0$, the series

$J_1(\lambda_n)$ alternates in sign with the first term positive. Therefore the field components with odd indices are all positive on the axis and even ones are negative. The sign of E_{z1} obviously agrees with our

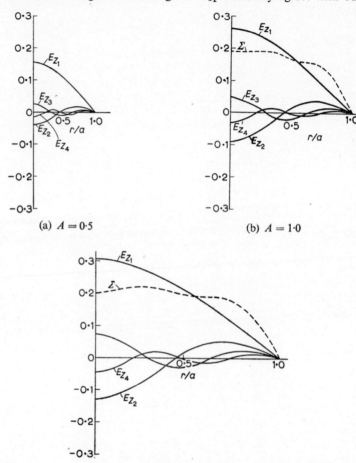

(a) $A = 0.5$

(b) $A = 1.0$

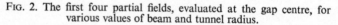

(c) $A = 1.5$

FIG. 2. The first four partial fields, evaluated at the gap centre, for various values of beam and tunnel radius.

sign convention, since the corresponding force on an electron is $-eE_z$, which is decelerating. E_{z2} then, is negative on the axis, goes to zero when $J_0(5.52r/a) = J_0(2.405) = 0$, i.e., when $r/a = 0.44$, and then becomes positive. Similarly, E_{z3} is positive for $r/a < 0.29$, negative for $0.29 < r/a < 0.64$ and then positive. We notice that as $r/a \to 1$, all the field components are positive. Figs. 2(a), (b) and (c) show the first four field components evaluated at $z = 0$ for constant ω_p (constant beam current density) for different values of A. The very marked increase in E_{z1} due to increase in F_n with A is very noticeable. Equation (15) shows that the current waves behave in exactly the same way. Fig. 3 shows the relative amplitudes of the first four current waves as functions of z for $A = 1$. To determine the amplitude at a given radial position we simply multiply by $J_0(\lambda_n r/a)$.

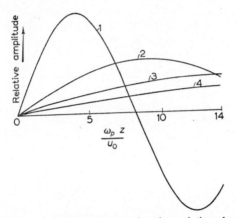

FIG. 3. The first four current waves, showing the variation along the beam.

This figure allows us to understand an experiment done by CHO-DOROW et al.,[2] who moved a phase-sensitive current probe radially through a modulated beam. When the probe was sufficiently far from the input, they found that the phase of the observed current changed by 180° as they moved the probe through the beam. Fig. 3 shows that this is just what we should expect, since for $\omega_p z/u_0 \doteqdot$ 8·0 the amplitude of the first wave is near zero and, especially for a beam with $A < 1$, the current is mostly in the second wave. But this wave changes sign at $r/a = 0·44$. The experiment constitutes a proof of the physical reality of higher order modes, if such were needed.

It might be thought that this would be disastrous from the point of view of extracting power from the beam, but reflection shows that the situation at the output gap must be the inverse of that in the

---

[2] CHODOROW, GINZTON and NALOS; *Proc. Inst. Radio Engrs.*, N.Y., 1953, **41**, 999.

M

input gap where the waves were set up. The component of the gap field changes sign at the same nodal rings as does the beam current so that all parts of the beam contribute, in phase, to the r.f. power induced in the output. This is, however, subject to the important assumption, certainly valid in the infinite magnetic field case, that any particular electron passes through the output at the same radial distance as it passed the input gap. We can prove this mathematically by inspecting the result of averaging over the beam which, from Eqs. (11) and (13), eliminates the $J_1(\lambda_n)$ terms from all the expressions.

It is now appropriate to form the expression for the current induced into the output resonator. By definition, this is simply $\sum M_n i_{zn}$ and the average over the beam must be taken. The result is

$$i_T = -j\frac{I_0\alpha\omega}{2\omega_p} \sum_1^\infty \frac{\langle M_n{}^2\rangle}{F_n} \sin\left(\frac{F_n\omega_p z}{u_0}\right) \quad (17)$$

For the gap without grids, we can write this, in a form which lends itself to computation, as

$$i_T = -j\frac{I_0\alpha}{2} \cdot \frac{\omega}{\omega_p}J_0{}^2\left(\frac{L}{2}\right)F(\omega_p, z) \quad (18)$$

where
$$F(\omega_p, z) = \frac{4\omega_p z}{u_0} \sum_1^\infty \frac{\lambda_n{}^2}{(A^2 + \lambda_n{}^2)^2} \frac{\sin Z_n}{Z_n} \quad (19)$$

and
$$Z_n = \frac{F_n\omega_p z}{u_0} \quad (20)$$

Equation (12) has been used for $\langle M_n{}^2\rangle$.

Fig. 4 shows a plot of $F(\omega_p, z)$ against $\omega_p z/u_0$ for several values of A or B as parameter. For comparison, the results of a single wave theory are included in which $\langle M^2\rangle$ has been substituted for the summation, i.e., the plot is of

$$\frac{4\omega_p z}{u_0}\left(\frac{I_0{}^2(A) - I_1{}^2(A)}{I_0{}^2(A)}\right)\frac{\sin(F_1\omega_p z/u_0)}{F_1\omega_p z/u_0} \quad (21)$$

The accurate theory gives somewhat larger values of the maximum r.f. current at somewhat greater distances from the input gap. The most important feature is, however, that the current does not fall off nearly so rapidly after the maximum when the exact theory is used as it does when the first-order theory is applied. This phenomenon is again capable of experimental proof. Three resonator klystrons have been made with both the resonator spacings approximately equal to 4, for $A = 1$. The gain could then be measured from resonator 1–2 and from resonator 1–3, with the second resonator detuned. Simple theory would predict zero gain from resonator 1–3 but, in fact, the gain was only slightly less than that from resonator 1–2. This is just what the accurate curves predict. In the experiments, the beam did not quite fill the tunnel so better numerical agreement could have been obtained using the results of the next section.

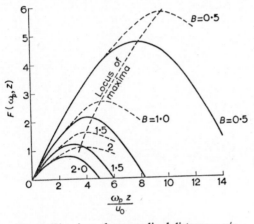

FIG. 4. $F(\omega_p, z)$ vs. the normalized distance $\omega_p z / u_0$.

– – – – = single mode theory

———— = accurate theory

Before leaving this section it is as well to say a little about the evaluation of the various series concerned. As n increases $\lambda_{n+1} - \lambda_n \to \pi$ and $\sin Z_n / Z_n \to 1$. Thus the series terms in Eq. (19) tend to $1/\lambda_n^2$ and the series is absolutely convergent. However, convergence is slow; a number of terms must be used and an approximate value derived for the rest. The series terms in Eqs. (13)–(19) however, are not absolutely but only conditionally convergent. The only practical method of summation appears to be to take the sum to n terms where n is to be chosen such that the $(n + 1)$th term is negligible compared with S_n. This relies on the easily proved fact that $S_n - a_{n+1} < S_\infty < S_n$, for a series with alternating signs.

5.2.   A CYLINDRICAL BEAM, NOT FILLING THE TUNNEL

We next consider a beam of normalized radius B centrally located in a tunnel of radius A. The allowed values of the radial propagation constant are given by Eq. (26) of Chapter 4, which we rewrite as

$$\frac{-(\gamma_r b) J_1(\gamma_r b)}{J_0(\gamma_r b)} = B \left[\frac{I_1(B)K_0(A) + I_0(A)K_1(B)}{I_0(B)K_0(A) - I_0(A)K_0(B)} \right] \tag{22}$$

Equation (22) is, however, merely an approximation for we have used $\beta = \omega/u_0$, instead of $\beta = (\omega \pm F_n\omega_p)/u_0$ in going from Chapter 4, Eq. (26). But the approximation turns out to be exceedingly good, for two reasons: first, $F_n\omega_p/\omega$ has been consistently assumed much smaller than unity and second, if we plot the R.H.S. of Eq. (22), which we do by putting $n = a/b$ obtaining

$$\phi(B) = B \left[\frac{I_1(B)K_0(nB) + I_0(nB)K_1(B)}{I_0(B)K_0(nB) - I_0(nB)K_0(B)} \right] \tag{23}$$

we find that $\phi(B)$ varies only very slowly with B for a fixed n. Such a plot is shown in Fig. 5. A small inaccuracy in β, reflected in a

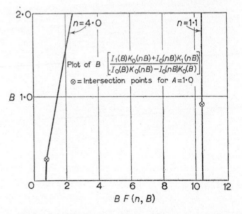

FIG. 5. This plot shows that $\phi(B)$ varies very little with B.

similar inaccuracy in B, therefore produces an even smaller error in $\phi(B)$ and the R.H.S. is for all practical purposes independent of F_n, so that for a fixed n, Eq. (22) can be written

$$\frac{-(\gamma_r b) J_1(\gamma_r b)}{J_0(\gamma_r b)} = h, \qquad (h = \text{constant}) \tag{24}$$

Now, Eq. (24) is another example of a type of boundary condition which permits an expansion in orthogonal functions (Appendix 9).

The work is best organized by the use of the "finite Hankel transforms" defined by SNEDDON.[3] If we wish to expand a given function $f(r)$ in a series using the eigenfunctions $J_0(\gamma_r . r)$ we use the transformation pair, over the range $o < r < b$

$$\bar{f}(\gamma_r) = \int_0^b rf(r)J_0(\gamma_r . r) \, \mathrm{d}r \tag{25}$$

$$\bar{f}(r) = 2 \sum_1^\infty \frac{\gamma_r^2 \bar{f}(\gamma_r)}{h^2 + \gamma_r^2 . b^2} \frac{J_0(\gamma_r . r)}{J_0^2(\gamma_r b)} \tag{26}$$

the sum being taken over all the positive roots of Eq. (24).

If we now use the expression for $\bar{f}(r)$ appropriate to gaps without grids

$$\bar{f}(\gamma_r) = \frac{1}{\beta_e^2 + \gamma_r^2} \frac{J_0(L/2)}{I_0(A)} \{BI_1(B)J_0(\gamma_r b) + (\gamma_r b)I_0(B)J_1(\gamma_r b)\} \tag{27}$$

Averaging over the gap, to obtain M^2, only involves averaging $J_0(\gamma_r.r)$, which is the only function of r appearing in (26). But $J_0(\gamma_r.b) \neq 0$, now, and the average contributes $J_1^2(\gamma_r.b) + J_0^2(\gamma_r.b)$.

The final result, after simplification, using the boundary condition Eq. (24) is

$$\sum \langle M_n^2 \rangle = \frac{4J_0^2(L/2)I_0^2(B)}{I_0^2(A)} \left\{ \frac{BI_1(B)}{I_0(B)} + h \right\}_2$$
$$\times \sum_1^\infty \frac{\gamma_r^2.b^2}{h^2 + \gamma_r^2.b^2} \frac{1}{(B^2 + \gamma_r^2 b^2)^2} \tag{28}$$

The current in this case is obtained by replacing $\langle M_n^2 \rangle$ in Eq. (17) by Eq. (28).

Values computed for this case are shown in Fig. 6. This figure compares the currents for $B = A = 1\cdot2$ with the values when $B = 1\cdot0$ and $B = 0\cdot6$. It will be observed that the maximum current when $B = 0\cdot6$ is only about 20% of that obtained when the beam fills the tunnel. Even a $1\cdot2:1$ ratio quite seriously diminishes the maximum current. It is therefore necessary for good interaction between the beam and circuit to make the beam fill the tunnel. This is, of course, not practicable but it would seem reasonable to design the beam so that $B \doteq 0\cdot9A$ and to adjust the magnetic

---

[3] SNEDDON; *Fourier Transforms*. McGraw-Hill, 1951. A briefer account is in TRANTER; *Integral Transforms in Mathematical Physics*. Methuen, 1951.

field so that the scalloping did not exceed $\pm 10\%$. If these conditions are achieved in a valve one can probably assume that, for all practical purposes, the beam fills the tunnel. Since only relatively small

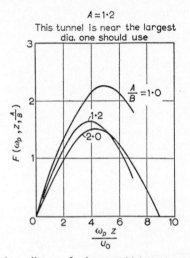

FIG. 6. $F(\omega_p, z)$ vs. distance for beams which do not fill the tunnel.

scalloping is allowed, the magnetic field will be a good deal greater than the Brillouin value and there is then little error in assuming that the field tends to infinity.

5.3. ANNULAR BEAMS

We now proceed to discuss two cases of annular flow. The first is that of an annular beam filling the space between metallic conductors. The second, of more practical importance, is that of a beam which just grazes the inner wall of a drift tube and only partially fills the tunnel.

5.3.1. Annular beam filling annular tunnel

Since the electric field is identically zero on both sides of the beam, the boundary conditions are met by a wave function

$$B_0(\gamma_r.r) = J_0(\gamma_r.r) Y_0(\gamma_r.a) - J_0(\gamma_r a) Y_0(\gamma_r.r) \qquad (29)$$

Here a is the outer diameter and d will be used for the inner diameter. $B_0(\gamma_r.r)$ is identically zero at $r = a$ and is made to vanish at $r = d$ by choice of the γ_r's so that $B_0(\gamma_r d) = 0$. It has been proved in Appendix 9 that this wave function yields an orthogonal expansion of $f(r)$ if we define

$$\bar{f}(\gamma_r) = \int_d^a r f(r) B_0(\gamma_r r)\, dr \qquad (30)$$

$$\bar{f}(r) = \frac{\pi^2}{2} \sum_{n=1}^{\infty} \frac{a^2 J_0^2(\gamma_r.d)}{J_0^2(\gamma_r a) - J_0^2(\gamma_r d)} \bar{f}(\gamma_r) B_0(\gamma_r.r) \qquad (31)$$

We find

$$\bar{f}(\gamma_r) = \frac{1}{\beta_e{}^2 + \gamma_r{}^2} \frac{2}{\pi} \left\{ \frac{J_0(\gamma_r a)}{J_0(\gamma_r d)} M_d - M_a \right\}$$

$$\bar{f}(r) = \pi \sum_{n=1}^{\infty} \frac{\gamma_r{}^2.a^2}{A^2 + \gamma_r{}^2.a^2}$$
$$\times \frac{\{J_0(\gamma_r a) M_d - J_0(\gamma_r d) M_a\}}{J_0(\gamma_r a) - J_0^2(\gamma_r d)} J_0(\gamma_r d) B_0(\gamma_r.r)$$

and

$$\sum \langle M_n{}^2 \rangle = \frac{4}{1 - (d/a)^2} \sum_{n=1}^{\infty} \frac{\gamma_r{}^2.a^2}{(A^2 + \gamma_r{}^2.a^2)^2}$$
$$\times \frac{\{M_a J_0(\gamma_r d) - M_d J_0(\gamma_r a)\}^2}{J_0^2(\gamma_r a) - J_0^2(\gamma_r d)} \qquad (32)$$

We may note that[4] if $d/c = k$, where k is less than 2·0 acceptable approximations for the γ_r's are given by

$$\gamma_r d = \frac{n\pi}{k-1}$$
$$\gamma_r a = \frac{k \cdot n\pi}{k-1} \qquad (33)$$

The expressions derived above could be used for a strip beam by replacing the Bessel functions by their asymptotic values for large arguments, while retaining a finite difference between a and d.

5.3.2. An annular beam in a hollow tunnel

The inner radius of the tunnel is a and the beam extends inwards to radius c. The required Hankel transform is not among those given by Sneddon, but is derived in Appendix 9. It ensures that the wave function is identically zero at the outer edge of the beam and

---

[4] JAHNKE and EMDE; *Tables of Functions*, pp. 204–205. Dover, 1945.

satisfies the correct boundary condition at the inner edge of the beam. The boundary condition can be obtained either directly or by application of Eq. (45) in Chapter 4 to this case. $B_0(\gamma_r.r)$ is still defined by Eq. (29) but the boundary condition at $r = c$ is now

$$-\frac{(\gamma_r.c)B'_0(\gamma_r c)}{B_0(\gamma_r c)} = \frac{CI_1(C)}{I_0(C)} \tag{34}$$

Equation (34) is an approximation of the same type as Eq. (22) and analysis shows that it is valid for most practical purposes, unless C is much larger than usual. Equation (30) still applies but Eq. (31) is now replaced by

$$\bar{f}(r) = \frac{\pi^2}{2} \sum_{n=1}^{\infty} \frac{\gamma_r^2}{\{1 - [(h^2 + \gamma_r^2.c^2)/W_n^2]\}} B_0(\gamma_r.r)\bar{f}(\gamma_r) \tag{35}$$

where $W_n = \dfrac{\gamma_{rn}.c Y_1(\gamma_{rn}.c) + h Y_0(\gamma_{rn}.c)}{Y_0(\gamma_{rn}.a)}$

$$= \frac{J_0(\gamma_{rn}.a)}{\gamma_{rn}.c J_1(\gamma_{rn}.c) + h J_0(\gamma_{rn}.c)} \tag{36}$$

The result for the mean square coupling factor then becomes

$$\sum \langle M_n^2 \rangle = \frac{4J_0^2(L/2)}{1 - (c/a)^2} \sum_{n=1}^{\infty} \frac{\gamma_r^2 a^2}{(A^2 + \gamma_r^2 a^2)^2} \frac{1}{[1 - \{h^2 + \gamma_r^2.c^2/W^2\}]} \tag{37}$$

Equation (37) is easily shown to reduce correctly to Eq. (12) as $c \to 0$.

The r.f. current factors are plotted for this case in Fig. 7, which shows that $F(\omega_p, z)$ is much larger now than for a solid beam of the same outer diameter and that the current maximum is at a greater distance from the origin. If, however, we keep ω_p constant, the annular beam current is only $[1 - (c/a)^2]I_0$ so that the actual r.f. current may not be much increased. If ω_p is increased for the annular beam, then considerably greater r.f. current can be obtained. This possibility is most interesting because it is well known that the perveance for a given value of potential depression is much greater for an annular beam than it is for a solid beam.

I have also been able to derive the general result for an annular beam which does not graze the inside of the tunnel, but, in view of its rather formidable aspect and the relatively small increase in information which it gives, I forbear from quoting it here.

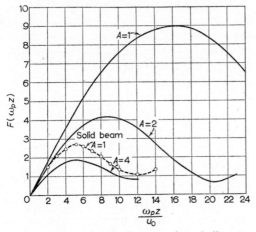

FIG. 7. $F(\omega_p,z)$ for an annular beam grazing a hollow tunnel.
$c/a = 0\cdot8$

5.4. THE BRILLOUIN BEAM

The cylindrical Brillouin beam is an interesting special case of a beam in a non-infinite magnetic field. In Section 4.6 we showed that the space-charge field varies as $I_0(R)$. We can therefore match the field in a gridless gap with only one space-charge mode in this case. Thus:

$$E_z = CI_0(R)$$

$$= \frac{F_B\omega_p\alpha u_0 J_0(L/2)}{2\eta} \sin Z \exp j(\omega t - \beta_e z) \tag{38}$$

and $\qquad E_r = \frac{j}{\beta_e}\frac{\partial E_z}{\partial r}$

so that we can now obtain an explicit expression for the a.c. variation in beam radius, Eq. (56) chapter 4, viz.,

$$r_1(b) = j\alpha \frac{M(b)z}{2}\frac{I_1(B)}{I_0(B)}\frac{\sin Z}{Z} \tag{39}$$

The symbol (b) indicates that values are taken at $r = b$. All the quantities on the R.H.S. are of the order unity, except for α and z, so we see that if the distance z is greater than about 10 times the beam radius, the a.c. spread of the beam can exceed the original diameter, even for small values of α. It is this fact which constitutes one of the major objections to the use of Brillouin focusing in power tubes. Having obtained Eq. (39) it is easy to write down the explicit relation for the current induced in an output resonator. The most direct way of doing this is to write

$$M_{tT} = \int_0^{b+r_1(b)} M(r)(J_z - \rho_0 u_0)2\pi r\ dr + \int_0^b M(r)\rho_0 u_0 2\pi r\ dr$$

and, to obtain, after approximating for $I_1(B + \beta_e r_1(b))$

$$i_T = -j\frac{I_0 \alpha z}{2b} M^2(b) \frac{\sin Z}{Z}\left\{\frac{2I_1(B)}{I_0(B)} - \frac{F_B \omega_p B}{\omega}\left(\frac{I_0{}^2(B) - I_1{}^2(B)}{I_0{}^2(B)}\right)\right\}$$

(40)

The first term can be recognized as $M(b)$ times the surface current. The second term, which is usually negligible, represents the averaged $\rho_0 u_1$ contribution.

5.5. THE CONFINED BEAM

In studying the confined beam an entirely rigorous treatment would attempt to include the effects due to the scallops in the absence of r.f. field and the T.E. fields which must be set up in addition to the T.M. fields once transverse motions are allowed. Here we make no attempt to be exact, we assume *ab initio* that the magnetic field is strong enough to make d.c. scalloping negligible and to allow us to ignore the T.E. modes. We put Eq. (95) of Section 4.7 into Eq. (80) of the same section to get

$$r_1 = \frac{\eta E_r}{F_c{}^2 \omega_p{}^2 - 2(m^2 - 1)\omega_p{}^2}$$

(41)

and form E_r from E_z, obtaining

$$r_1 = \frac{-j\alpha z}{2\beta_e} \sum_{n=1}^{\infty} \frac{F_n{}^2}{2(m^2 - 1) - F_n{}^2} \frac{\sin Z_n}{Z_n} \frac{\partial M_n}{\partial r}$$

(42)

Allowing for the slight difference in notation, the leading term in Eq. (42) is $F_1{}^2/[2(m^2 - 1) - F_1{}^2]$ times the Brillouin value. This is likely to be a small number, less than 0·125, in practical cases. Subsequent terms are much smaller, so that we must conclude that the a.c. beam spreading is very much less than in the Brillouin case. It is not difficult to keep the spreading down to any desired value.

5.6. THE GENERAL BOUNDARY

We have now considered all the cases of interest when the beam flows through a continuous metal tunnel. We now take up the case in which a cylindrical surface of arbitrary characteristics is substituted for the cylinder. This is done by assuming that the boundary condition at $r = a$ is

$$-\frac{H_\theta}{E_z} = Y_s \tag{43}$$

Y_s being the surface admittance of the sheet. This will allow us to consider several cases including a helix of internal radius A, a resistive wall and capacitative or inductive walls. We also limit ourselves to cases in which the beam is centred on the tube axis and in which the magnetic field is strong.

The fields inside the beam are then of the form

$$E_{z1} = AJ_0(\gamma_r.r)$$

and outside $\qquad E_z = BI_0(\beta r) + DK_0(\beta r)$

The equation analogous to Eq. (26) of Chapter 4 is readily found to be

$$-(\gamma_r b)\frac{J_1(\gamma_r b)}{J_0(\gamma_r b)}$$

$$= \left[\frac{\beta b\left(I_1(\beta b)\left\{K_0(\beta a)-\frac{j\omega\epsilon_0}{\beta Y_s}K_1(\beta a)\right\}+K_1(\beta b)\left\{I_0(\beta a)+\frac{j\omega\epsilon_0}{\beta Y_s}I_1(\beta a)\right\}\right)}{I_0(\beta b)\left\{K_0(\beta a)-\frac{j\omega\epsilon_0}{\beta Y_s}K_1(\beta a)\right\}-K_0(\beta b)\left\{I_0(\beta a)+\frac{j\omega\epsilon_0}{\beta Y_s}I_1(\beta a)\right\}}\right] \tag{44}$$

For the drift tube $Y_s \to \infty$ and Eq. (44) then reduces to Eq. (22). Equation (44) was first given by CHU and JACKSON[5] in their study of travelling-wave tubes.

When Y_s is a pure imaginary, the R.H.S. of Eq. (44) is real and, apart from the extra complication due to additional terms, Eq. (44) is not difficult to handle numerically. If, as in the resistive wall amplifier, Y_s is real, then the R.H.S. is complex and one has to work with tables of complex Bessel functions. But, as we shall see later, this special case has been treated by pole and zero expansions based on the electrolytic trough method.[6]

If Y_s only varies slowly with the general propagation constant

---

[5] CHU and JACKSON; *Proc. Inst. Radio Engrs.*, N.Y., 1948, **36**, 853.
[6] BIRDSALL and WHINNERY; *J. Appl. Phys.*, 1953, **24**, 314.

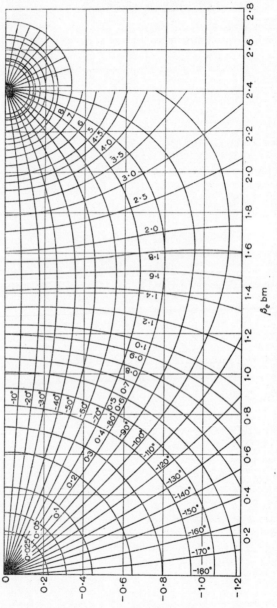

FIG. 8. Contours of constant phase and magnitude of $\gamma_2 b I_1(\gamma_2 b)/J_0(\gamma_2 b)$ in the plane of the argument $\gamma_2 b = \beta_e b(m + jn)$.

β, then, on the same reasoning as in earlier cases, we can form orthogonal expansions using the roots of Eq. (44).

As a first example of the procedure let us take the simplest possible case—that of the beam completely filling a tunnel with highly resistive walls. Equation (44) then reduces to

$$\frac{(\gamma_r a)J_1(\gamma_r a)}{J_0(\gamma_r a)} = \frac{-j\beta aG}{\omega\epsilon_0} = re^{-j\pi/2} \tag{45}$$

As usual, we assume for a start that $\beta \doteq \beta_e = \omega/u_0$. The other quantities in the middle term of Eq. (45) are taken as known. The map of the left-hand side, taken from BIRDSALL and WHINNERY,[6] is reproduced in Fig. 8. Suppose as a concrete example that $r = 0\cdot4$, then from the $-90°$, $0\cdot4$ point we find $\gamma_r.a = 0\cdot67 - j0\cdot6$, which is next expressed in the form $\gamma_r.a = \beta_e a(m + jn)$, i.e., for $\beta_e.a = 1\cdot0$, $m + jn = 0\cdot67 - j0\cdot6$. We next have to determine the exact propagation constant β which is done, as before, through

$$\beta = \frac{\omega}{u_0} \pm \frac{\omega_p}{u_0} \left[1 + \left(\frac{\gamma_r a}{\beta_e a} \right)^2 \right]^{-1/2}$$

or, in a more convenient form for this case,

$$\beta = \frac{\omega}{u_0} \pm \frac{\omega_p}{u_0} \left(p + jq \right) \tag{46}$$

where $$p + jq = [1 + (m + jn)^2]^{-1/2} \tag{47}$$

Birdsall and Whinnery give a plot of Eq. (47), reproduced in Fig. 9, which allows the conversion to be readily made. For the numerical values under discussion

$$p + jq = 0\cdot8 + j0\cdot266$$

and $$\beta = \frac{\omega}{u_0} \pm \frac{\omega_p}{u_0}(0\cdot8 + j0\cdot266) \tag{48}$$

Since Eq. (48) is written in terms of the phase constant, the imaginary part of Eq. (48) is the attenuation constant α. We see that $\alpha = \pm0\cdot266\omega_p/u_0$ and deduce that the fast space-charge wave is attenuated at the rate of $2 \times 0\cdot266\omega_p/u_0$ nepers/metre or $4\cdot53\omega_p/u_0$ dB/m, while the slow wave is amplified at the same rate. This, of course, bears out what we have said before on the physical behaviour of this tube. It should be stressed that no significance should be

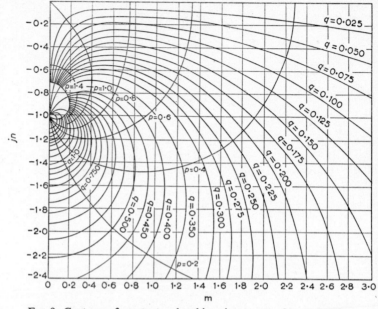

FIG. 9. Contours of constant real and imaginary parts of $pj + q$ in the m, n-plane.

attached to the numbers chosen above—they are merely convenient. In fact, they lead to values of β sufficiently different from β_e to require that a second approximation be used. Equation (48) could be put back into Eq. (45) and the second bracket would become complex instead of imaginary, resulting in modified values of m and n and therefore of p and q. This procedure can be repeated until p and q reach stationary values. We defer the actual discussion of real tube behaviour until later.

5.7. A BEAM IN A HELIX

A second example of general boundary conditions, which is of much more practical importance, is the helix containing an electron beam. We shall now proceed to set up the expressions for this case. We use fields whose explicit form is that appropriate to the sheath helix, for we have already shown that these are sufficiently accurate, provided the magnitudes are adjusted in the light of the results on tape helices.

We consider, then, a sheath helix of mean diameter a containing an electron beam of smaller diameter b. The beam is focused by a strong magnetic field so that only the current component J_z can be excited and there is no θ dependence. The wave function is exp $(j\omega t - \gamma z)$ since γ is now, in general, complex and, to keep the treatment as general as possible, we for the moment retain terms in k^2. Under these conditions the T.E. and T.M. modes, given in the table in Chapter 4 (p. 114), are slightly modified. We find

T.M. modes

$$\frac{1}{r}\frac{\partial}{\partial r}\left(r\frac{\partial E_z}{\partial r}\right) + \left(\gamma^2 + k^2\right)E_z = \frac{j(\gamma^2 + k^2)}{\omega\epsilon_0} \cdot J_z \tag{49}$$

$$E_r = -\frac{\gamma}{(\gamma^2 + k^2)}\frac{\partial E_z}{\partial r} \tag{50}$$

$$H_\theta = -\frac{j\omega\epsilon_0}{(\gamma^2 + k^2)}\frac{\partial E_z}{\partial r} \tag{51}$$

T.E. modes

$$\frac{1}{r}\frac{\partial}{\partial r}\left(r\frac{\partial H_z}{\partial r}\right) + (\gamma^2 + k^2)H_z = 0 \tag{52}$$

$$H_r = \frac{-\gamma}{(\gamma^2 + k^2)}\frac{\partial H_z}{\partial r} \tag{53}$$

$$E_n = \frac{j\omega\mu_0}{(\gamma^2 + k^2)}\frac{\partial H_z}{\partial r} \tag{54}$$

Let us dispose of the T.E. modes first. We expect that γ will have a large imaginary part $\doteq \beta_e = \omega/u_0$ and a small real part so that γ^2 is negative. We then write $p^2 = -(\gamma^2 + k^2)\dagger$ and Eq. (52) then gives

$$H_z = AI_0(pr) \exp(j\omega t - \gamma z) \tag{55}$$

Equations (53) and (54) then yield

$$H_r = A\frac{\gamma}{p}I_1(pr)\exp(j\omega t - \gamma z) \tag{56}$$

$$E_\theta = -A\frac{j\omega\mu_0}{p}I_1(pr)\exp(j\omega t - \gamma z) \tag{57}$$

The electron dynamics of the T.M. mode case were discussed in

---

† If $\gamma^2 \gg k^2$ as usual, we see that $p \doteq \beta$.

detail in Chapter 4, Section 3 and lead to the wave equation

$$\frac{1}{r}\frac{\partial}{\partial r}\left(r\frac{\partial E_z}{\partial r}\right) + \gamma_r^2 E_z = 0 \tag{58}$$

where
$$\gamma_r^2 = p^2\left(\frac{\omega_p^2}{(\omega + j\gamma u_0)^2} - 1\right) \tag{59}$$

A difficulty now arises as to the sign of the second bracket. Most American writers[7],[8] assume, without discussion, that $\omega_p^2/(\omega + j\gamma u_0)^2 < 1$, so that γ_r^2 is negative and the I_0 functions must be used. However, our studies of space-charge waves have shown that this is not the case in drift tubes, where the bracket equals $(1/F^2 - 1)$ which is > 1. In the present case we are not yet able to assign a value to γ but, if we anticipate a little, and try, for instance, the values given by the simplest version of Pierce's ballistic theory[9] we find that the bracket is in fact positive unless the gun perveance is extremely low. For a typical medium power tube, the bracket is quite large numerically. This invalidates the results of FRIEDMAN,[8] based on a value of $\doteq 1$. We therefore take (suppressing the phase functions)

$$E_z = BJ_0(\gamma_r.r) \tag{60}$$

$$E_r = \frac{-\gamma\gamma_r}{p^2}BJ_1(\gamma_r.r) \tag{61}$$

$$H_\theta = \frac{-j\omega\epsilon_0}{p^2}\gamma_r BJ_1(\gamma_r.r) \tag{62}$$

The quantity which most interests us is the radial impedance or admittance looking back into the beam. For T.M. modes, the admittance is the ratio $-H_\theta/E_z$ evaluated at $r = b$, or

$$bY_b = \frac{j\omega\epsilon_0}{p^2}(\gamma_r b)\frac{J_1(\gamma_r b)}{J_0(\gamma_r b)} \tag{63}$$

We now turn to the waves set up on the helix. Outside the helix the TE field components are exactly as they were in the case of no

[7] CHU and JACKSON; *Proc. Inst. Radio Engrs.*, *N.Y.*, 1948, **36**, 853.
[8] FRIEDMAN; *J. Appl. Phys.*, 1951, **22**, 443.
[9] PIERCE; *Traveling-Wave Tubes*, Chapter II. Van Nostrand, 1950.

beam. They can be written down as slight and obvious modifications of those in Appendix 3. They are

$$H_z = CK_0(pr) \tag{64}$$

$$H_r = -\frac{C\gamma}{p}K_1(pr) \tag{65}$$

$$E_\theta = C\frac{j\omega\mu_0}{p^2}K_1(pr) \tag{66}$$

The T.M. components are coupled to the beam and although their form is unaltered outside the beam, the magnitude must be allowed to change. Therefore

$$E_z = DK_0(pr) \tag{67}$$

$$E_r = -D\frac{\gamma}{p}K_1(pr) \tag{68}$$

$$H_\theta = -D\frac{j\omega\epsilon_0}{p}K_1(pr) \tag{69}$$

In the space $b < r < a$, the form of the expressions must be modified because, when $r = 0$ is not included in the region, both I_0 and K_0 functions are allowed.

The T.M. fields are

$$E_z = FI_0(pr) + GK_0(pr) \tag{70}$$

$$E_r = \frac{\gamma}{p}[FI_1(pr) - GK_1(pr)] \tag{71}$$

$$H_\theta = \frac{j\omega\epsilon_0}{p}[FI_1(pr) - GK_1(pr)] \tag{72}$$

The boundary conditions on the helix are now used to eliminate all but one of the constants A, C, D, F and G. The resultant admittance, looking outwards from $r = b$ is then equated to the beam admittance, Eq. (63), to give the desired matching condition. The standard boundary conditions of the sheath helix at $r = a$ are (i = internal, e = external)

$$\begin{gathered} E_z{}^i = E_z{}^e \\ E_\theta{}^i = E_\theta{}^e \\ E_z{}^{i,e} = -E_\theta{}^{i,e}\cot\psi \\ H_z{}^i + H_\theta{}^i\cot\psi = H_z{}^e + H_\theta{}^e\cot\psi \end{gathered} \tag{73}$$

N

If we form Y_r from Eqs. (70) and (72) we find

$$bY_r = \frac{-j\omega\epsilon_0 \cdot b}{p}\left[\frac{FI_1(pr) - GK_1(pr)}{FI_0(pr) + GK_0(pr)}\right] \qquad (74)$$

so that we only require to find G/F. It is left to the reader as an exercise to carry out the derivation which results in

$$\phi(pa) = \frac{G}{F} = \frac{I_0(pa)}{K_0(pa)}\left[\frac{k^2a^2\cot^2\psi}{p^2a^2}\frac{I_1(pa)K_1(pa)}{I_0(pa)K_0(pa)} - 1\right] \qquad (75)$$

Equating the admittances at $r = b$ we have

$$\frac{-(\gamma_r b)J_1(\gamma_r b)}{J_0(\gamma_r b)} = pb\left[\frac{I_1(pb) - \phi(pa)K_1(pb)}{I_0(pb) + \phi(pa)K_0(pb)}\right] \qquad (76)$$

The particular case $r = a$, is of some interest. If we put $r = a$ in Eq. (74) and insert the value of $\phi(pa)$ we find

$$aY_a = \frac{-j\omega\epsilon_0 a}{p}\frac{K_1}{K_0}\left[\frac{1 + I_1K_0/I_0K_1 - I_1K_1/I_0K_0 \cdot (k^2a^2\cot^2\psi)/p^2a^2}{I_1K_1/I_0K_0 \cdot (k^2a^2\cot^2\psi)/p^2a^2}\right] \qquad (77)$$

the arguments of the Bessel functions all being pa. If we now insert the value of Y_a for Y_s in Eq. (44), Eq. (76) is easily verified.

If the beam is absent G, and therefore $\phi(pa)$, is zero. From Eq. (75) this means that

$$\frac{k^2a^2\cot^2\psi}{p_0^2a^2}\frac{I_1(p_0a)K_1(p_0a)}{I_0(p_0a)K_0(p_0a)} - 1 = 0 \qquad (78)$$

which is just the ordinary determinantal equation for the sheath helix. This observation is the basis for perturbation expansions of the R.H.S. in Eq. (76) because we can expand $\phi(pa)$ by Taylor's theorem, yielding

$$\phi(pa) \doteq \phi(p_0a) + (pa - p_0a)\phi'(pa)_{p=p_0} = (pa - p_0a)\phi'(p_0a) \qquad (79)$$

since $\phi(p_0a) = 0$. This expansion has been much used.

We next observe from Eq. (74) that Y_r has two poles at $p = 0$ and at $\phi(p_p'a) = -I_0(p_p'r)/I_1(p_p'r)$ and a zero at $\phi(p_z'a) = I_1(p_z'r)/K_1(p_z'r)$. The pole at $p = 0$ is unimportant in our work. The other pole and zero are vital. We start by considering the case $r = a$ and note that $Y_a \to \infty$ is equivalent to replacing the helix by a drift tube. We see that this can only happen when the square bracket in Eq. (75) is equal to -1, which in turn means $p'_p a \to \infty$. Investigation of a practical case shows that $p'_p a$ has to be equal to 5 to 10 times $p_0 a$ to make the equivalence reasonable. We have thus proved that the helix never behaves like a drift tube except to space-charge waves set up on the beam when the beam velocity is very much below the synchronous value and is quite outside the inter-action region used in T.W.A.s.

Examining Y_b we find that the equation

$$\frac{I_0(p_p a)}{K_0(p_p a)}\left[\frac{k^2 a^2 \cot^2 \psi}{p_p^2 a^2}\frac{I_1 K_1}{I_0 K_0} - 1\right] = \frac{-I_0(p_p b)}{K_0(p_p b)} \tag{80}$$

is satisfied for values of $p_p a$ much more nearly equal to $p_0 a$ than those given above, especially when b/a is less than $0 \cdot 7$. Since $Y_b \to \infty$ corresponds with a drift tube closely surrounding the beam, it is *a priori* likely that this condition represents one boundary to the zone of interaction. If we denote the root of Eq. (80) by p_p, then $p_p a > p_0 a$.

On the other hand the zero of Y_b is given by

$$\frac{I_0(p_z a)}{K_0(p_z a)}\left[\frac{k^2 a^2 \cot^2 \psi}{p_z^2 a^2}\frac{I_1 K_1}{I_0 K_0} - 1\right] = \frac{I_1(p_z b)}{K_1(p_z b)} \tag{81}$$

Since I and K are both positive, as are I_0 and K_0, the R.H.S. of Eq. (81) is opposite in sign to that of the R.H.S. of Eq. (80) so that $p_z a < p_0 a$. By inspection of Eq. (74) it can be seen that Y_b is an negative imaginary quantity between p_p and p_z. It is therefore a inductive susceptance and we know from the work of BIRDSALL and WHINNERY[6] that this is a necessary condition if complex pro-pagation constants, and therefore waves with exponential increase, are to be obtained. Below p_z the susceptance is capacitive and gain is, according to the above authors, impossible. We therefore propose the hypothesis that, without any reference to the actual conditions set up when circuit loss, etc., are present, travelling-wave gain is only possible for the range $p_z < p < p_p$. Practically, we would not be surprised if a much more restricted range is encountered. We also recall that p_0 lies in the operating range. This is important, for at p_0 Eq. (76) takes on the simple form

$$-\frac{(\gamma_r b)J_1(\gamma_r b)}{J_0(\gamma_r b)} = \frac{p_0 b I_1(p_0 b)}{I_0(p_0 b)} \tag{82}$$

If we assume that the condition for optimum operation is $p_0 b =$

$\beta_e \cdot b$, then Eq. (82) can be solved for $\gamma_r b$ and we can obtain a space-charge reduction factor

$$F_H^2 = \frac{1}{1 + [(\gamma_{rH} \cdot b)/(\beta \cdot b)]^2} \tag{83}$$

Equation (82) has no solutions in the range $\gamma_r b < 2.405$, so that even the first space-charge reduction factor determined from Eq. (83) is less than the value obtained for a similarly disposed drift tube.† Finally, we note that when pa is less than $p_z a$, $\phi(p, a)$ is positive and increasing quite rapidly. K_1 and K_0 both increase as their arguments decrease so that it soon becomes permissible to approximate Eq. (76) by

$$\gamma_r b \frac{J_1(\gamma_r b)}{J_0(\gamma_r b)} = \frac{pb K_1(pb)}{K_0(pb)} \tag{84}$$

Equation (84) will be recognized as the determinantal equation for a beam of radius b in a drift tube of infinite radius, that is, of the beam in free space. Thus, when the electron velocity is above the upper limit for travelling-wave tube gain, the space-charge waves set up have the propagation constants of those of the same beam in free space.

Fig. 10 shows plots of $\lambda J_1(\lambda)/J_0(\lambda)$, $\lambda K_1(\lambda)/K_0(\lambda)$, $-\lambda I_1(\lambda)/I_0(\lambda)$ from which the solutions of Eqs. (82) and (84) and the corresponding values of F can be calculated. However, these values of F only relate to certain special cases and in particular we have assumed in their derivation that p is a real number, whereas in the range of amplification it is obviously complex. This may well influence the behaviour of the solution. The main point brought out so far is that the space-charge reduction factor depends now on the propagation constant in a much more complicated way than in the drift tube case. Moreover, since we have shown that the R.H.S. of Eq. (76) goes from a zero to a pole in a range comparable with the interaction range, we have also shown that an expansion of the r.f. current in a set of orthogonal modes is impossible, for Eq. (76) obviously does not satisfy the necessary boundary condition, Eq. (24).

Little work appears to have been done on the higher space-charge modes, with the exception of a little-known paper by RYDBECK.[10] Some interesting relations are derived by Rydbeck and we now quote these.

---

† This solution gives rise to a field variation with a node. It is therefore a higher order wave. Other solutions exist for complex valves of p.

[10] RYDBECK; *A.E.Ü.*, 1953, 7, 409.

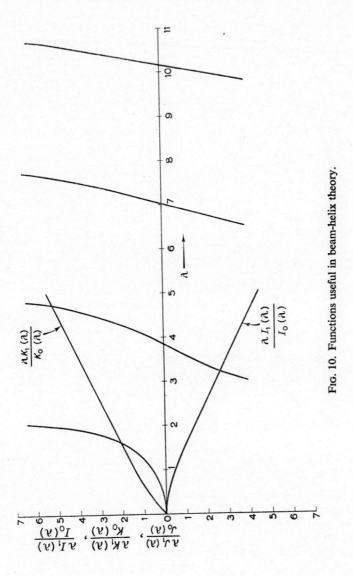

Fig. 10. Functions useful in beam-helix theory.

Write $\phi(pa) = G(pa)[I_0(pa)/K_0(pa)]$ and $F(\gamma_r b) = (\gamma_r b)[J_1(\gamma_r b)/J_0(\gamma_r b)]$ then by solving Eq. (76) for $\phi(pa)$ and multiplying both sides of the result by $F(\gamma_r.b) - pb[K_1(pb)/K_0(pb)]$ we obtain

$$G(pa)\left\{F(\gamma_r b) - pb\frac{K_1(pb)}{K_0(pb)}\right\} = \frac{I_0(pb)K_0(pa)}{K_0(pb)I_0(pa)}\left\{F(\gamma_r b) + \frac{pbI_1(gb)}{I_0(pb)}\right\}$$

(85)

Rydbeck considers the L.H.S. of this equation as representing the perturbation of the uncoupled helix waves $G(p_0a) = 0$ and the uncoupled beam waves $\{F(\gamma_r b) - [pbK_1(pb)/K_0(pb)]\} = 0$. The first term on the R.H.S. is simply a geometrical factor influencing the tightness of the coupling. Again, Rydbeck writes

$$\psi(\gamma_r b) = \frac{J_0(\gamma_r b)}{pb}\left\{F(\gamma_r b) + \frac{pbI_1(pb)}{I_0(pb)}\right\} = \frac{\gamma_r b}{pb}J_1(\gamma_r b) + \frac{I_1(pb)}{I_0(pb)}J_0(\gamma_r b)$$

(86)

Now, the R.H.S. of Eq. (86) is very similar to the function derived in Eq. (27). In fact, we can easily show that

$$\psi(\gamma_r b) = \frac{1 + \gamma_r^2 b^2/\beta_e^2 b^2}{pbI_0(pb)}\int_0^{pb} prI_0(pr)J_0(\gamma_r.r)\,\mathrm{d}(pr) \qquad (87)$$

The integral clearly represents an interaction integral between the space-charge waves and the circuit waves. Similarly

$$F(\gamma_r b) - \frac{pbK_1(pb)}{K_0(pb)}$$

$$= -\frac{1}{J_0(\gamma_r b)K_0(pb)}\left\{1 - \left(1 + \frac{\gamma_r^2 b^2}{p^2 b^2}\right)\int_0^{pb} prK_0(pr)J_0(\gamma_r.r)\,\mathrm{d}(pr)\right\}$$

(88)

Then for the beam in free space we have

$$1 = \left(1 + \frac{\gamma_r^2 b^2}{p^2 b^2}\right)\int_0^{pb} prK_0(pr)J_0(\gamma_r.r)\,\mathrm{d}(pr) \qquad (89)$$

Equation (89) is an integral equation, which only has solutions for particular values of the multiplier $(1 + \gamma_r^2 b^2/p^2 b^2) = 1/F^2$. In this instance the integral equation is trivial as the functions under the integral are determined. In a more general case we should not know, for example, that the correct function of $(\gamma_r.r)$ was $J_0(\gamma_r.r)$ but instead have an indeterminate kernel $K(\gamma_r.r)$. Then, normal techniques for the solution of integral equations of the Fredholm type would provide the eigenvalues and eigenfunctions.

If we put Eq. (88) and (89) into Eq. (85) we find

$$1 = \frac{1}{F^2}\left[\int_0^{pb} prK_0(pr)J_0(\gamma_r.r)\,\mathrm{d}(pr) + \right.$$
$$\left. + \frac{K_0(pa)}{G(pa)I_0(pa)}\int_0^{pb} prI_0(pr)J_0(\gamma_r.r)\,\mathrm{d}(pr)\right] \quad (90)$$

as the general integral equation for our problem.

Rydbeck does not attempt the solution by integral equation methods but by approximation using infinite products. We do not follow him further because he makes assumptions which are valid only for beams of diameters much greater than those now used.

We have now reached a point at which further general discussion of the T.W.A. is impossible until we have developed relations more appropriately derived when we come to the detailed description of its operation.

6

SPACE-CHARGE WAVES IN KLYSTRONS

WE BEGIN the study of the application of space-charge wave theory to actual valve structures by considering klystron amplifiers. These constitute an especially simple example and one which is also of practical importance; for modern klystrons are capable of giving higher powers than are available from any other known type of tube. As we shall see, it is easy to obtain high values of gain but the bandwidth is relatively limited, although this defect can be overcome to a limited extent by the circuit technique of stagger tuning, as carried out in I.F. amplifiers.

6.1. TWO-RESONATOR AMPLIFIER, SINGLE-MODE THEORY

The basic amplifier, shown in Fig. 1, consists of two resonators coupled to a single beam carrying a current I_0 at a d.c. voltage V_0. The beam entering the first gap is free of either current or velocity modulation. The voltage $V_1 \exp(j\omega t)$ established across the first gap

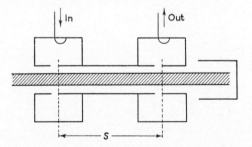

FIG. 1. Schematic two-resonator klystron amplifier.

causes velocity modulation of the beam. The action of the drift space converts the velocity modulation into convection current modulation. The second resonator, spaced s metres in the z direction from the first, then receives an induced current $M . i_c$ which flows through the parallel impedance of the resonator and creates a voltage V_2, which tends to slow down all the electrons present in the output gap during the negative half-cycle. The beam loses kinetic energy in the output gap. This energy is gained by the output resonator in the form of a.c. power so the device converts the part of the d.c. energy supplied by the battery into a.c. Apart from the main conversion of d.c. into a.c. there are interchanges of a.c. power. The unmodulated beam damps the input resonator because, although the transit angle across the gap is short ($< \pi$), the modulation process still takes up a small amount of power from the beam. Exactly the same thing happens in the output gap, the higher voltage V_2 remodulates the electron beam, and if the r.f. current is looked upon as a small perturbation the loss of power must be given by the same laws as in the first gap. More exact analysis shows that this is a good approximation for greater current modulations.

In this treatment we let the cold loss resistance of the cavity be R_c, the beam impedance $R_0 = V_0/I_0$ and the beam loading† $= 2R_0/MM'$. Then, the conductance of the cavity in parallel with the beam loss conductance is

$$G_T = \frac{1}{R_c} + \frac{MM'}{2R_0} \tag{1}$$

We assume small signal conditions and that the input and output feeders are matched to the transformed values of G_T so that there are no standing waves on either feeder. The loaded conductance of the output resonator is $2G_T$ and we assume that the gap dimensions are identical in the two resonators. The space-charge wave matrix, Eq. (104) of Chapter 4 gives the required information as to the r.f. current produced by the input voltage V_1, which creates an initial kinetic voltage of MV_1. Then,

$$\begin{vmatrix} V_2 \\ i_2 \end{vmatrix} = \begin{vmatrix} \cos Z_1 & jZ_0 \sin Z_1 \\ \dfrac{j \sin Z_1}{Z_0} & \cos Z_1 \end{vmatrix} \begin{vmatrix} MV_1 \\ i_{10} \end{vmatrix} \tag{2}$$

and $i_{10} = \rho_0 u_{10} = MV_1 . \tfrac{1}{2}R_0$.

Since we are working with a.c. amplitudes and not R.M.S. values, the power input is simply

$$W_{\text{in}} = \frac{V_1^2 G_T}{2} \tag{3}$$

---

† See Section 4.10.1 for the present symbols.

and
$$W_{\text{out}} = \frac{M^2 i_2 \cdot i_2{}^*}{4G_T} \tag{4}$$

but only half of this power appears as useful output across the load. The power gain is thus

$$G = \frac{M^2 i_2 \cdot i_2{}^*}{4V_1{}^2 \cdot G_T{}^2} = \frac{M^4}{4G_T{}^2}\left[\frac{\sin^2 Z_1}{Z_0{}^2} + \frac{\cos^2 Z_1}{4R_0{}^2}\right] \tag{5}$$

or, since,
$$Z_0{}^2 = 4R_0{}^2 \cdot \frac{F^2 \omega_p{}^2}{\omega^2}$$

$$G = \frac{M^4}{16R_0{}^2 G_T{}^2}\left[\frac{\omega^2 \sin^2 Z_1}{F^2 \omega_p{}^2} + \cos^2 Z_1\right] \tag{6}$$

If, as is usual, $\omega/F\omega_p \gg 1$ the first term in Eq. (6) is much bigger than the second. If this is the case, $Z_1 = F\omega_p z/u_0$ should be made equal to $\pi/2$ for $z = s$, to obtain the maximum gain and

$$G = 20 \log_{10}\left(\frac{M^2 \omega}{4R_0 F\omega_p G_T}\right)\ \mathrm{d}B$$

The condition for gain is obviously that the bracketed term should exceed unity.

Since these space-charge wave results are only valid for small signals and include no information which would allow us to calculate the maximum power output, it is natural to enquire if the Webster theory[1] can be extended to include the space-charge wave modifications. This can be done as follows:—In the Webster theory, the time of arrival at the second resonator of an electron which passed through the centre line of the buncher at $t = t_0$ is

$$t_2 = t_0 + \frac{s}{u_0 + u_{10} \sin \omega t_0} \tag{7}$$

since the a.c. velocity is supposed to be constant in the drift tube. Here, the a.c. velocity $u_1 = u_{10} \cos Z_1$. Let $S_1 = F\omega_p s/u_0$. Then the analogue of Eq. (7) is

$$t_2 = t_0 + \frac{s}{u_0 + 1/S_1 \int_0^{S_1} u_{10} \cos \zeta\, \mathrm{d}\zeta}$$

or
$$t_2 = t_0 + \frac{s}{u_0 + u_{10} (\sin S_1)/S_1 \sin \omega t_0} \tag{8}$$

---

[1] BECK; *Thermionic Valves*, p.363. Cambridge University Press, 1953.

i.e., the average a.c. velocity is lower than the initial a.c. velocity by the ratio $(\sin S_1)/S_1$. With this alteration the Webster theory can be applied exactly as before and we find that the a.c. current can be expanded as a Fourier series.

$$i_2 = I_0\left[1 + 2\sum_1^\infty J_m\left(\frac{mS\alpha M}{2}\frac{\sin S_1}{S_1}\right)\cos m(\omega t_2 - S)\right] \qquad (9)$$

However, Eq. (9) is only valid so long as the assumption of no overtaking is obeyed, i.e., until $dt_2/dt_0 = 1$ or, in other words, until the argument of the Bessel function reaches unity. The peak value of the fundamental component of the current wave then has the value $2I_0J_1(1{\cdot}0) = 0{\cdot}88I_0$. This value leads to an electronic efficiency of 44% and to output efficiencies from 22% upwards, depending on the valve parameters in the manner detailed by BECK.[2] This is distinctly encouraging since it indicates that, with high-powered valves, in which R_0 is small and the circuit losses are a small proportion of the beam losses, efficiencies of up to about 40% can be forecast without invalidating the basic assumptions of our theory. We do not, moreover, wish to imply that the efficiency ceases to increase with increasing α beyond this point, but merely that it will increase at a different, probably slower, rate.

Let us, for a moment, consider the fundamental component of Eq. (9). Inserting the explicit value of M for single-mode theory, we have

$$i_2 = 2I_0J_1\left(\frac{S\alpha}{2}\cdot\frac{J_0(L/2)I_0(R)}{I_0(A)}\frac{\sin S_1}{S_1}\right) \qquad (10)$$

Equation (10) shows that i_2 is not constant over the beam but depends on the radius through the $I_0(R)$ factor. The current induced in the output resonator is Mi_2. If we make a usual small-signal assumption and put $J_1(X) \doteq X/2$ and average over the beam we merely recover the factor $\langle M^2\rangle$ and the treatment leads to the results already given in Chapter 5. If we do not do this we have to average over the beam and obtain an integral of the form

$$\int_0^A rI_0(R)J_1(KI_0(R))\,dr$$

or, if we limit ourselves to the case in which $KI_0(A) = 1{\cdot}0$

$$\int_0^A rI_0(R)J_1\left(\frac{I_0(R)}{I_0A}\right)dr \qquad (11)$$

---

[2] BECK; *Velocity Modulated Thermionic Tubes*, p. 81. Cambridge University Press, 1948.

Table 1 gives some values of this function and compares them with the results of taking $\langle M^2 \rangle$. The results are different for small values of A but tend to the small-signal results as A gets larger. This is understandable since $J_1(X) \to X/2$ as $X \to 0$.

TABLE 1

Comparison between Eq. (11) and the mean square coupling coefficient

A	Eq. (11)	$\langle M^2 \rangle$
0·5	0·85	0·94
1·0	0·72	0·80
1·5	0·59	0·64
2·0	0·48	0·51

To summarize, space-charge wave theory differs sharply from the Webster theory in that it gives a maximum length for the drift tube, beyond which the gain decreases instead of increasing. This length is very nearly $s = (\pi/2)(u_0/F\omega_p)$, or one quarter space-charge wavelength. The effect of the cosinusoidal variation in the a.c. velocity along the draft tube can easily be taken over into the Webster theory resulting in a somewhat lower value of r.f. current for any given distances along the tunnel. The requirement that no overtaking of electrons should be allowed limits the validity of this modified theory to the range of α defined by $\alpha < (2/SM)(S_1/\sin S_1)$, but this does not restrict the theory to unduly small signals.

In conclusion, let us return to the gain expression in Eq. (6) and convert it into the symbols used elsewhere.[1] It is easily shown that the klystron parameter P, used there, is equivalent to $4R_0 G_T/M^2$ in the present notation. The normalized drift length $S = \omega s/u_0$ is to be reduced to $S(\sin S_1)/S_1$ or at optimum, $S_{\text{opt}} = \omega/F\omega_p \cdot 2/\pi$. Thus, the present analysis gives

$$G = 2P \log_{10} \left\{ \frac{S(\sin S_1/S_1)}{P} \right\} \tag{12}$$

instead of $20 \log_{10}(S/P)$, for the maximum gain at small signals. This is, of course, what we should expect from the remarks already made on the comparison of the analyses.

6.2. TWO-RESONATOR AMPLIFIER, MULTI-MODE THEORY

There is no difficulty in writing down the small-signal gain in this case, because the necessary results for the current induced in the output gap can be taken from Chapter 5. Equation (4) (of this Chapter) must be written

$$W_{\text{out}} = \frac{i_T \cdot i_T{}^*}{4G_T}$$

since M is already taken into account in Eq. (18) of Chapter 5. Still neglecting the correction due to the finite value of i_{10}, we find the gain is now given by

$$G = 20 \log_{10}\left(\frac{\omega J_0{}^2(L/2)F(\omega_p, z)}{4GR_0\omega_p}\right)$$

$$= 20 \log_{10}\left(\frac{\omega/\omega_p J_0{}^2(L/2)F(\omega_p, z)}{M^2 P}\right) \qquad (13)$$

where the M^2 is to be understood as the average overall gap factor as used in calculating P (BECK[1]). The appropriate value of $F(\omega_p, z)$ for the system under consideration is to be taken from curves similar to those given in Chapter 5, which already cover a wide range of situations of practical interest. It is to be noted that the gain depends on ω/ω_p as well as on $F(\omega_p, z)$. This means that changes in beam geometry which alter the plasma frequency alter the multiplier or, in other words $F(\omega_p, z)$ is only a measure of relative gain at fixed ω_p and therefore designs with high values of $F(\omega_p, z)$ do not necessarily give the highest overall gains. Inspection of Fig. (4) in Chapter 5 shows that Eq. (11) gives somewhat greater values of optimum gain than does Eq. (6), and also greater values of optimum drift length. The increase is only a matter of 2 dB in a two-cavity amplifier but is much more important in multiple-cavity tubes, as we shall see later.

Turning now to the connexion with the Webster theory, we use the series expression for the a.c. velocity taken from the last chapter. Term by term integration of the series is permissible, under canonical conditions. To be concrete, let us take again the case of the beam filling the tunnel. The a.c. velocity is given by Eq. (13) of Chapter 5 and integration from $0 \rightarrow s$ gives

$$\langle u_2 \rangle = \frac{\alpha u_0}{2} J_0\left(\frac{L}{2}\right) \sum_n \frac{2\lambda_n}{A^2 + \lambda_n{}^2} \frac{J_0(\lambda_n r/a)}{J_1(\lambda_n)} \frac{\sin S_n}{S_n} \qquad (14)$$

which is used in Eq. (7) to obtain a result analogous to Eq. (9).

If the d.c. beam current density is $J_0(= I_0/\pi a^2)$, the current in an annulus of thickness Δr at radius r is,

$$i_2(r) = 2J_0 \cdot \pi r \Delta r \cdot \left[1 + 2 \sum_{m=1}^{\infty} J_m\left(\frac{mS\alpha}{2} \cdot J_0 \left(\frac{L}{2} \right) \right. \right.$$

$$\left. \left. \times \sum_{n=1}^{\infty} \frac{2\lambda_n}{A^2 + \lambda_n^2} \frac{J_0(\lambda_n r/a)}{J_1(\lambda_n)} \frac{\sin S_n}{S_n} \right) \cos m(\omega t_2 - S) \right] \quad (15)$$

and the corresponding value of the fundamental component is

$$4J_0 \cdot \pi r \Delta r J_1\left(\frac{S\alpha}{2} J_0\left(\frac{L}{2} \right) \sum_n \frac{2\lambda_n}{A^2 + \lambda_n^2} \frac{J_0(\lambda_n r/a)}{J_1(\lambda_n)} \frac{\sin S_n}{S_n} \right) \quad (16)$$

The gap coupling factor for this annulus of current is $J_0(L/2)I_0(R)/I_0(A)$ and the total current induced by the beam into the resonator becomes:—

$$i_2 = \frac{4I_0}{a^2} \frac{J_0(L/2)}{I_0(A)} \int_0^a I_0(R)J_1(F(R))r \, \mathrm{d}r \quad (17)$$

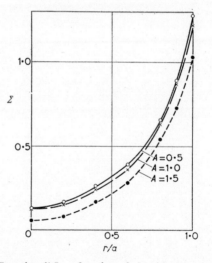

FIG. 2. Equation (16) as function of r/a with A as parameter.

To illustrate these results the series in Eq. (16) has been evaluated as a function of r/a, for several values of A as parameter, at an axial distance S from the origin which is known from the small-signal multi-mode theory to give rise to the first maximum in the small-signal r.f. current. These results are shown in Fig. 2. Then $\alpha J_0(L/2)$ is chosen so as to make the argument of $J_1\{F(R)\}$ unity at the edge of the beam, $r/a = 1$. In physical terms this means that conditions are chosen so that the limiting small-signal case is reached at the beam edge, but nowhere else. This, together with the results of Fig. 2, determines $J_1\{F(R)\}$ everywhere. This quantity is then multiplied by $rI_0(R)$ and the integration of Eq. (17) is carried out numerically. The integrand of Eq. (17) is shown, in normalized form, in Fig. 3, where the integrand $0.44RI_0(R)$ appropriate to the assumption of a uniform velocity distribution is also shown.† The

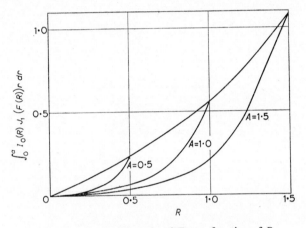

FIG. 3. Integrand of Equation (17) as a function of R.

integrand of Eq. (17) is, apart from the factor $I_0(R)$, which is not very much different from unity over the range considered, the r.f. beam current as a function of radius. Fig. (3) therefore shows that the current decreases sharply towards the beam centre so that about two-thirds of the r.f. current is in the annulus for which $r/a > 0.7$. The situation is somewhat analogous to the skin effect phenomenon on a metallic conductor but the physical causes are different, as one of the major variables is the ratio of beam diameter to tunnel diameter. If the beam had been made small in comparison with the tunnel the fields and velocities would be nearly uniform

† My thanks are due to my colleague Mr. P. E. Deering, for his painstaking evaluation of the very tedious alternating series involved. He is also responsible for many of the curves in Chapter 5.

over the beam and the effect would be much less marked. This is not to be taken as an argument for the actual use of fine beams in large tunnels, to which there are overriding objections. Table 2 shows $i_2 \div 2I_0 J_0(L/2)$ evaluated in three different ways. First, by the use of Eq. (17), second, from the small-signal theory of Chapter 5, Eq. (18) and Fig. 4 and last from the Webster theory, i.e., $i_2 = 2I_0 \times 0.44\langle M \rangle$, where M is the overall gap-coupling factor.

TABLE 2

Normalized output current, according to three different analyses

A	Eq. (17)	Small signal	Webster
0·5	0·21	0·23	0·43
1·0	0·20	0·21	0·39
1·5	0·19	0·20	0·34

The quantity tabulated in Table 2 is closely related to the efficiency and it is actually equal to the efficiency when the circuit has zero losses and the catcher voltage is just equal to the d.c. beam voltage. It will be seen that the results from the present section differ inappreciably from those of the small-signal theory but both are only about half those of the Webster theory. It is rather hard to say what precise statement one can make as to the limiting efficiency. The above results are worked out on a particular assumption about the maximum velocity given to the edge electrons; if this velocity were increased somewhat, the r.f. current at the edge of the beam would not be as high as the revised calculation would indicate, but the new calculation would be valid over the inner part of the beam and the efficiency would go up. On the whole it seems likely that the results in Table 2 must be restricted to relate to gain and efficiency at a particular value of drive voltage and not extended too far. It is also interesting that the value of A has very little bearing on the results of this section. The mathematical reason for this is that A only influences the first few terms of the series, for which λ_n is fairly small and with alternating series of this type, the first few terms have little effect on the final sum.

As a final comment on this subject, it is worth noting that the a.c. velocity never becomes negative in the results considered. However, for slightly greater values of S than those used above, the first term of the series changes sign and the axial velocity first drops to zero and then becomes negative. When this is the case, one would be better off without the central part of the beam. The drift distance can be chosen for maximum gain without reaching this condition.

6.3.   THREE-CAVITY AMPLIFIER, SINGLE-MODE THEORY

We next take up the discussion of the three-cavity klystron on the basis of a simple space-charge wave theory, assuming that only one mode is appreciably excited by the initial gap. Since we shall need to introduce the cavity voltage, now and in subsequent sections, it will prove more convenient to use U's for the kinetic voltages on the beam and V's for the peak r.f. cavity voltages. Thus if V_n is the voltage on the nth cavity and i_n is the r.f. beam current at the centre of the cavity we have

$$V_n = -Mi_n\left(\frac{1}{R_c} + \frac{1}{R_b} + \frac{1}{R_L}\right)^{-1} = \frac{-i_nM}{G_{Tn}} \qquad (18)$$

where R_c = parallel cavity resistance

R_b = beam loading resistance, calculated as shown elsewhere[3]

R_L = load resistance if present, transformed into cavity.

If we put $(1/R_c + 1/R_b)^{-1} = G$, then for a matched load which is the normal small-signal condition, $G_T = 2G$. We recall that the kinetic voltage is defined as u_0/η times the a.c. velocity, u_1, so that at the first gap we have

$$U_1 = \frac{u_0}{\eta} \cdot u_1 = MV_1 \qquad (19)$$

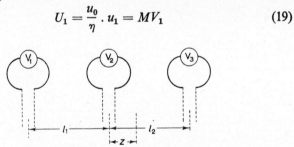

FIG. 4. Notation for klystron amplifier.

The rest of the notation is shown in Fig. 4, $L_1 = F\omega_p l/u_0$, $Z_1 = F\omega_p z/u_0$, etc. We now write down the expression for the kinetic

---

[3] BECK; *Thermionic Valves*, Chapter 12, Section 4. Cambridge University Press, 1953.

voltage and beam current at z, which is between the second and output resonators. We find

$$
\begin{vmatrix} U_3 \\ i_3 \end{vmatrix} = \begin{vmatrix} \cos(L_1 + Z_1) & jZ_0 \sin(L_1 + Z_1) \\ j\dfrac{\sin(L_1 + Z_1)}{Z_0} & \cos(L_1 + Z_1) \end{vmatrix} \begin{vmatrix} MV_1 \\ 0 \end{vmatrix} +
$$

$$
+ \begin{vmatrix} \cos Z_1 & jZ_0 \sin Z_1 \\ j\dfrac{\sin Z_1}{Z_0} & \cos Z_1 \end{vmatrix} \begin{vmatrix} -\dfrac{i_2 M^2}{G_{T2}} \\ 0 \end{vmatrix} \tag{20}
$$

and i_2 is given by Eq. (2) where we, for simplicity, take $i_{10} = 0$. Inserting i_2 into Eq. (20) and carrying out the operations we easily find

$$
\begin{vmatrix} U_3 \\ i_3 \end{vmatrix} = \begin{vmatrix} \cos(L_1 + Z_1) & -j\dfrac{\sin L_1 \cos Z_1}{G_{T2} \cdot Z_0} M^2 \\ j\dfrac{\sin(L_1 + Z_1)}{Z_0} & \dfrac{M^2 \sin Z_1 \sin L_1}{G_{T2} \cdot Z_0{}^2} \end{vmatrix} \begin{vmatrix} U_1 \\ U_1 \end{vmatrix} \tag{21}
$$

The power input is $W_{in} = V_1{}^2 G/2$. The total power output is $Mi_3{}^2/2G_{T3}$, but if the load is matched, only half of this appears as useful power, in the load. Thus the power gain A is

$$
\frac{M^2 i_3{}^2}{2G_{T3} \cdot G \cdot V_1{}^2} = \frac{M^4 i_3{}^2}{2G_{T3} \cdot G \cdot U_1{}^2} \tag{22}
$$

or, from Eq. (21)

$$
A = \frac{M^4}{2G_{T3} \cdot G} \left| j\frac{\sin(L_1 + Z_1)}{Z_0} + \frac{M^2 \sin Z_1 \sin L_1}{G_{T2} \cdot Z_0{}^2} \right|^2
$$

$$
= 10 \log_{10}\left\{ \frac{M^4}{2G_{T3} \cdot G} \left(\frac{\sin^2(L_1 + Z_1)}{Z_0{}^2} + \frac{M^4 \sin^2 Z_1 \sin^2 L_1}{G_{T2}{}^2 \cdot Z_0{}^4} \right) \right\} \mathrm{dB} \tag{23}
$$

Equation (23) is the general expression for the gain to a resonator located at Z_1. We now consider some special cases. The first is that for which $l_1 = l_2$ and the centre cavity is not loaded, i.e., $G_1 = G = G_{T2}$, and the ouput is matched, $G_{T3} = 2G$. Then,

$$
A = 10 \log_{10} \left\{ \frac{M^4}{4G^2} \left(\frac{\sin^2 2L_1}{Z_0{}^2} + \frac{M^4 \sin^4 L_1}{G^2 \cdot Z_0{}^4} \right) \right\} \tag{24}
$$

In such a case one would normally choose l_1 so that $L_1 = \pi/2$ and A then simplifies to

$$A_{\pi/2} = 10 \log_{10} \frac{M^8}{4G^4 Z_0{}^4} = 40 \log_{10} \frac{M^2}{\sqrt{2} G Z_0} \qquad (25)$$

The question then arises as to whether Eq. (25), which gives the maximum gain for each stage, gives the maximum overall gain. To investigate this let $L_2 = \pi/2 + \delta$. Equation (23) then gives

$$A = A_{\pi/2} + 10 \log_{10} (G^2 Z_0{}^2 \sin^2 \delta + M^4 \cos^2 \delta) \qquad (26)$$

When the term in the bracket exceeds unity Eq. (26) gives more gain than Eq. (25) and vice versa. This clearly depends mainly on the value of $G^2 Z_0{}^2$, which in turn depends on the design parameters. However, in normal valves $M^2/\sqrt{(2)}G Z_0 \doteqdot 10$ and Eq. (26) represents a loss and not a gain.

From the results of the first section of this chapter we see that the gain of 2 two-cavity amplifiers in cascade is

$$40 \log_{10} \frac{M^2}{2 G Z_0} \qquad (27)$$

Here, we do somewhat better since the centre cavity is not loaded, in fact the difference is 6 dB. As the three-cavity tube is simpler to use, its advantages are very great.

6.4.   MULTICAVITY KLYSTRONS

At the moment, a great deal of interest is taken in the performance of klystrons with more than three cavities because such tubes can be given a bandwidth of at least a few per cent by the circuit technique of staggering. This means that the resonant frequencies of the intermediate cavities are off-set from the mid-band frequency and their Q's are adjusted by loading to predetermined values. If this is properly done a frequency characteristic with a flat top and steep sides is obtained just as in an I.F. amplifier. The klystron theory is, however, a good deal more complicated, because the gain function of each stage is not independent of that in the preceding stages. An example of this is Eq. (24) which clearly contains terms, those in $\sin 2L_1$, due to the first gap as well as the term from the second gap. In this simple case it is possible to choose L_1 so as to make $\sin 2L_1$ vanish and therefore attain a condition of independence. Another difficulty is the possible difference between the cavity resonances and Q's which prevents us from utilizing matrix methods, for these are only of value in that it is easy to raise a matrix to any desired power but very cumbersome to multiply out n different matrices. For these reasons we base our analysis on Fig. 5. Here, no attention has been paid to vertical scale. The cavities, indicated as perfect grids are shown displaced. Each cavity originates, on single-mode theory, a pair of space-charge waves, of which only the current wave influences the later cavities. The total current exciting a particular cavity is the sum of all the currents evaluated on the vertical line through the cavity centre.

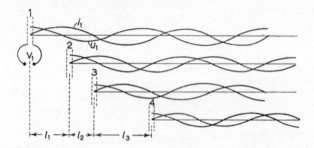

FIG. 5. The current velocity waves in a multicavity klystron.

We continue to use the short gap assumptions implicit in the last section, viz., the current and kinetic voltage waves are continuous at a gap but at each gap a new velocity, and consequently a new current wave, of initial amplitude MV_n, where V_n = voltage on nth cavity, is set up. We put $MV_n = U_n$. V_n is given by $-M$ times the sum of the current waves from all the preceding cavities. The distances between cavities are assumed different and the loaded admittance of the nth cavity is Y_n. In general

$$Y_n = Y_{cn} + G_b \qquad (28)$$

where Y_{cn} is the admittance of the nth cavity, which may include an external load. We write i_n for the amplitude of the current wave originating at the nth cavity. Then

$$i_n = j\frac{U_n}{Z_0} \qquad (29)$$

If we assume a matched load coupled to the output cavity the overall gain is simply

$$\frac{W_0}{W_i} = \frac{1}{2}\left|\frac{1}{Y_n \cdot Y_1}\right| \left|\frac{M i_T}{V_1}\right|^2 = \frac{M^4}{2}\left|\frac{1}{Y_n \cdot Y_1}\right| \left|\frac{i_T}{U_1}\right|^2 \quad (30)$$

where i_T is the sum of all the currents driving the last gap, evaluated in the beam. Thus we have now to evaluate i_T in terms of U_1. Starting with i_1 we have

$$i_1(z) = j\frac{U_1}{Z_0} \sin Z_1 \quad (31)$$

Therefore, the current driving the second cavity

$$= j\frac{M U_1}{Z_0} \sin L_1$$

Therefore

$$U_2 = -j\frac{M^2 U_1}{Y_2 Z_0} \sin L_1$$

and

$$i_2 = \frac{M^2 U_1}{Y_2 Z_0^2} \sin L_1 \quad (32)$$

The current driving the third cavity

$$= M[i_1 \sin (L_1 + L_2) + i_2 \sin L_2] -$$

$$- j\frac{U_1 M}{Z_0} \sin (L_1 + L_2) + \frac{M^3 U_1}{Y_2 Z_0^2} \sin L_1 \sin L_2 \quad (33)$$

$$\therefore \quad U_3 = -\frac{M U_1}{Y_3}\left(\frac{jM \sin (L_1 + L_2)}{Z_0} + \frac{M^3}{Y_2 Z_0^2} \sin L_1 \sin L_2\right) \quad (34)$$

$$i_3 = U_1\left(\frac{M^2 \sin (L_1 + L_2)}{Y_3 Z_0^2} - j\frac{M^4}{Y_2 Y_3 Z_0^3} \sin L_1 \sin L_2\right) \quad (35)$$

The current driving the fourth cavity is:—

$$[i_1 \sin (L_1 + L_2 + L_3) + i_2 \sin (L_2 + L_3) + i_3 \sin L_3]$$

$$= U_1\left[\frac{j}{Z_0} \sin (L_1 + L_2 + L_3) + \frac{M^2}{Y_2 Z_0^2} \sin L_1 \sin (L_2 + L_3) + \right.$$

$$\left. + \frac{M^2 \sin (L_1 + L_2) \sin L_3}{Y_3 Z_0^2} - j\frac{M^4}{Y_2 Y_3 Z_0^3} \sin L_1 \sin L_2 \sin L_3\right] \quad (36)$$

The gain of a four-cavity klystron then depends on the square of the modulus of the bracketed term on the R.H.S. of Eq. (36). This can be made much simpler if we take $L_1 = L_2 = L_3$. The result is

$$\frac{i_T}{U_1} = j\frac{\sin 3L}{Z_0} + \frac{M^2}{Z_0^2}\sin L \sin 2L\left(\frac{1}{Y_2} + \frac{1}{Y_3}\right) - j\frac{M^4}{Y_2 Y_3 Z_0^3}\sin^3 L \tag{37}$$

If $L = \pi/2$, $\sin L = 1$, $\sin 2L = 0$, $\sin 3L = -1$

$$\frac{i_T}{U_1} = -\frac{j}{Z_0} - j\frac{M^4}{Y_2 Y_3 Z_0^3} \tag{38}$$

and the gain is

$$\frac{M^4}{2}\left|\frac{1}{Y_4 \cdot Y_1}\right|\left|\frac{1}{Z_0} + \frac{M^4}{Y_2 Y_3 Z_0^3}\right|^2 \tag{39}$$

Equation (39) clearly depends on the frequency characteristics of all four cavities but the tuning of the intermediate cavities can be adjusted independently of the input and output cavities. Naturally, this condition only relates to single-mode theory.

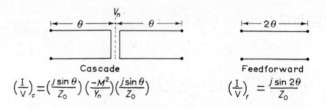

$$\left(\frac{I}{V}\right)_c = \left(\frac{j\sin\theta}{Z_0}\right)\left(\frac{-M^2}{Y_n}\right)\left(\frac{j\sin\theta}{Z_0}\right) \qquad \left(\frac{I}{V}\right)_f = \frac{j\sin 2\theta}{Z_0}$$

Fig. 6. The two-gain mechanisms.

The calculation of the gain for more resonators is equally straightforward but is, naturally, very tedious. The results analogous to Eq. (37) may, however, be written down directly, using the following observations, due to BERS.[4] By examination of the processes leading to Eq. (37) it may be observed that there are two gain mechanisms operative, the "cascade" mechanism and the "feed forward"

[4] BERS; *M.I.T. Quarterly Progress Report*, October 15, 1956.

mechanism. These are illustrated in Fig. 6. The terms in Eq. (37) represent

1st. Feedforward gain over two cavities at a time.

2nd. Feedforward gain over one cavity at a time.

3rd. Cascade gain for both central cavities.

We can now write down the ratio i_T/U_1 for a five-cavity klystron. This is done in a long-winded manner so as to illustrate the process. The resonator spacings are assumed equal but the resonator parameters are not identical.

The cascade gain term is

$$\frac{-M^6}{Z_0{}^4}\frac{\sin^4 L}{Y_2 Y_3 Y_4}$$

There are three terms due to feedforward gain from pairs of cavities with the third cavity detuned.   The sum is

$$-j\frac{M^4}{Z_0{}^3}\sin^2 L \sin 2L\left(\frac{1}{Y_2 Y_3}+\frac{1}{Y_2 Y_4}+\frac{1}{Y_3 Y_4}\right)$$

There are three terms due to feedforward gain from single cavities with the two other cavities detuned. The sum is

$$\frac{M^2}{Z_0{}^2}\sin L \sin 3L\left(\frac{1}{Y_2}+\frac{1}{Y_4}\right)+\frac{M^2}{Z_0{}^2}\frac{\sin^2 2L}{Y_3}$$

Finally feedforward over the whole length gives

$$j\frac{\sin 4L}{Z_0}$$

Collecting terms

$$\frac{i_{T(5)}}{U_1}=\left[-\frac{M^6}{Z_0{}^4}\frac{\sin^4 L}{Y_2 Y_3 Y_4}+\frac{M^2}{Z_0{}^2}\left\{\sin L \sin 3L\left(\frac{1}{Y_2}+\frac{1}{Y_4}\right)+\frac{\sin^2 2L}{Y_3}\right\}+\right.$$
$$\left.+j\frac{\sin 4L}{Z_0}-j\frac{M^4}{Z_0{}^3}\sin^2 L \sin 2L\left(\frac{1}{Y_2 Y_3}+\frac{1}{Y_2 Y_4}+\frac{1}{Y_3 Y_4}\right)\right] \quad (40)$$

Equation (40) has eight terms; the addition of each successive resonator doubles the number so that a six-cavity tube has to be described by 16 terms and an eight-cavity tube by 64. Such tubes have been built and it is obvious that their stagger tuning must be carried out more by art than science. The reader is left to write down the six-cavity gain as an exercise, and, if he has patience, the eight-cavity gain.

Some general considerations on the gain × bandwidth product of synchronously tuned multicavity klystrons with identical cavities have been given by MULLER[5] who writes down the current in the nth gap as the sum of all the preceding currents and then deduces from it the voltage, obtaining

$$V'_{(n)} = \zeta \sum_{k=1}^{n-1} V'_{(n-k)} \frac{\sin (n-k)L}{(n-k)L} \tag{41}$$

where

$$V_n = \exp\left(-j(n\omega l/u_0)\right)$$

$$\zeta = -j \frac{M^2 R_p}{1 + j2Q(\Delta\omega/\omega)} \cdot \frac{I_0}{2V_0} \cdot \frac{\omega l}{u_0} \tag{42}$$

Equation (41) leads to the difference equation

$$V'_{(n+2)} - \left[2\cos L + \zeta\frac{\sin L}{L}\right]V'_{(n+1)} + V'_n = 0 \tag{43}$$

If Eq. (43) is solved for $L \to 0$, we find on using the boundary conditions

$$\frac{V'_{(n)}}{V'_1} = \frac{\zeta}{2\sqrt{\zeta + \zeta^2/4}}$$

$$\times \left[\left(1 + \frac{\zeta}{2} + \sqrt{\zeta + \frac{\zeta^2}{4}}\right)^{n-1} - \left(1 + \frac{\zeta}{2} - \sqrt{\zeta + \frac{\zeta^2}{4}}\right)^{n-1}\right] \tag{44}$$

where the second term is negligible for large gain. Muller uses the limiting cases $|\zeta| \gg 1$, $|\zeta| \ll 1$ to discuss the gain bandwidth product and to show that this is, in general, smaller than that of the T.W.A. For instance, $|\zeta| \gg 1$

$$\frac{\Delta f(K)}{\Delta f(TWA)} = 3.85 C^{5/2} \exp\left(-2.78C\right) \tag{45}$$

This ratio only reaches unity when $C \doteq 0.34$ which is, of course, a very high value. However, these considerations are not really of much importance because they do not show what can be done by

---

[5] MULLER; *Onde Electrique*, 1956, **26**, 893.

circuit techniques and one would certainly not employ a synchronously tuned tube if bandwidth were important. Details of the performance of stagger-tuned klystrons are hard to come by. Muller cites an S band tube of 1·5 MW pulsed output with 40 dB gain and 3·5% Δf for four cavities. The efficiency was 30%. A pulsed T.W.A. for an output of 0·2 MW at the same frequency had a gain of 23 dB, an efficiency of 23% and a bandwidth of 9·0%. The gain × bandwidth product of these tubes is thus roughly equal in magnitude but whether either or both represents the best available performance is not known.

The literature on the technique of staggering is sparse. An E.M.I. report[6] discusses some of the more important points, but it appears to the writer that the most immediately productive technique would be to make a systematic computer study of the question, using gain expressions similar to Eq. (40). It should also be recalled that, for simplicity, we have neglected the influence of the higher order space-charge modes, which complicate the problem still further. Such neglect is justified only in the initial work.

6.5. HIGH EFFICIENCY WORKING OF MULTICAVITY KLYSTRONS

In the last section we have mainly been interested in gain and bandwidth and have implied that the cavities would usually be located roughly one quarter space-charge wavelength apart. Another possibility exists; we may operate a three-cavity klystron so as to

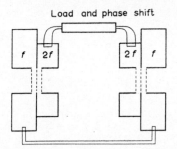

FIG. 7. A possible type of klystron with improved efficiency.

obtain the maximum output efficiency by arranging the transit angles so that more of the electrons enter the catcher during the retarding half-period than would otherwise be the case.

---

[6] KREUCHEN, AULD and DIXON; *J. Electronics*, 1957, **2**, 529.

If it were possible to bunch an electron beam with a saw-tooth voltage, then, ignoring space-charge effects, it would clearly be possible to arrange matters so that all the electrons which passed through the buncher in a cycle arrived together at the catcher and the conversion efficiency would be 100%. It is not possible to achieve saw-tooth bunching with existing circuit means but by appropriate rearrangements it is possible to approach more closely to the ideal than is the case with sinusoidal bunching. One obvious way is to couple harmonic resonators to the beam, attempting to build up the saw-tooth from a Fourier series. Fig. (7) shows an oscillator using first and second harmonics due to GUÉNARD et al.[7] This tube appears to have been built but experimental results have not been reported, leaving the practicability in some doubt. However, it was long ago pointed out by Feenberg, in unpublished work, that similar results could be obtained in a correctly adjusted three-cavity klystron. The condition required is that the voltages on the first and second cavities are not very different and that the phasing of the second cavity should be correct. The effect is clearly a non-linear one and cannot be treated by superposition of current waves. A theoretical treatment must therefore be based on a modification of the Webster theory and not on space-charge wave theory alone. This has been done by Warnecke in the reference cited. To avoid unduly complicated expressions we have to introduce several special notations. The gap spacings are l_1, l_2 and normalized become L_1, L_2. The corresponding space-charge distances $F\omega_p l_1/u_0$, $F\omega_p l_2/u_0$ are written L'_1, L'_2. ωt_0, ωt_2, ωt_3 are replaced by the phases θ_0, θ_2, θ_3. The phase of arrival at the centre of the catcher gap is given by

$$\theta_3 = \theta_2 + \frac{l_2}{u_0 + u_{10}\left[\sin(L'_1 + L'_2)/L'_1 + L'_2\right]\sin\theta_0 + } \qquad (46)$$
$$+ u_{20}(\sin L'_2/L'_2)\sin(\theta_2 + \alpha)$$

where θ_2 is defined through Eq. (8). Using a binomial approximation

$$\theta_2 + \alpha \doteqdot \theta_0 + L_1 + \alpha - \frac{\omega l u_{10}\sin L'_1}{u_0^2 L'_1}\sin\theta_0$$

$$= \theta_0 - \delta_1\sin\theta_0 - \gamma \qquad (47)$$

the definitions of δ_1 and γ being obvious.

---

[7] GUÉNARD, WARNECKE and FAURE; Ann. Radioélec., 1948, 3, 302.

We define

$$\delta_2 = \frac{\omega l_2 u_{20} \sin L'_2}{u_0{}^2 L'_2} \tag{48}$$

$$\delta_{12} = \frac{\omega l_1 u_{10} \sin L'_1}{u_0{}^2 L'_1} + \frac{\omega l_2 u_{10} \sin (L'_1 + L'_2)}{u_0{}^2 (L'_1 + L'_2)} \tag{49}$$

Using these expressions and, again, a binomial approximation

$$\theta_3 = \theta_0 + L_1 + L_2 - \delta_{12} \sin \theta_0 - \delta_2 \sin (\theta_0 - \delta_1 \sin \theta_0 - \gamma) \tag{50}$$

and the conversion efficiency for a catcher voltage V_3 is

$$\eta = \frac{-V_3}{2\pi V_0} \int_0^{2\pi} \cos \theta_3 \, d\theta_0$$

Clearly the terms L_1, L_2 make no contribution to the integral. Moreover, it can be shown that when γ is small, its presence only introduces terms of order γ^2 and therefore negligible. We thus omit this quantity for the present. The efficiency for $V_3 = V_0$ is now

$$\eta \doteq \frac{-1}{2\pi} \int_0^{2\pi} \{\cos (\theta_0 - \delta_{12} \sin \theta_0) - \delta_2 \sin (\theta_0 - \delta_1 \sin \theta_0)\} \, d\theta_0 \tag{51}$$

and the integral can be evaluated by expanding $\sin (\theta_0 - \delta_1 \sin \theta_0)$ in a series of Bessel functions. The resulting powers of $\sin \theta$, $\cos \theta$ are expressed as multiple angles and terms higher than the second harmonic are discarded to obtain

$$\theta_3 \doteq \theta_0 - \{\delta_{12} + \delta_2[J_0(\delta_1) - J_2(\delta_1)] \} \sin \theta_0 + \\ + \delta_2[J_1(\delta_1) + J_3(\delta_1)] \sin 2\theta_0 \tag{52}$$

$$= \theta_0 + a \sin \theta_0 + b \sin 2\theta_0 \tag{53}$$

Carrying out the integration we obtain

$$\eta_3 = J_0(b) J_1(a) - \sum_{n=1}^{\infty} J_{2n}(b)[J_{4n-1}(a) - J_{4n+1}(a)] + \\ + \sum_{n=1}^{\infty} 2(2n-1) J_{2n-1}(b) J_{4n-2}(a) \tag{54}$$

GUÉNARD[7] et al. have investigated this expression intensively and find that it gives a maximum of 74% in the vicinity of $a = 1.9$,

$b = 0.9$. The addition of a third harmonic term does not improve matters very much, only about 75% being obtained for the optimum case. The use of the second harmonic has increased the conversion efficiency for $V_3 = V_0$ by about 30% (58–74%). The restrictions under which this result is obtained are rather severe and the authors have calculated the efficiency by numerical means and have presented the results as efficiency contours in the δ_1, δ_2 plane for various

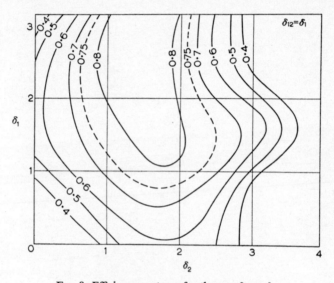

FIG. 8. Efficiency contours for the case $\delta_{12} = \delta_1$.

values of δ_{12} as parameter. Fig. (8) shows the best of these, obtained for $\delta_1 = \delta_{12}$. The figure shows that the efficiency probably reaches a value of about 90% for $\delta_1 \doteq 1.8$, $\delta_2 \doteq 1.6$. Further investigations show that the efficiency is, in fact, best for γ small. For $\gamma = \pi/4$, the best efficiency is still above 80% for $\delta_1 \doteq 2.1$, $\delta_2 \doteq 1.6$ but for $\gamma = \pi/2$ the efficiency is reduced.

We now discuss the significance of the condition $\delta_{12} = \delta_1$. From Eq. (49)

$$\delta_{12} = \delta_1 + \frac{\omega l_2 u_{10} \sin (L'_1 + L'_2)}{u_0{}^2 (L'_1 + L'_2)}$$

so this condition means that $L'_1 + L'_2 = 0$, π, 2π, etc. This might be satisfied by $L'_1 = L'_2 = \pi/2$ but this would mean that the penultimate cavity would have to be very heavily loaded to achieve the condition $\delta_2 \doteqdot \delta_1$. This condition could be much more easily satisfied if L'_2 was made smaller than L'_1 so that the gain between first and second cavities is reduced. Even so loading would have to be resorted to, to bring δ_2 below δ_1. It also follows that the gain of the klystron will be very much reduced, to a value about equal to that of the second and third cavities alone. In order of magnitude the gain might be less than 13 dB instead of 36–40 dB for a klystron designed for full gain. Naturally, the status quo could be restored by the addition of a preliminary high-gain stage. It should be mentioned that in their book WARNECKE and GUÉNARD,[8] make a mistake in their definition of their δ_3 which should correspond with our δ_{12} and Eq. (49) but does not. This invalidates their argument leading to the condition $2L'_1 + L'_2 = \pi$.

Experimental work bearing on this point is meagre, the very large values of drive power necessary to obtain the required conditions in the sort of high-power high-efficiency valve which might disclose the effect constitute a distinct difficulty. Also, the effects of the true radial current distribution discussed in Section 2 would probably be very marked in reducing the efficiency in a solid-beam klystron. It would appear desirable that the point be investigated as the gain in efficiency, if realizable, would be a very real advance.

6.6. LARGE SIGNAL EFFECTS

We conclude this chapter by a brief discussion of large-signal effects. Three points are of major interest in this connection. These are the maximum amplitude of the r.f. current wave, the maximum amplitude of the r.f. voltage on the cavity and the last is the effect of the radial field variation.

On the first of these questions we can shed little light, this regrettably seems to be a problem for the digital computer.

As regards the second we can make progress by assuming that the catcher is placed at a plane of maximum r.f. current. In single-mode theory this means that the r.f. velocity is zero at the catcher, while in multi-mode theory, while the velocity is not zero, it is small compared with the initial value. We make, then, the assumption, not far from the truth, that the r.f. velocity is zero at the catcher and the electrons therefore all have the same velocity u_0 at entry to the gap. We then wish to determine the value of the decelerating voltage

---

[8] WARNECKE and GUÉNARD; *Tubes à modulation de Vitesse*, p. 283. Gauthier Villars, 1951.

which will just bring the electrons to rest at the plane of exit from the gap, as a function of the gap length. This problem is readily solved for gridded gaps, for instance, by the use of Llewellyn's electronics equations. As we only need to use this condition in the immediate vicinity of the gap walls we can use this result directly. It is shown in Fig. 9 in a form first computed by WARNECKE and BERNIER,[9] which we now consider to be a plot of α_2 vs. gap length L. Consider values for $L = 2$; the edge coupling factor is $J_0(L/2) = 0.765$ so that Fig. 9 shows that the voltage seen by an edge electron may be as high as $1.430 V_0$ without stopping it in the gap. Fig. 9

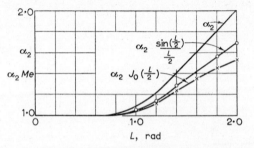

FIG. 9. Effect of gap length on value of α_2 which just stops some electrons.

also shows that electrons nearer the axis, which are acted on by the field over longer angles, require larger voltages to bring them to rest but are actually subjected to smaller voltages. Therefore, if an edge electron is just brought to rest all electrons at smaller radial distances from the axis will cross the gap. We may thus consider the data of Fig. 9 as determining the limiting voltage on the cavity, instead of the arbitrary condition $V_2 = V_0$.

The efficiency of a klystron amplifier in non-linear theory is given by BECK[10] as

$$\eta = \alpha_2 M J_1\left(\frac{S\alpha_1 M}{2}\right) - (\alpha_2 M)^2 \frac{P}{8} \qquad (55)$$

where the J_1 term comes from the Webster theory. If we optimize Eq. (55) by forming $\partial \eta/\partial \alpha_2$ we find that $P = [4J_1(S\alpha_1 M/2)/\alpha_2 M]$, while the maximization with respect to α, yields $(\alpha_2 M)_{\text{opt}} = 3.68$.

[9] WARNECKE and BERNIER; *Rev. Gen. Élect*, 1942, **101**, 117.

[10] BECK; *Velocity Modulated Thermionic Tubes*, p. 81, Eq. (4). Cambridge University Press, 1948.

These results combine to give

$$(\alpha_2 M)_{\text{opt}} = \frac{2 \cdot 34}{P} \tag{56}$$

Equation (56) together with Fig. 9, determines the minimum value of P for which the optimum load adjustment $\partial \eta / \partial \alpha_2 = 0$ gives a cavity voltage low enough not to turn back electrons in the gap. The question then arises as to what happens when P is lower than this value, which is very frequently the case in high-power klystrons. Clearly, we have to go back to Eq. (55) and insert the optimum value of $\alpha_2 M$ and the known value P to calculate the efficiency numerically. However, we note that the M's in Eq. (55) are the R.M.S. values averaged over the beam whereas we have used the edge value in conjunction with Fig. 9. If the beam fills the tunnel, which is desirable in the output gap,

$$M = M_e \left(\frac{I_0{}^2(A) - I_1{}^2(A)}{I_0{}^2(A)} \right)^{1/2} \tag{57}$$

and at optimum drive

$$\eta = 0 \cdot 584 \alpha_2 M_e \left(\frac{I_0{}^2 - I_1{}^2}{I_0{}^2} \right)^{1/2} - (\alpha_2 M_e)^2 \left(\frac{I_0{}^2 - I_1{}^2}{I_0{}^2} \right) \frac{P}{8} \tag{58}$$

For comparison, when P is larger than the limit given in Eq. (56)

$$\eta = \frac{0 \cdot 63}{P} \tag{59}$$

Equation (59) depends much less strongly on A (here equal to the beam radius) than does Eq. (58). It is therefore necessary to be more careful about the dimensioning of the gaps of high-output klystrons than simple considerations would indicate. It is also not necessarily disadvantageous to increase the gap length beyond the values used in the earlier stages. This procedure has other advantages: it tends to reduce the liability to multipactor† effect and it reduces the

---

† Multipactor effect is a heavy loading of the output gap which in severe cases may lead to an arc across the gap. It is due to secondary emission from the lips of the gap. If the secondaries are emitted when the gap field decelerates the main bunch, the secondaries are accelerated. They then hit the opposite lips giving rise to further secondaries which are in turn accelerated if the transit time is favourable. A large swinging charge may be built up which may cause gas ionization and arcing. Since the secondaries have relatively low velocities, making the gap longer tends to prevent their gaining much energy in a single transit and therefore reduces the severity of the phenomenon.

gap capacitance and therefore increases the bandwidth. This latter point is, however, rather unimportant because the loading may easily be seen to be so heavy that the bandwidth of the output cavity is large compared with that of the middle cavities. Table 3 shows some results relevant to the effect of dimensions on efficiency.

TABLE 3

Overall efficiency as a function of beam radius

R	$\eta\%$			
	P = 1·0		P = 0·5	
	Eq. (55)	Eq. (58)	Eq. (55)	Eq. (58)
1·0	45·9	42·0	52·15	47·0
1·2	45·9	41·0	52·15	45·7
1·4	45·9	39·5	52·15	43·7
1·6	45·9	37·35	52·15	41·7
1·8	45·9	36·80	52·15	40·3
2·0	45·9	35·10	52·15	38·3

It should be remembered that these results do not take into account the concentration of current on the surface of the beam but even so they give values consistent with those obtained on well-designed high-power klystrons which range from 30–50%.

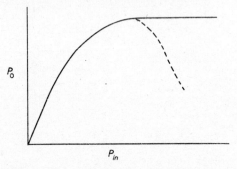

FIG. 10. Power saturation in multicavity klystron.

An experimental point which has some bearing on the high-level behaviour is that klystrons designed and operated for full gain show a very marked saturation effect when overdriven. Fig. 10 illustrates this, the full curve being the typical observed behaviour while the dotted curve indicates the behaviour expected on the basis of uniform beam theory. This finding can possibly be explained by the fact that as electrons on the beam surface start to turn back and oscillate in the output gap, and therefore remove energy from the catcher, the electrons nearer to the axis are bunched more tightly and transfer their energy more efficiently. Even so, the linearity of the saturation characteristic is often very marked and appears worthy of comment.

P

7

TRAVELLING-WAVE TUBES AND BACKWARD-WAVE OSCILLATORS

In this chapter we give a unified discussion of the operation of travelling-wave amplifiers and backward-wave oscillators of the type in which the magnetic field, normally used for focusing, is in the direction of electron motion. In the French terminology these are the "O" type devices. In the travelling-wave amplifier we require a slow-wave circuit in which the phase and group velocities are in the same direction while the B.W.O. uses a circuit which has phase and group velocities oppositely directed. In both cases, however, the phase velocity of the circuit waves is directed in the same line as the direction of electron motion. It is also necessary, for interaction to take place, that the electron velocity be approximately equal to the phase velocity of the waves on the circuit.

7.1. THE TRAVELLING-WAVE TUBE

The travelling-wave amplifier consists of the following elements: an electron gun adapted for the production of an electron beam which can be introduced properly into the focusing magnetic field, a slow-wave circuit which is provided with input and output transformers used to couple the circuit to the input and output feeders, which may be either coaxial lines or waveguides, and a collector capable of dissipating the necessary power, which removes the electrons from the device after they have traversed the circuit. Fig. 1 gives a much simplified sketch of a particular type of T.W.A. using a helical delay line and waveguide feeders.

The major physical features of the operation of the device are as follows:—Power is fed from a driving generator into the input transformer which effects a matched impedance transformation to the helix impedance. These transformers must be carefully designed if the full wide-band performance of the helix is even to be approximately realized. The waves on the circuit give rise to relatively weak fields in the region occupied by the beam. However, if the beam velocity is in approximate synchronism with the waves the electrons

214

travel with the beam and are acted on for a considerable time. The action of the fields is thus to set up velocity modulation of the beam, and power is taken from the fields to produce such modulation.

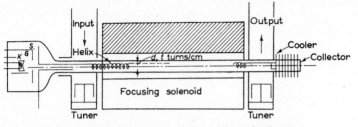

FIG. 1. Travelling-wave amplifier—schematic diagram.

Coincident with the setting up of velocity modulation the beam begins to exhibit variations of density, or, in other words, it becomes bunched. Now suppose that the beam is not in exact synchronism with the wave. If the beam velocity is slightly higher than the wave velocity the bunches will travel forward through the wave, the initial position of a bunch centre being at the position of a reference electron which entered the system at an instant when the field was changing from negative to positive. Conversely, if the beam velocity is lower the bunch tends to drift back through the field. If the bunch moves forward from its initial position with respect to the field, it moves into a region of decelerating field and therefore the electrons of the bunch are all slowed down. The energy lost by the electrons is gained by the field and amplification results. If, on the other hand, the bunch falls back with respect to the field it gains energy and the wave is damped. The electrons must therefore travel slightly faster than the wave, if amplification is to result.† In reality, matters are more complicated because analysis shows that, in the presence of the electron beam, the circuit wave splits up into four components, three in the direction of p and one backward. In the range of relative velocities for which gain is possible the three forward waves exhibit respectively no change in amplitude, exponential attenuation and exponential gain. Gain and loss per unit length are equal in magnitude. Both these latter waves travel more slowly than the electron velocity and this is a prerequisite if gain is to be observed.

The T.W.A. has a major defect in that there is a direct electrical connection from the output back to the input. Not only is there a

---

† See Appendix 10 for further discussion of this point.

backward wave as a result of the fundamental electronic behaviour of the device, but we must also allow for the effects of unintentional or unavoidable mismatches at the output transformer. The original tubes, made by Kompfner at the Clarendon Laboratories, Oxford, suffered from the onset of oscillations at low beam currents for just this reason. The major contribution of Pierce was to realize that the judicious use of circuit attenuation considerably eased this problem. Analysis shows that the use of circuit attenuation is fully effective in reducing the amplitude of reflected waves but only about one-third of the inserted attenuation is effective in reducing the forward gain. If we have a T.W.A. which will only give 10 dB gain before oscillation sets in, and we insert 60 dB of circuit attenuation, we should be able to increase the beam current until about 50 dB of forward gain is observed, before oscillation sets in again.

7.2. INTERACTIONS WITH FORWARD AND BACKWARD WAVES

We now wish to describe the physics of the backward-wave oscillator and the first step is to obtain a clear understanding of how an electron beam reacts with forward and backward circuits. The argument is due to WARNECKE and GUÉNARD,[1] with minor corrections. Fig. 2 shows three cells of some kind of periodic circuit. According to the considerations of Chapter 3, a snapshot of the

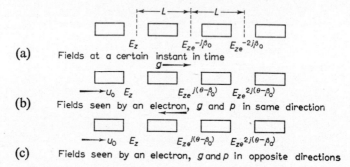

$$\begin{array}{c}
\vdash \!\!-\! L \!-\!\!\!\to \!\!\vdash\!\!-\! L \!-\!\!\!\to\\
E_z \qquad E_{ze}^{-j\beta_0} \quad E_{ze}^{-2j\beta_0}
\end{array}$$

(a)   Fields at a certain instant in time

$g \longrightarrow$

$\longrightarrow u_0 \; E_z \qquad E_{ze}^{j(\theta-\beta_0)} \quad E_{ze}^{2j(\theta-\beta_0)}$

(b)   Fields seen by an electron, g and p in same direction

$\longrightarrow u_0 \; E_z \qquad E_{ze}^{j(\theta-\beta_0)} \quad E_{ze}^{2j(\theta-\beta_0)}$

(c)   Fields seen by an electron, g and p in opposite directions

FIG. 2. The fields in periodic structures.

fields at a single instant in time will show that they differ only by the phase factor $\exp(-j\beta_0)$, Fig. 2(a). Fig. 2(b) gives an electron's

[1] WARNECKE and GUÉNARD; *Proc. I.E.E.*, 1953, **100**, Pt. 111, 351.

eye view of the same fields. This is obtained by multiplying by the additional factor per cell of $j\theta$, where $\theta = \omega L/u_0$ and u_0 is the electron velocity. Fig. 2(b) is drawn for the case where g and p are in the same direction, that of the electrons. Fig. 2(c), which is incorrectly printed in the reference, shows the situation when g is reversed. The fields are, of course, unchanged. This already indicates that interaction should be possible in both cases, if it is possible in either. Now consider that a bunched electron beam interacts with the circuit, on which the initial modulating waves are assumed to have decayed. For forward wave interactions, synchronism demands that

$$\theta = \beta_0 + 2n\pi, \qquad \begin{aligned} &n = 0, 1, 2, 3, \text{ etc.}, \beta_0 > 0 \\ &n = 1, 2, 3, \text{ etc.}, \beta_0 < 0 \end{aligned} \tag{1}$$

The r.f. currents at the three gaps are i, $i \exp(-j\theta,)$ $i \exp(-2j\theta)$, which induce voltages E, $E \exp(-j\theta)$, $E \exp(-2j\theta)$ int the capacitances of the gaps. The negative signs are taken into the E. Each of the induced voltage pulses propagates in both directions away from the gap in which it was induced. Fig. 3(a) shows the situation at the instant the bunch reaches the centre of the third

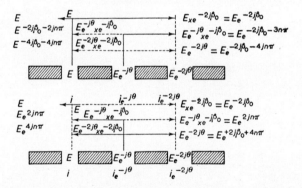

FIG. 3. How the overall fields build up by reflection and transmission.

gap. It will be seen that the three elementary pulses add up in the forward direction, since their phases only differ by multiples of $2n\pi$. In the backward direction, however, the phases differ by multiples of $2\beta_0$, which can only give equality of phase when $\beta_0 = 0$ or π, cases which we already know to give rise to zero group velocity. Thus, for this type of synchronism a forward wave results and the backward components all cancel.

Fig. 3(b) shows what happens when

$$\theta = -\beta_0 - 2n\pi, \qquad n = 0, 1, 2, 3, \text{etc.}, \beta_0 > 0$$

$$n = 1, 2, 3, \text{etc.}, \beta_0 < 0 \qquad (2)$$

Here, the elementary pulses add up in the backward direction and tend to cancel in the forward direction. We have therefore demonstrated that the two different possibilities for approximate equality of phase velocity do, in fact, lead to different directions of energy flow, that is, of group velocity.

Now let us write down the expressions for the voltage induced in a line by an arbitrary distribution of sources whose intensity in the range Δz at z is $A_{(z)}\Delta z$. Consider first the forward wave amplifier. A driving generator feeds power to the right into a line of length l terminated at either end in its characteristic impedance. The field at a distance $z = a$ from the origin is made up of the following components, the part due to the input generator, the part of the field propagating to the right from all the sources in the range $0 < z < a$, and the part of the field propagating to the left from the sources in the range $a < z < l$. Therefore

$$E_{(a)} = E_t \exp\left(-\Gamma_0 a\right) + \tfrac{1}{2}\int_0^a A_{(z)} \exp\left[-\Gamma_0(a - z)\right] \mathrm{d}z +$$

$$+ \tfrac{1}{2}\int_a^l A_{(z)} \exp\left[\Gamma_0(a - z)\right] \mathrm{d}z \quad (3)$$

Here we have written the propagation constant as Γ_0 to emphasize that it, in general, has both real and imaginary parts. Equation (3) is widely used in T.W.A. theory, where it is utilized by carrying out two differentiations and introducing the coupling impedance Z_c. The result is known as the "circuit" equation in contrast with the "electronic" equation, which gives the r.f. convection current in terms of the circuit voltage. The two equations together give a quartic equation for the perturbed or "hot" propagation constants, i.e., the values of propagation constant measured when the beam interacts with the circuit. This is the basis of PIERCE's[2] theory of the T.W.A. which has been widely used and is largely responsible for our present good understanding of the operation of these tubes.

Turning now to the B.W.O., the generator is located at the far

---

[2] PIERCE; *Traveling-Wave Tubes*, Van Nostrand, 1950.

end of the circuit. Writing down the sum of the three contributions, as before, we obtain

$$E_{(a)} = E_i \exp\left[\Gamma_0(l - a)\right] + \tfrac{1}{2} \int_0^a A_{(z)} \exp\left[\Gamma_0(a - z)\right] dz +$$

$$+ \tfrac{1}{2} \int_a^l A_{(z)} \exp\left[-\Gamma_0(a - z)\right] dz \quad (4)$$

Equations (3) and (4) give rise to the same second order homogeneous differential equation, but the inhomogeneous parts are reversed in sign.

Having studied the details of the interaction, let us now return to the operation of the B.W.O. Here, as in all oscillators, the oscillation builds up from noise or other random variations which may be taken as providing a value of E_i in Eq. (4). The resulting field acts on the beam and produces a certain small degree of bunching. The bunches interact with the circuit in the way described above, so producing a flow of energy towards the gun end of the oscillator. This in turn increases the bunching field which reacts on the beam, causing increased r.f. conduction current, consequent increase in the induced field and so on. We have here assumed that the loop gain is greater than unity. The state of steady oscillation is reached when any further increase in oscillation amplitude is accompanied by a decrease in r.f. current. There are many non-linear effects which might cause such a decrease, an instance being the loss of electrons by deflexion to the circuit before traversing the whole interaction space.

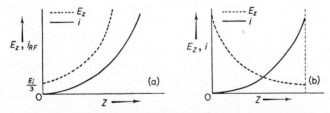

FIG. 4. (a) R.F. field and current in a travelling-wave amplifier.
(b) The same, for a backward-wave oscillator.

Before leaving the qualitative discussion of the behaviour of T.W.A.s and B.W.O.s, it is useful to consider the plots of the longitudinal variation of electric field and r.f. convection current which are shown very schematically in Fig. 4. Fig. (4a) shows the situation in the

T.W.A. Here the electric field of the amplified wave and the r.f. current both increase exponentially from the beginning of the helix to the output device. E_z increases from the finite initial value, due to the input generator, which is roughly $E_t/3$ while the r.f. current builds up from zero. In Fig. 4(b), which applies to the B.W.O., the electric field is strong where the unmodulated beam enters the system, as this is the output end of the circuit, but the r.f. field builds up sinusoidally along the direction of beam travel. The difference in behaviour is important in large-signal theory. In the T.W.T. the behaviour near the output is very complicated because the r.f. currents and fields are simultaneously large. On the other hand in the B.W.O. the field is only strong where the currents are weak and vice versa, so that the large-signal theory should be inherently simpler than that of the T.W.A.

7.3.　THE BALLISTIC THEORY OF THE T.W.A.

The theory of the T.W.A. is usually treated from one of two distinct points of view. These are the ballistic viewpoint adopted by the originators of the device, Kompfner and Pierce, which is fully described in Pierce's well-known book,[2] and the field theory, in which the tube is treated as a problem in Maxwellian electromagnetic theory in which the proper modes of the cold helix are modified by the presence of the charges in the beam. Theories of this type go back to RYDBECK[3] and CHU and JACKSON.[4] In view of the preoccupation of the present work with field theories it may easily appear strange that the ballistic theory should be discussed. There are two reasons for including it. First, a very good general theory of the T.W.A. can be established by this means, one, moreover, in which the initial approximations can be systematically refined until further improvement ceases to yield significant changes. Secondly, the ballistic theory is widely known and used to such an extent that it would be silly, even if it were otherwise desirable, to expect engineers to change to another presentation. This section then, gives a brief presentation of Pierce's theory which is, however, modified to take account of the space-charge bunching of the beam in a manner different, and, to my mind, preferable, to that of Pierce. The method employed was originated by DOEHLER and KLEEN[5] and leads naturally to the ideas on matching of space-charge waves already discussed in Chapter 5.

As has already been said, the ballistic theory derives an electronic

[3] RYDBECK; *Ericsson Technics*, No. 46, 1948.
[4] CHU and JACKSON; *Proc. I.R.E.*, 1948, **36**, 853.
[5] DOEHLER and KLEEN; *Ann. Radioélec*, 1948, **3**, 184.

equation which gives the value of r.f. current in terms of the supposedly known r.f. field producing it. A circuit equation then gives the field in terms of the current. The overall equation is obtained as a condition of compatibility and results in four allowed values for the "hot" propagation constant.

7.3.1. The electronic equation

The electronic equation is derived by a very similar method to that employed in deriving the space-charge wave expressions of the first few sections of Chapter 4. The wave functions here are of the form $\exp(j\omega t - \Gamma z)$ since we now expect Γ to be complex instead of imaginary. The small-signal assumption then leads to the r.f. current.

$$i_1 = (u_0\rho_1 - \rho_0 u_1)\exp(j\omega t - \Gamma z) \tag{5}$$

where $\rho_0 =$ charge density per unit beam length. Continuity gives

$$\frac{\partial i_1}{\partial z} = -\frac{\partial \rho_1}{\partial t}$$

or

$$-\Gamma i_1 = -j\omega\rho_1 \tag{6}$$

while the force law becomes

$$\frac{du}{dt} = -\eta E_T \tag{7}$$

where

$$E_T = E_z + E_{sc} \tag{8}$$

Here E_z is taken as the impressed field set up by the circuit while E_{sc} is a local space-charge field caused by the bunches in the beam, which modifies the circuit field. E_{sc} is determined by considering the one-dimensional case, in which Poisson's equation gives

$$\frac{\partial E_{sc}}{\partial z} = \frac{\rho_1}{\epsilon_0} \tag{9}$$

or, if the initial condition $i_1 = 0$ at $z = 0$ is used in the continuity equation, Eq. (6)

$$E_{sc} = -\frac{i_1}{j\omega\epsilon_0} \tag{10}$$

Then, since the operator d/dt in Eq. (7) is equivalent to $u_0\partial/\partial z + \partial/\partial t$, we have

$$u_1(j\omega - \Gamma u_0) = -\eta\left(E_z - \frac{i_1}{j\omega\epsilon_0}\right) \tag{11}$$

From Eqs. (5) and (6) we easily find that

$$u_1 = -\frac{i_1}{j\omega\rho_0}(j\omega - \Gamma u_0) \qquad (12)$$

whence
$$i_1 = \frac{j\omega\rho_0\eta E_z}{(j\omega - \Gamma u_0)^2 + \eta\rho_0/\epsilon_0} \qquad (13)$$

If we put $\rho_0 = I_0/u_0$ since ρ_0 is here the charge per unit beam length, $u_0^2 = 2\eta V_0$, $\omega/u_0 = \beta_e$, $\omega_p^2 = \eta\rho_0/\epsilon_0 u_0$, Eq. (13) becomes

$$i_1 = \frac{j\beta_e}{(j\beta_e - \Gamma)^2 + \omega_p^2/u_0^2} \cdot \frac{I_0 E_z}{2V_0} \qquad (14)$$

If the ω_p^2/u_0^2 term, i.e., the term due to E_{sc}, is neglected, Eq. (14) is identical with the result of the simplified T.W.A. theory, i.e., PIERCE,[2] Eq. 2.22 or BECK,[6] Eq. 14.8. Often, to take account of the actual field conditions, that is, of the fact that we are dealing with fields which are very far from being one-dimensional, a modified value $\omega_q^2 = F^2\omega_p^2$ is used instead of ω_p^2, where F^2 is a space-charge reduction factor of some kind. It will be part of our work to attach precise meanings to F^2.

7.3.2. The circuit equation

This is established by differentiating Eq. (3) twice to obtain

$$\frac{d^2 E_z}{dz^2} - \Gamma_0^2 E_z = -\Gamma_0 A_{(z)}$$

But $d/dz = -\Gamma$ when the beam is present. Therefore,

$$(\Gamma^2 - \Gamma_0^2)E_z = -\Gamma_0 A_{(z)} \qquad (15)$$

The coupling impedance is introduced by defining

$$A_{(z)} = \Gamma^2 Z_c i_1$$

$$E_z = \frac{\Gamma^2 \Gamma_0 Z_c}{(\Gamma_0^2 - \Gamma^2)} \cdot i_1 \qquad (16)$$

Equation (16) is the desired circuit equation.

In Pierce's treatment the local space-charge fields are treated as passive modes of the circuit and his space-charge term appears in

---

[6] BECK; *Thermionic Valves*, Chapter 14. Cambridge University Press, 1953.

the circuit equation. For the details the reader should see his Chapter 7. His result is

$$E_z = \left[\frac{\Gamma^2 \Gamma_0 Z_c}{(\Gamma_0{}^2 - \Gamma^2)} - j \frac{\Gamma^2}{\omega C_1} \right] i_1 \qquad (17)$$

where C_1 is a lumped capacitance representing the effects of the passive modes. It is more natural to keep the space-charge terms with the beam, as we have done in the last section.

7.3.3. The determinantal equation

Combining Eqs. (14) and (16) we obtain the determining equation for the propagation constants

$$\frac{(\Gamma_0{}^2 - \Gamma^2)[(j\beta_e - \Gamma)^2 + F^2 \omega_p{}^2 / u_0{}^2]}{\Gamma^2 \Gamma_0 \cdot j\beta_e} = \frac{I_0 Z_c}{2V_0} = 2C^3 \qquad (18)$$

where the last form introduces Pierce's parameter C. Equation (18) is of the fourth power in Γ and therefore leads to four possible propagation constants. We shall discuss the solutions of Eq. (18) later.

Pierce obtains an equation equivalent to Eq. (18) by introducing a space-charge parameter Q defined by

$$Q = \frac{\beta_e}{2\omega C_1 Z_c} \qquad (19)$$

the result being

$$(j\beta_e - \Gamma)^2 - 4\Gamma^2 Q C^3 = \frac{2C^3 \Gamma^2 \Gamma_0}{(\Gamma_0{}^2 - \Gamma^2)} \cdot j\beta_e \qquad (20)$$

Comparing this with Eq. (18) and remembering that, for a strong interaction, $\Gamma^2 \doteq -\omega^2/u_0{}^2$ we see that

$$4QC \equiv \frac{F^2 \omega_p{}^2}{C^2 \omega^2} \qquad (21)$$

or

$$\frac{F\omega_p}{\omega} \equiv 2C\sqrt{QC} \qquad (22)$$

The last two expressions are written as equivalences and not as equations because the physical identity of the quantities defined has not been proved. If we are able to find an acceptable and reliable method of calculating F^2 in the sequel we may use its numerical value in conjunction with Eq. (20) by the use of the equivalence just demonstrated. This is important because extensive studies of the numerical solution of Eq. (20) with various values of QC as parameter have been published.

We now take up the question of the solution of Eq. (18). This is approached by what is essentially a perturbation method. We already know that interaction is strong only when the electron velocity is so adjusted that $\Gamma_0 \doteq j\beta_e$ so we put

$$\Gamma = \Gamma_0 - \zeta = j\beta_e - \zeta \qquad (23)$$

where ζ is a small quantity.

Inspection of Eq. (18) shows that for vanishingly small values of I_0 for which $C^3\dagger$ and ω_p^2 both $\to 0$, this procedure leads to a correct solution. The next step is to retain C^3 but not ω_p^2. If Eq. (23) is put into Eq. (18) we obtain

$$\beta_e^3 C^3 = j\zeta^3 \qquad (24)$$

by neglecting ζ in comparison with $2j\beta_e$ and ζ^2 in comparison with $2j\zeta\beta_e$.

From Eq. (24)

$$\zeta = (-j)^{1/3}\beta_e C \qquad (25)$$

If we insert the three roots of $(-j)$ and use Eq. (23) to determine the Γ's we find

$$\Gamma_1 = \beta_e \left[j\left(1 + \frac{C}{2}\right) - \frac{\sqrt{3}C}{2} \right] \qquad (26)$$

$$\Gamma_2 = \beta_e \left[j\left(1 + \frac{C}{2}\right) + \frac{\sqrt{3}C}{2} \right] \qquad (27)$$

$$\Gamma_3 = \beta_e[\, j(1 - C)] \qquad (28)$$

and putting these back into the original equations

$$\Gamma_4 = -\beta_e \left[j\left(1 - \frac{C^3}{4}\right) \right] \qquad (29)$$

It will be observed that Γ_1 and Γ_2 are complex, while Γ_3 and Γ_4 are imaginary. Since the wave functions are $\exp(-\Gamma)$, Γ_1, which has a negative real part, gives rise to a wave which increases exponentially in the direction of travel, the amplification constant being $\sqrt{(3)}\beta_e C/2$. The second wave is attenuated at the same rate. The phase velocities are the same for these two waves and equal $u_0(1 + C/2)^{-1}$, so they

---

† C^3 is a small number, <1 so that $C > C^3$.

are a little less than the electron velocity. The third wave has a phase velocity of $u_0(1 + C)$, i.e., slightly above u_0 while the fourth wave travels in the backward direction. It must be realized that this wave exists quite independently of the output coupling arrangements and is not a consequence of mismatching but is a basic feature of the electronic behaviour of the T.W.A.

Having obtained an analytical solution to Eq. (18), valid in the degree of approximation stated, we find that further progress depends on the adoption of numerical methods, which are much facilitated by the use of the initial solution based on the above analysis. The results so obtained do not concern us for the moment but we shall return to them later.

7.3.4. Initial amplitudes and gain

Knowing the propagation constants of the various waves we can now proceed to calculate their amplitudes at the input to the helix, using the initial values. At $z = 0$ these are $E = E_i$, $u_1 = 0$, $i_1 = 0$. Let E_1, E_2, E_3 be the amplitudes of the three forward waves, then we find

$$E_1 + E_2 + E_3 = E_i \tag{30}$$

From Eq. (11)
$$\frac{E_1}{\zeta_1} + \frac{E_2}{\zeta_2} + \frac{E_3}{\zeta_3} = 0 \tag{31}$$

From Eq. (14)
$$\frac{E_1}{\zeta_1{}^2} + \frac{E_2}{\zeta_2{}^2} + \frac{E_3}{\zeta_3{}^2} = 0 \tag{32}$$

$\omega_p{}^2$ is neglected in Eq. (32)

Solving for E_1 we find

$$E_1 = \frac{E_i}{(1 - \zeta_2/\zeta_1)(1 - \zeta_3/\zeta_1)} \tag{33}$$

the other E's being found by permuting the ζ's. If the values of ζ from Eq. (25) are used in Eq. (33) etc., we find that all the waves have the same initial amplitude $E_i/3$.

If the helix is long enough for the amplified wave to be much bigger than the unattenuated wave, which is the second largest wave, the gain in dB is merely $G = 20 \log_{10}(E_0/E_i)$ where $E_0 = E_i/3 \exp [\sqrt(3)\beta_e l C]/2$, $l =$ active length of helix. Thus

$$G = (7 \cdot 5CL - 9 \cdot 54) \text{ dB}† \tag{34}$$

† I find that I made a stupid mistake in the formula equivalent to Eq. (34) in *Thermionic Valves*. I seem to have put $\log_{10} = 2 \cdot 303 \log_e$ instead of the correct value. I apologize to anyone who was misled.

$L = \omega l/u_0$ length of helix in terms of transit angle. Equation (34) is often written in terms of the length expressed in wavelengths $2\pi N = L$, the result being

$$G = (47\cdot3CN - 9\cdot54)\,\text{dB} \tag{35}$$

These equations apply for a lossless helix operated very near to the velocity for maximum gain. Real T.W.A.s all include lumped loss so as to obtain increased forward gain and stability at the cost of increased beam current. The limiting case of very large lumped loss can be considered equivalent to two separate helices which are coupled by the velocity modulation and r.f. beam current, quantities which persist in the space between the two helices. These matters are fully treated by Pierce and need not detain us here, except to remark that very high gain (55–60 dB at 4 kMc/s) has been obtained by the use of separated helices with the output helix operated at a slightly different voltage. For details see KLEIN.[7]

7.4. THE FIELD THEORY OF THE T.W.A. AND THE SPACE-CHARGE FACTOR

We now discuss the field theory of the T.W.A. The fundamental relations have already been derived in Chapter 5, but they are repeated here for convenience. Using the sheath helix model, the determinantal equation is

$$\frac{I_1(\gamma_0 a)K_1(\gamma_0 a)}{I_0(\gamma_0 a)K_0(\gamma_0 a)}\left(\frac{ka}{\gamma_0 a}\right)^2 \cot^2\psi = 1 \tag{36}$$

this gives the helix propagation constant in the absence of the beam. The radial impedance defined by

$$Y_{(r)} = \sqrt{\frac{\mu}{\epsilon}}\,\frac{H_\theta}{E_z} \tag{37}$$

is given by

$$j\left(\frac{ka}{\gamma_0 a}\right)$$

$$\times \left[\frac{I_1(\gamma_0 r) - K_1(\gamma_0 r)\left\{\left(\dfrac{ka}{\gamma_0 a}\right)^2 \dfrac{\cot^2\psi\, I_1(\gamma_0 a)K_1(\gamma_0 a) - I_0(\gamma_0 a)K_0(\gamma_0 a)}{K_0^2(\gamma_0 a)}\right\}}{I_0(\gamma_0 r) + K_0(\gamma_0 r)\left\{\left(\dfrac{ka}{\gamma_0 a}\right)^2 \dfrac{\cot^2\psi\, I_1(\gamma_0 a)K_1(\gamma_0 a) - I_0(\gamma_0 a)K_0(\gamma_0 a)}{K_0^2(\gamma_0 a)}\right\}}\right]$$

$$\tag{38}$$

---

[7] KLEIN; *A.E.Ü.*, 1955, **9**, 55.

the surface admittance Y_s is, by definition, the value of $Y_{(r)}$ at $r = a$, i.e.,

$$Y_s = j\left(\frac{ka}{\gamma_0 a}\right)\left[\frac{K_1}{K_0}\frac{1 + (I_1K_0/I_0K_1) - (I_1K_1/I_0K_0)(ka/\gamma_0 a)^2 \cot^2 \psi}{(I_1K_1/I_0K_0)(ka/\gamma_0 a)^2 \cot^2 \psi}\right]$$
(39)

all the Bessel functions being of the same argument $\gamma_0 a$. If we insert Eq. (36) into Eq. (39) we find that

$$Y_{s(\text{cold})} = j\left(\frac{ka}{\gamma_0 a}\right)\frac{I_1(\gamma_0 a)}{I_0(\gamma_0 a)}$$
(40)

which can easily be directly verified using the cold fields. Equation (38) was first derived by CHU and JACKSON[4] who also indicated an approximate solution which we deal with here, since it is freely used in the literature. Inspection of Eq. (38) shows that it has a pole at $\gamma = 0$, a zero very close to $\gamma_0 a$ and another pole at $\gamma_0 a$. Then, we can approximate the function by making a Taylor expansion round the zero, and expressing the function as a quotient of factors. Let γ_z, γ_p be the values at the zero and second pole respectively. Then

$$Y_{(r)} = \frac{f(\gamma)}{\gamma - \gamma_p}$$
(41)

and

$$f(\gamma) = f(\gamma_z) + (\gamma - \gamma_z)f'(\gamma_z), \text{ etc.}$$
(42)

but, by definition

$$f(\gamma_z) = 0$$

and from Eq. (41)

$$f'(\gamma_z) = (\gamma_z - \gamma_p)Y'_{(r)}$$
(43)

Therefore

$$Y'_{(r)} \doteq (\gamma_z - \gamma_p)\frac{(\gamma - \gamma_z)}{(\gamma - \gamma_p)}\left(\frac{\partial Y_{(r)}}{\partial \gamma}\right)_{\gamma = \gamma_z}$$
(44)

To utilize Eq. (44) the indicated differentiation is carried out and the d.c. evaluated at the zero. The pole is found and Eq. (44) can then be used to approximate Eq. (38).

Chu and Jackson proceed by determining the T.M. wave admittance within the beam, which in their notation is

$$Y'_{(r)} = -j\frac{k}{\gamma} \cdot \frac{\phi}{\gamma} \cdot \frac{I_1(\phi r)}{I_0(\phi r)}$$
(45)

where

$$\phi = -(\gamma^2 + k^2)\left[1 + \frac{\eta I}{\pi b^2 \epsilon_0 u_0{}^3(j(\omega/u_0) - \gamma)^2}\right]$$
(46)

They have thus tacitly assumed that the term in the square bracket, which in our notation is just $[1 - \omega_p{}^2/(\omega - \beta u_0)^2]$, is positive, whereas we know that it is, in general, negative. However, they approximate Eq. (45) by

$$Y'_{(r)} = -j\frac{ka}{a} \cdot \frac{\phi^2}{\gamma^2} \cdot \frac{b}{2} \qquad (47)$$

By equating the expressions for $Y'_{(r)}$ in Eqs. (44) and (47) a cubic is obtained which gives the values of γ corresponding with the three forward waves. Over a range of values of β_e it is found that complex γ's arise in conjugate pairs, one giving gain, the other, attenuation. The curves resulting from this work are instructive, one being reproduced in Fig. 5. Fig. 5(a) shows the phase constants, Fig. 5(b) the attenuation constants. From Fig. 5(a) it will be observed that the complex roots appear when β_e equals the phase constant

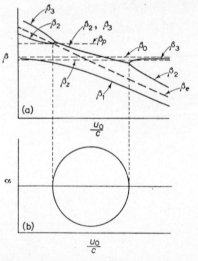

FIG. 5. Real and imaginary parts of the hot propagations constants, calculated from field theory for a particular set of conditions.

at the pole of the circuit equation. The cold propagation constant β_0, here lies at about the centre of the range of operation. On closer examination it turns out that the electrons have to travel faster than the increasing wave (α_2, β_2) to give energy to it. At the other extreme the departure from synchronism is so great that no bunching results as the electrons move forward and through the wave.

The results of Chu and Jackson were used to form the basis of another, better, approximation by FRIEDMAN.[8] He introduces the function

$$G(pa) = \frac{I_0(pa)}{K_0(pa)}\left[\left(\frac{ka\cot\psi}{pa}\right)^2 \frac{I_1(pa)}{I_0(pa)}\cdot\frac{K_1(pa)}{K_0(pa)} - 1\right] \quad (48)$$

which transforms the secular equation, obtained by equating the expressions for $Y'_{(r)}$ in Eqs. (45) and (38) into

$$\frac{\phi}{p}\frac{I_1(\phi b)}{I_0(\phi b)}\frac{I_0(pb)}{I_1(pb)} = \frac{1 - [K_1(pb)/I_1(pb)]G(pa)}{1 + [K_0(pb)/I_0(pb)]G(pa)} \quad (49)$$

But it is obvious, from (36), that $G(p_0 a) = 0$ so we can use a Taylor series to write

$$G(pa) = (p - p_0)G'(p_0 a) \quad (50)$$

Equation (50) is a much more attractive starting point for perturbation procedures than is Eq. (44). Friedman uses this to obtain another cubic equation giving the desired values for the propagation constants. His work is still subject to the effects of the incorrect form of beam impedance.

The best known use of the approximate field admittance is, however, FLETCHER's[9] work on the evaluation of Pierce's space-charge parameter Q. If we write down Pierce's electronic equation for a thin annular beam (field constant over the beam) we get

$$\frac{E_1}{i_1} = \frac{1}{2\pi bY} = -\frac{\Gamma^2\Gamma_0 Z_c}{\Gamma^2 - \Gamma_0^2} - \frac{2jQZ_c\Gamma^2}{\beta_e} \quad (51)$$

If we subtract Eq. (45) from Eq. (38) to form Y, the equations are equivalent if

$$\Gamma_0^2 = -\gamma_0^2 - k_0^2 \quad (52)$$

$$\frac{2Q}{\beta_e} = \left(1 + \frac{k_0^2}{\gamma_0^2}\right)^{-1/2}\frac{\gamma_0}{\gamma_p^2 - \gamma_0^2} \quad (53)$$

and

$$\frac{1}{Z_c} = -j\pi b\gamma_z^2\left(1 + \frac{k_0^2}{\gamma_0^2}\right)\left(\frac{\partial Y_c}{\partial \gamma}\right)_{\gamma=\gamma_0} \quad (54)$$

where we have utilized the fact that the zero of γ as defined, occurs at the unperturbed circuit value γ_0. The important relation is Eq. (53)

---

[8] FRIEDMAN; *J. Appl. Phys*, 1951, **22**, 443.
[9] FLETCHER; *Proc. I.R.E.*, 1950, **38**, 413, reprinted in Appendix VI of PIERCE; *Traveling-Wave Tubes*, p. 242. Van Nostrand, 1950.

which allows one to calculate Q. Fig. 6 shows part of Fletcher's plot of $Q(\gamma_0/\beta_e)(1 + \beta_0^2/\gamma_0^2)^{-1/2} \to Q$, as a function of $\gamma_0 a$. These curves have been very widely used for design purposes but it now seems probable that they underestimate Q, although their derivation depends on Pierce's form of the beam impedance and not on that to which we have taken exception.

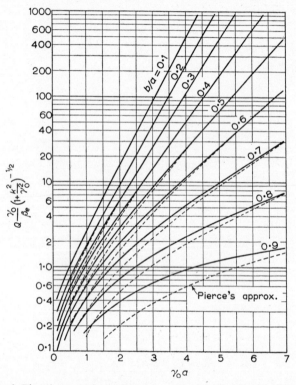

FIG. 6. Pierce's space-charge factor Q, as calculated by Fletcher (*loc. cit.*).

The thick beam is handled in this method by finding the position and current of a thin beam so that the admittance is the same as that of the thick beam, which is uniform out to radius b. This part of the derivation is subject to the field forms assumed within the beam and is therefore more suspect than Eq. (53). Since the details are somewhat elaborate they are not given here. The results are plotted in Fig. 7 for comparison. The problem of the solid beam has been treated from the viewpoint of integral equations by PAR-ZEN.[10] The integral equation is solved by use of a trial function. For this Parzen uses $I_0(pr)$, in the spirit of all the above authors and obtains results for Q which are smaller than Fletcher's, especially for small $\gamma_0 a$.

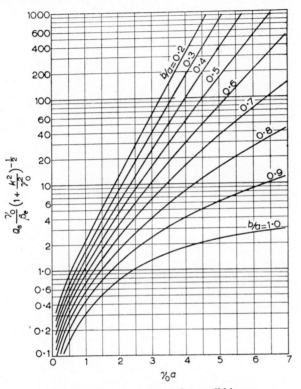

FIG. 7. The same as Fig. 6 for a solid beam.

Yet another approach to a simplified calculation of $F\omega_p$ or Q is to utilize superposition theory. Equation (8) shows that the total field is the sum of the circuit field and the space-charge fields. The real problem is a non-linear one, since the space-charge field at any z plane is due to the bunching action of the sum of circuit and space-charge fields up to the point under consideration. However, a first approximation to the result is to superpose the field

[10] PARZEN; *Trans, I.R.E.*, 1955, ED-2, 242.

due to the circuit in the absence of the beam on the space-charge field due to a beam traversing the region but with the circuit removed. This method has been used widely by the Warnecke school of writers on the problem,[11] but they go unnecessarily far in approximating the space-charge reduction factor for the case of the infinite beam. Instead of using their approximation, better results are obtained by using the curves of Fig. 3 in Chapter 4, using the $n \to \infty$ curve, which obviously represents the case in which a beam of any specified diameter traverses a space in which the radial distance to any conductor is extremely large. The resulting value of F can either be used in conjunction with Eq. (14) or can be converted into a Q value by the use of Eq. (22). It will be observed that for usual values of beam diameter $1 < \gamma_0 b < 2$, F ranges from about 0·6–0·8 which are rather large numerical values. However, this estimate of F may be expected to overshoot the correct value. Warnecke's values are 10–15% higher still but his approximate field is known to exceed the true debunching field in the drift tube case. Before leaving this estimate it should be remembered that, unlike the Fletcher analysis, it is applicable to any type of cylindrical circuit and not merely to the helix. In fact, since the helix is apt to give rise to the strongest field interactions, the superposition method is likely to give better results for other types of circuit.

Two much more fundamental studies of the reduction factor have been made. Space does not permit us to give more than an outline of the ideas. The first is due to KINO[12] who after a careful re-examination of the normal mode expansion, derives a form which converges more rapidly than the usual one. In the circuit equation, terms due to the electron current, the slow-wave mode and the lumped effect of other modes are included but Kino is able to show numerically that the final result is close to that for the beam in free space, at least for $\gamma_0 a > 1$. His result for QZ_e is

$$QZ_c \doteq 30\left(\frac{\gamma_0}{\beta_0}\right)\left(\frac{\gamma_0}{k}\right)I_0(\gamma_0 b)K_0(\gamma_0 b) \qquad (55)$$

subject to the condition $\gamma_0 a > 1$. Equation (55) applies to a hollow beam of mean radius b. For beams roughly equal in radius to the helix radius, Kino's results give values of Q which are roughly double those of Fletcher.

The second study by VAINSHTEIN[13] is even more fundamental.

[11] WARNECKE, DOEHLER and KLEEN; *Wireless Eng.*, 1951, **57**, 167.
[12] KINO; *Stanford Electronics Research Lab. Rept. No. 84*, 1955.
[13] VAINSHTEIN; *Soviet Physics* (translation of *J. Tech. Phys. U.S.S.R.*), 1956, **1**, 119.

Here, an integral equation is set up and solved on the basis of normal mode expansions. Several results, in different approximations, are obtained; the author considers that the most reliable is

$$F^2 = \frac{1}{2}\left\{ (\gamma_0 b)^2 [I_0 K_0 + I_1 K_1] - \frac{I_1{}^2}{I_0{}^2 - I_1{}^2} \right\} \qquad (56)$$

all the Bessel functions having the same argument $(\gamma_0 b)$. Fig. 8 shows a plot of Eq. (56), which applies to a solid beam compared

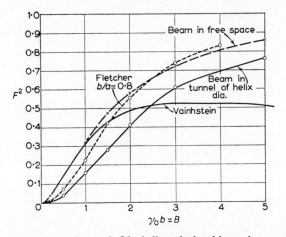

FIG. 8. Space-charge factors for the helix, calculated by various methods.

with the values taken from Fig. 3, Chapter 4. As expected, Eq. (56) yields lower values of F. We conclude that Fig. (8) shows results which are sufficiently good for practical purposes.

7.5. EXACT RESULTS FOR THE PROPAGATION CONSTANTS

Having attached a definite numerical meaning to the quantities Q or F, we now revert to the question of solutions of the secular equations, Eqs. (18) or (20). Several authors, starting with Pierce, have treated the solution of these equations in the general case of a non-sychronous beam, a slightly lossy circuit and non-zero space-charge. The method is straightforward; one attempts, by suitable substitutions and combination of parameters, to express the secular equations in the simplest possible form. Numerical values are then inserted and the roots extracted by standard procedures. The merit of one set of computations over another then merely consists in compactness, freedom from unnecessary approximation and range of conditions studied. The paper by WARNECKE *et al.* cited in Section 7.4 gives a range of such solutions but uses a notation which is very unfamiliar to Anglo-American readers. The best compilation known to me is that of BREWER and BIRDSALL.[14] In this, Pierce's form of the secular equation and notations are used as the starting point. In Eq. (20) then, put

$$\Gamma_0 = j\beta_e(1 + Cb - jCd) \tag{57}$$

$$\Gamma = j\beta_e(1 + jC\delta) \tag{58}$$

to obtain

$$\left(\delta + \frac{j\sqrt{4QC}}{1 - C\sqrt{4QC}}\right)\left(\delta - \frac{j\sqrt{4QC}}{1 + C\sqrt{4QC}}\right)(\delta + jb + d)$$

$$\times \left(\delta - jb - d - \frac{2j}{C}\right) = \left(\delta - \frac{j}{C}\right)^2 \frac{2C(1 + Cb - jCd)}{1 - 4QC^3} \tag{59}$$

To consider Eq. (59) we start from the condition in which the beam is very weakly coupled to the circuit so that Z_c, and therefore $C, \to 0$ but QC is finite. In this event Eq. (20) yields

$$(\delta + j\sqrt{4QC})(\delta - j\sqrt{4QC})(\delta + jb + d)\left(\delta - jb - \frac{2j}{C} - d\right) = 0 \tag{60}$$

and the four δ's are easily identified as two space-charge waves $\delta_{1,2} = \pm j\sqrt{(4QC)}$, δ_3 the forward circuit wave and δ_4 the backward wave. However, as the interaction region is approached the waves change their roles and this identification cannot be retained. What is done is to call δ_1 the growing wave parameter, δ_2 the attenuating wave parameter and δ_3 the fast wave parameter. The backward wave parameter δ_4 can be disposed of at once for it is always sufficiently well given by

$$\delta_4 = d + j\left(b + \frac{2}{C}\right) \tag{61}$$

The solutions of Eq. (59) are now considered as functions of C, b, d and QC and are tabulated and plotted in the form

$$\delta_n = x_n + jy_n \tag{62}$$

---

[14] BREWER and BIRDSALL; *Tech. Memo. No.* 331. Hughes Aircraft Co. A shortened version appears in *Trans. I.R.E.*, 1954, ED 1, 1.

At this point we remind readers of the physical significance of b and d. b depends on the difference between the phase constant β_0 of the unperturbed circuit mode and the phase constant of the electron beam, i.e.,

$$\beta_0 = \beta_e(1 + Cb)$$

or
$$b = \frac{1}{C}\left(\frac{\beta_0}{\beta_e} - 1\right) \tag{63}$$

d is a positive number associated with the cold circuit loss so that the attenuation over a length z is given by $\exp(-\beta_e Cd \cdot z)$ or if L dB is the loss per circuit wavelength

$$d = \frac{0 \cdot 1836L}{C} \tag{64}$$

In a study on a practical tube, then, b is a variable directly related to the voltage and can be adjusted to assume the optimum value while d is fixed once the helix dimensions and material are fixed. To obtain a large gain per unit length we require that Γ_1 should have a large negative real part. But

$$\Gamma_1 = j\beta_e(1 - Cy_1) - \beta_e Cx_1 \tag{65}$$

so that x_1 has to be large and positive. Figs. 9 and 10 show some results taken from the reference cited.

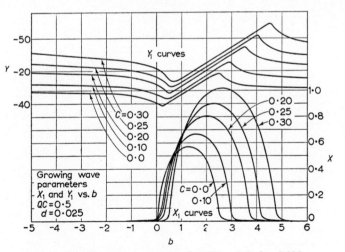

FIG. 9. Growing wave parameters for $QC = 0 \cdot 5$, $d = 0 \cdot 025$.

As we have seen, the initial excitation loss has also some influence on the overall gain of the T.W.A. Equation (33) is only valid for the approximations discussed in sections 7.3.3 and 7.3.4, since the simple

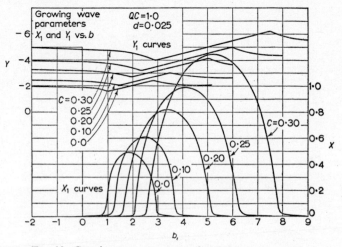

FIG. 10. Growing wave parameters for $QC = 1$, $d = 0\cdot025$.

expressions for the propagation constants do not apply. Moreover, the field at entry to the helix has to be modified to take account of the space-charge. The effects are best considered separately so that inserting our present notation and solving† for V_1/V we find

$$\frac{V_1}{V} = \left[1 + \left(\frac{1 + jC\delta_1}{1 + jC\delta_2}\right)\left(\frac{\delta_2}{\delta_1}\right)^2\left(\frac{\delta_3 - \delta_1}{\delta_2 - \delta_3}\right) + \left(\frac{1 + jC\delta_1}{1 + jC\delta_2}\right)\left(\frac{\delta_3}{\delta_1}\right)^2\left(\frac{\delta_1 - \delta_2}{\delta_2 - \delta_3}\right)\right]^{-1}$$
(66)

We see that to make use of this, we have to know δ_2 and δ_3 as well as δ_1. The results are plotted in the form of the loss $A_1 = 20\log_{10}|V_1/V|$.

Then, modifying Eq. (30) to

$$E_1 + E_2 + E_3 = E_t\left(1 - j\frac{2(\Gamma_0{}^2 - \Gamma^2)}{\beta_e Q\Gamma_0}\right)^{-1}$$
(67)

we similarly find that $\quad A_2 = 20\log_{10}|V_c/V|$

---

† See Appendix 11.

where
$$\frac{V_c}{V} = \left[1 - \frac{4QC(1 + jC\delta_1)^2}{\delta_1{}^2 + 4QC(1 + jC\delta_1)^2}\right] \qquad (68)$$

Figs. 11 and 12 show plots of A_1 and A_2.

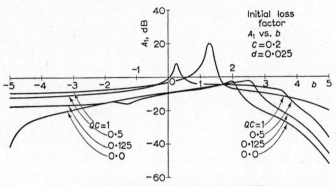

FIG. 11. Initial loss factors, $C = 0.2$, $d = 0.025$.

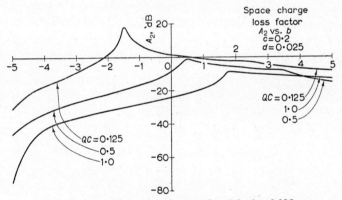

FIG. 12. Space-charge loss factor. $C = 0.2$, $d = 0.025$.

The overall gain can now be expressed in the standard form

$$G = (A_1 + A_2) + BCN \qquad (69)$$

where
$$B = 54.6x_1 \qquad (70)$$

Since x_1 is of the order unity, C may be around 0·05 in a medium-power tube and N might be 30, and the loss factors do not exceed 10 dB in the range of interest near optimum b, Eq. (69)

predicts gains of the order 70 dB. The use of heavily attenuating sections reduces this somewhat; first, by reducing the effective length and secondly by introducing a severing loss, which Pierce shows to be around 6 dB. If we estimate that the sum is 12 dB, we reduce the expected gain to below 60 dB and high-gain tubes have, in fact, been made with gains of this order. A careful comparison of theory and experiment has been made by LAICO, MCDOWELL and MOSTER[15] on a 5 W tube for 6 kMc/s. The observed gain for a beam current of 40 mA and 5 W output was 34 dB. The gain calculated for $b/a = 0.4$ was 31.5 dB and for $b/a = 0.6$, 38.5 dB. However, the estimated $b/a = 0.5$ agreed rather poorly with the value of 0.7 obtained from a beam tester. The authors ascribe the difference to the concentration of current on the axis of the tube. Another factor which may well account for some of the difference is that they used the value of F appropriate to a solid cylinder equal in mean diameter to that of the helix. As we have said, this gives too low a value of F and therefore of QC. The gain for a given b/a would therefore be reduced and the agreement in this respect, improved. One may comment that, in general, the most uncertain parameter in a design is always b/a. First, this is because it is difficult to measure this parameter except in a separate beam tester, a method which leads to uncertainties in reproduction of the mechanical dimensions, vacuum conditions, precisely equivalent magnetic fields, etc., and secondly, because the beam is inevitably scalloped to a greater or less degree and some sort of longitudinal average has to be considered. Finally, only in the best electron optical systems is the beam truly uniform in density over its cross-section. Many good and useful guns give beams which vary from annular to solid along their length. It is, perhaps, mainly for these reasons that few workers have considered it worthwhile subjecting the theory which, in general, is well confirmed by experiment, to a really detailed experimental proof. This is a pity, because such experiments would give, for instance, valuable information on values of F and Z_c.

We now revert, for a moment, to the connexion between F and Q. Equation (22) relies on the approximation $\Gamma^2 \doteq -\omega^2/u_0^2$ which we have just seen to be inexact. A better result is obtained by solving the first two brackets of Eq. (59) for the space-charge waves. Then, from Eq. (58) we find

$$\beta = \beta_e \left(1 \pm \frac{C\sqrt{4QC}}{1 \pm C\sqrt{4QC}} \right) \qquad (71)$$

[15] LAICO, MCDOWELL and MOSTER; B.S.T.J., 1956, 35, 1285.

But, for space-charge waves

$$\beta = \beta_e\left(1 \pm \frac{F\omega_p}{\omega}\right)$$

or
$$\pm \frac{F\omega_p}{\omega} = \frac{\pm C\sqrt{4QC}}{1 \pm C\sqrt{4QC}} \tag{72}$$

This is identical with the earlier approximation if C is small, but it can be seen that when $F\omega_p/\omega$ takes on the maximum values associated with modern high perveance guns, the approximation is not good and Eq. (72) should be used.

We have now discussed the major features of the low-level operation of T.W.A.s. The factors we have not mentioned, such as regions of lumped attenuation and breaks, are treated by obvious extensions of the methods used above. Details are given by Pierce.

7.6. TRAVELLING-WAVE TUBE EFFICIENCY

We have commented before on the inability of small-signal theories to say anything about the efficiency. Early estimates of this quantity were not much more than guesses. Because of the practical importance of the subject very extensive computational studies have been made on high-speed digital computers. It is impossible to say anything useful about this work in a short space so we limit ourselves to a fairly complete bibliography and some conclusions. The best technique appears to be that introduced by NORDSIECK[16] who used the Lagrangian technique of setting up equations of motion for the trajectories of typical electrons instead of the Eulerian technique of determining the velocity, charge density, etc., as functions of position and time which we have used almost exclusively in our earlier work. This work has been extended by POULTER[17] by including, at any rate partially, the space-charge effects. A small C theory including space-charge is given by TIEN, WALKER and WOLONTIS.[18] ROWE,[19] in work which has excited a good deal of controversy has used Poulter's space-charge expression (helix replaced by solid tunnel, bunches show no radial variation) but has calculated the field based on the electron distribution in time instead of in space.

[16] NORDSIECK; *Proc. I.R.E.*, 1953, **41**, 630.
[17] POULTER; *Report 73*, Electronics Research Lab., Stanford University, 1954.
[18] TIEN, WALKER and WOLONTIS; *Proc. I.R.E.*, 1955, **43**, 260.
[19] ROWE; *Report 19*, Electron Tube Laboratory, University of Michigan, 1955. Parts appear in *Proc. I.R.E.*, 1956, **44**, 200; and *Trans. I.R.E.*, 1956, ED 3, 39.

Papers by BRILLOUIN[20] and by VAINSHTEIN[21] should also be consulted. The results given in the sequel are quoted from a paper by TIEN.[22]

On the experimental side, papers by BRANGACCIO and CUTLER,[23] CALDWELL and HOCH,[24] KLEIN and FRIZ[25] and by CUTLER[26] should be referred to.

Tien's computations cover the ranges of QC 0·1–0·4; b 0·46–2·56; k 1·25–2·50 and show that the efficiency varies from 23–37% for $C = 0·1$ to 33–40% for $C = 0·15$. Perhaps the most important finding of this work is the very large increase in the velocity spread which is a consequence of increases in C. The velocity spread diminishes the bunching which lowers the saturation level and the limiting efficiency. Increases of b and QC also act in the same direction. These remarks explain the differences between the finite C theory of Tien and the small C theory of Tien, Walker and Wolontis.

CUTLER[26] investigated the operation of a tube scaled to low frequency, so that its size became large and it became easy to obtain large values of C and QC, while accurate measurement techniques were also available. He concluded that:

(i) There are optimum values for QC and γb of $QC = 0·2$, $\gamma b = 0·5$ giving maximum efficiency.

(ii) The optimum value of C leads to a maximum efficiency of 38%.

Cutler not only measured the gain, efficiency, etc., as a function of beam current and diameter, but also used a velocity spectrograph at the collector of his tube to obtain information on the velocity distribution of the electrons at exit from the helix. Curves of efficiency as a function of QC and γb show general agreement with the work of Tien except for $C > 0·14$ where the value of η/C drops away from proportionality and a general lowering by about 25%. The other striking point was that the efficiency peaked for such a relatively small diameter as $\gamma b = 0·5$. This can hardly be said to be a departure from theory as the theoretical studies do not pay much attention to the radial fields but it does seem a low value, especially in relation to the considerations on klystrons given in Chapter 6.

Table 1, which is reproduced from Cutler, gives some measured and calculated values of efficiency with the relevant parameters.

[20] BRILLOUIN; *J. Appl. Phys.*, 1949, **20**, 1197; *Proc. Nat. Acad. Sci.*, 1955, **41**, 401.
[21] VAINSHTEIN; *Congrès International Tubes Hyperfréquences*, 1956.
[22] TIEN; *B.S.T.J.*, 1956, **35**, 349.
[23] BRANGACCIO and CUTLER; *Trans. I.R.E.*, PGED 3, 1953.
[24] CALDWELL and HOCH; *Trans. I.R.E.*, E.D. 3, 1956, 6.
[25] KLEIN and FRIZ.; *F.T.Z.*, 1954, **7**, 349.
[26] CUTLER; *B.S.T.J.*, 1956, **35**, 841.

TABLE 1

Comparison between measured and theoretical efficiencies of T.W.T.s.

Source	f (kMc/s)	QC	γb	C	Efficiency %		Theoretical corrected for circuit attenuation
					Measured	Theoretical	
McDowell ..	4·0	0·27	0·62	0·078	19·5	26·0	21·6
McDowell ..	6·0	0·29	0·80	0·058	13·2	16·2	12·5
Brangaccio and Cutler	4·0	0·61	0·87	0·041	11·0	6·0	6·0†
Danielson and Watson ..	11·0	0·35	1·20	0·05	6·6	7·0	4·8
R. Warnecke	0·87	0·32	0·3	0·125	27·0	33·0	33·0
W. Klein and Friz ..	4·0	0·50	0·43	0·05	7·8	11·5	5·7
W. Kleen ..	4·0	0·20	0·94	0·10	20·0	26·0	22·0
L. Brück ..	3·5	0·19	0·60	0·065	15·0	23·0	18·5
Hughes Aircraft ..	3·24	0·19	0·94	0·12	39·0	31·0	29·0
Hughes Aircraft ..	9·0	0·15	1·30	0·11	25·0	15·5	12·7

† A slight beam misalignment could account for most of this difference.

(—Cutler)

Agreement is good except for the tubes made by the Hughes Aircraft Co., whose efficiencies considerably exceed the calculated values. On the whole then, it seems that the large-signal performance of existing tubes is fairly well understood. We do not, however, know by what means, if any, tubes with better efficiencies than those mentioned can be designed. It is obvious from what has been said, that the performance of T.W.A.s with annular beams should be investigated both experimentally and theoretically.

7.7. THE BACKWARD-WAVE OSCILLATOR

We now turn from the T.W.A. to backward-wave oscillators, whose history was briefly given in Chapter 1. The most striking feature of B.W.O.s is the electronic tuning range which in one case[27] reaches the enormous figure of 2·6 to 13·3 kMc/s. This is obtained by varying the circuit voltage from 40 to 3000 V. This last fact highlights one of the inevitable defects of the B.W.O., the large range of variation in output power with frequency. This is somewhat

---

[27] Sullivan; Proc. I.R.E., 1954, 42, 1658.

reduced by the fact that the voltage increases with the frequency so that circuit couplings and normalized beam dimensions tend to remain constant but the input power inevitably varies. In the case cited the power at a constant 10 mA beam current varies from 4 mW at 4 kMc/s to 55 mW at 12 kMc/s. Other phenomena, which rank as deficiencies of B.W.O.s from some important viewpoints, are the microstructure exhibited by the power output $\sim$ voltage curve and the frequency $\sim$ voltage curve when examined on an open scale. For instance, the latter phenomenon makes the use of the device as an F.M. transmitter difficult or impossible.

The standard theories of the B.W.O. are those of HEFFNER[28] and JOHNSON.[29] These have been extended as to the efficiency by GROW and WATKINS.[30] The treatments by Heffner and Johnson are almost identical except that Heffner uses the electronic equation (14) while Johnson uses Pierce's form of circuit equation (17). As we have pointed out, if Eq. (22) is used for conversion of one form to the other, differences can arise for large values of C. Heffner solves the resulting equations by the use of Laplace transforms but this merely leads to a rather slight simplification of the working and since Johnson's results are given in more detail we usually use his numerical values.

In the B.W.O. the electronic equation is precisely the same as it is in the T.W.A., so that either Eq. (14) holds or in the Pierce–Johnson treatment Eq. (14) without the term in $\omega_p{}^2$. The circuit equation is, however, different as we see by comparing Eq. (4) with Eq. (3). By differentiating Eq. (4) twice with respect to a, we find for the field variation along the line

$$\frac{d^2 E_z}{dz^2} - \Gamma_0{}^2 E_z = \Gamma_0 A(z) \tag{73}$$

or
$$(\Gamma^2 - \Gamma_0{}^2)E_z = \Gamma_0 A(z) \tag{74}$$

which differs from Eq. (15) in the sign of the R.H.S. alone. If we now define the coupling impedance by

$$A(z) = -\Gamma^2 Z_e i_1 \tag{75}$$

which is in any case logical in view of the direction of energy flow, we retrieve Eqs. (18) or (20), respectively. On the other hand, we do

[28] HEFFNER; *Proc. I.R.E.*, 1954, **42**, 930.
[29] JOHNSON; *Proc. I.R.E.*, 1955, **43**, 684.
[30] GROW and WATKINS; *Proc. I.R.E.*, 1955, **43**, 848.

not wish to have C^3 a negative number, so in fact we retain the original definition $A_z = \Gamma^2 Z_c i_1$, and obtain the secular equation

$$(j\beta_e - \Gamma)^2 - 4\Gamma^2 Q C^3 = \frac{-2C^3 \Gamma^2 \Gamma_0 \cdot j\beta_e}{(\Gamma_0{}^2 - \Gamma^2)} \qquad (76)$$

which differs from Eq. (20) by a minus sign on the R.H.S. Following Johnson, we write by analogy with Eqs. (57) and (58)

$$\Gamma_0 = j\beta_e(1 + Cb + jCd) \qquad (77)$$

$$\Gamma = j\beta_e(1 + jC\delta) \qquad (78)$$

Inserting these into Eq. (76) and approximating for $C \ll 1$ we find

$$-\delta^2 = \frac{1}{-b - jd + j\delta} + 4QC \qquad (79)$$

In this approximation the fields and the voltages are found in just the same way as in Eqs. (30)–(33) so that (initial r.f. current and velocity still zero) we find

$$V_1 = \frac{V(O)}{(1 - \delta_2/\delta_1)(1 - \delta_3/\delta_1)} \text{ etc.} \qquad (80)$$

But we are now taking space-charge effects into account so that the actual circuit voltage is somewhat different, being given by

$$\frac{V_{c1}}{V_1} = \frac{\delta_1{}^2 + 4QC}{\delta_1{}^2} \qquad (81)$$

and
$$V_c = V_{c1} + V_{c2} + V_{c3} \qquad (82)$$

Using Eq. (80)
$$V_{c1} = \frac{V(O)(\delta_1{}^2 + 4QC)}{(\delta_1 - \delta_2)(\delta_1 - \delta_3)} \qquad (83)$$

with similar expressions for V_{c2} and V_{c3}. The corresponding expression for the value of this voltage at the output, $z = l$ is, using Eq. (78),

$$V_{c1}(l) = V_{c1} \exp(-j\beta_e l) \exp \beta_e C l \delta_1 \qquad (84)$$

or, introducing $\beta_e l = 2\pi N$ and summing over the three waves

$$\frac{V_c(l)}{V(O)} \exp(j2\pi N) = \frac{(\delta_1^2 + 4QC) \exp(2\pi CN\delta_1)}{(\delta_1 - \delta_2)(\delta_1 - \delta_3)} +$$
$$+ \frac{(\delta_2^2 + 4QC) \exp(2\pi CN\delta_2)}{(\delta_2 - \delta_1)(\delta_2 - \delta_3)} + \frac{(\delta_3^2 + 4QC) \exp(2\pi CN\delta_3)}{(\delta_3 - \delta_1)(\delta_3 - \delta_2)} \quad (85)$$

If now Eq. (79) is solved for the δ's as a function of b, d and QC, the gain of the B.W.O. can be calculated by putting the appropriate values into Eq. (85). When this is done it is found that the gain becomes infinite for certain values of CN which is, of course, the condition for the tube to start oscillating. In other words the oscillation conditions are found from the roots of the equation

$$\frac{V_c(l)}{V(O)} = 0 \quad (86)$$

It should be noted that Eq. (86) can be satisfied for a whole series of different values of CN. These represent higher order oscillations which occur in a particular tube, if the beam current is increased sufficiently far above the starting current. There is thus a difficulty in increasing the power output from a B.W.O. simply by increasing the input. This has to be overcome by circuit techniques, e.g., by the use of circuits in which the coupling impedance for the higher order mode is reduced.

Equation (85) can be easily solved using the first order δ's which ignore loss and space-charge. Heffner shows that when this is done, we find

$$(\beta - \beta_e)L = (2n + 1)\pi \quad (87)$$

where n is the order of the oscillation. In a backward-wave circuit β decreases as ω increases so that Eq. (87) shows that ω decreases as the order of the oscillation increases, which tends to make it more difficult to avoid interfering modes.

Table 2 shows Johnson's starting currents computed from Eq. (85) for three values of QC, while Table 3 shows the corresponding values of the δ's. In these tables D is the total circuit loss, defined similarly to Eq. (70), as

$$D = 54{\cdot}6dCN \text{ dB} \quad (88)$$

Figs. 13 and 14 show plots of CN and $(\beta - \beta_e)L$ vs. Q/N. On these, we have added points for the second oscillation, when

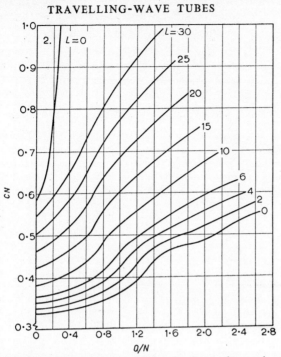

FIG. 13. CN vs. Q/N at start oscillation for first and second modes.

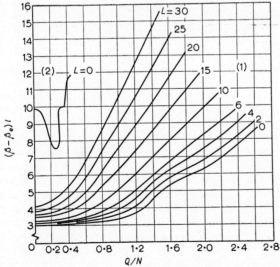

FIG. 14. $(\beta - \beta_e)l$ vs. Q/N at start oscillation for first and second modes.

R

$D = 0$, taken from the work of Heffner. These curves are used as follows—A reasonable beam current is assumed. C is then calculated, using the correct expression for the coupling impedance

TABLE 2

Theoretical starting conditions for backward-wave oscillator

QC	L	b	CN	$(\beta - \beta_e)$	QC/CN
	0	1·522	0·3141	3·003	0
	2	1·488	0·3275	3·062	0
	4	1·457	0·3414	3·125	0
	6	1·427	0·3556	3·188	0
0	10	1·375	0·3847	3·324	0
	15	1·318	0·4229	3·502	0
	20	1·271	0·4627	3·695	0
	25	1·231	0·5040	3·898	0
	30	1·197	0·5470	4·114	0
	0	1·533	0·3990	3·843	1·253
	2	1·526	0·4237	4·063	1·180
	4	1·526	0·4483	4·298	1·115
	6	1·530	0·4731	4·548	1·057
0·50	10	1·543	0·5207	5·048	0·9602
	15	1·553	0·5775	5·635	0·8658
	20	1·555	0·6344	6·198	0·7881
	25	1·551	0·6934	6·758	0·7211
	30	1·547	0·7554	7·343	0·6619
	0	2·072	0·4914	6·397	2·035
	2	2·064	0·5156	6·687	1·939
	4	2·059	0·5413	7·003	1·847
	6	2·058	0·5684	7·350	1·759
1·00	10	2·063	0·6218	8·060	1·608
	15	2·067	0·6866	8·917	1·456
	20	2·065	0·7537	9·779	1·327
	25	2·063	0·8249	10·69	1·212
	30	2·064	0·8982	11·65	1·113

determined for the desired backward-wave mode, which is often a space-harmonic. Q can be calculated as in Section 7.4 and then, knowing the circuit loss, a value of N suitable for the start of oscillation can be determined. If this is unsuitable, e.g., if the circuit is too long or stupidly short or conditions are too close to the start of the second oscillation, the current must be appropriately modified and another trial made.

TABLE 3. Theoretical propagation constants for waves in a backward-wave oscillator at start of oscillation

QC	L	δ_1		δ_2 (Fast space-charge wave)		δ_3	
0	0	0.72521	$+0.15046j$	-0.72521	$+0.15046j$	0	$-1.82293j$
	2	0.74390	$+0.13938j$	-0.71527	$+0.16864j$	0.083275	$-1.79602j$
	4	0.76168	$+0.12775j$	-0.70537	$+0.18423j$	0.15838	$-1.76898j$
	6	0.77885	$+0.11591j$	-0.69589	$+0.19784j$	0.22624	$-1.74075j$
	10	0.81036	$+0.09118j$	-0.67805	$+0.21964j$	0.34389	$-1.68582j$
	15	0.84560	$+0.05976j$	-0.65872	$+0.23995j$	0.46303	$-1.61770j$
	20	0.87594	$+0.02827j$	-0.64244	$+0.25459j$	0.55850	$-1.55386j$
	25	0.90220	$-0.00246j$	-0.62890	$+0.26552j$	0.63562	$-1.49407j$
	30	0.92476	$-0.03180j$	-0.61775	$+0.27382j$	0.69799	$-1.43902j$
0.50	0	0	$-0.79876j$	0	$+1.28250j$	0	$-2.01674j$
	2	0.04676	$-0.79680j$	-0.004494	$+1.28231j$	0.04423	$-2.01151j$
	4	0.08835	$-0.80145j$	-0.008465	$+1.28272j$	0.08361	$-2.00727j$
	6	0.12507	$-0.81025j$	-0.011934	$+1.28350j$	0.11926	$-2.00325j$
	10	0.18685	$-0.83442j$	-0.017663	$+1.28558j$	0.18272	$-1.99415j$
	15	0.24963	$-0.86576j$	-0.023288	$+1.28806j$	0.24956	$-1.97530j$
	20	0.30151	$-0.89517j$	-0.027729	$+1.29016j$	0.30392	$-1.95000j$
	25	0.34522	$-0.92156j$	-0.031282	$+1.29186j$	0.34666	$-1.92130j$
	30	0.38099	$-0.94662j$	-0.034054	$+1.29334j$	0.38076	$-1.89371j$
1.0	0	0	$-1.50029j$	0	$+1.93663j$	0	$-2.50834j$
	2	0.036174	$-1.49754j$	-0.001165	$+1.93652j$	0.036061	$-2.50298j$
	4	0.069266	$-1.49845j$	-0.002223	$+1.93650j$	0.068358	$-2.49705j$
	6	0.099034	$-1.50294j$	-0.003173	$+1.93656j$	0.097539	$-2.49163j$
	10	0.15005	$-1.51868j$	-0.004804	$+1.93685j$	0.14936	$-2.48117j$
	15	0.20269	$-1.54151j$	-0.006478	$+1.93725j$	0.20409	$-2.46373j$
	20	0.24689	$-1.56200j$	-0.007839	$+1.93752j$	0.24715	$-2.44052j$
	25	0.28204	$-1.58323j$	-0.008909	$+1.93780j$	0.28187	$-2.41857j$
	30	0.31087	$-1.60445j$	-0.009779	$+1.93807j$	0.31091	$-2.39762j$

TABLE 3a

Incremental propagation constants at start oscillation ($d = 0$)
First root ($n = 0$)

QC	b	CN	x_1	y_1	x_2	y_2	y_3
0·01	1·5208	0·31499	0·701126	0·151985	−0·701126	0·151985	−1·82477
0·15	1·51683	0·318892	0·595803	0·158194	−0·595803	0·158194	−1·83322
0·10	1·51213	0·32415	0·431820	0·166441	−0·431820	0·166441	−1·84501
0·15	1·5079	0·329905	0·143376	0·175225	−0·143376	0·175225	−1·85835
0·152	1·5076	0·33020	0·118393	0·175610	−0·118393	0·175610	−1·85882
0·154	1·5076	0·33040	0·0859972	0·175948	−0·0859972	0·175948	−1·85949
0·156	1·5076	0·33060	0·0278968	0·176288	−0·0278968	0·176288	−1·86017
0·158	1·5075	0·33100	0	0·10045	0	0·252839	−1·86078
0·16	1·5071	0·33111	0	0·0661599	0	0·287939	−1·86119
0·18	1·5052	0·33360	0	−0·09766	0	0·4593	−1·8668
0·19	1·5047	0·33490	0	−0·14920	0	0·5146	−1·87005
0·20	1·5042	0·33628	0	−0·193094	0	0·562197	−1·87330
0·25	1·5015	0·34337	0	−0·356192	0	0·744875	−1·89018

TABLE 3b

Incremental propagation constants at start oscillation (d = 0)
Second root ($n = 1$)

QC	b	CN	x_1	y_2	x_2	y_2	y_3
0·01	2·6312	0·59533	0·565253	0·0658452	−0·565253	0·0658452	−2·76289
0·05	2·4621	0·63023	0·434237	0·0754412	−0·43237	0·0754412	−2·61298
0·10	2·2095	0·68766	0·199324	0·0935656	−0·199324	0·0935656	−2·39663
0·11	2·15240	0·70150	0·113337	0·0984419	−0·113337	0·0984419	−2·34928
0·13	2·03120	0·73186	0	−0·0825726	0	0·302475	−2·25110
0·14	1·967	0·7485	0	−0·127713	0	0·361233	−2·20052
0·15	1·9009	0·76584	0	−0·159976	0	0·408682	−2·14961
0·20	1·5594	0·85924	0	−0·224975	0	0·575922	−1·91035
0·25	1·2663	0·9462	0	−0·216922	0	0·701252	−1·75063
0·26	1·22136	0·96427	0	−0·215066	0	0·725501	−1·73179
0·27	1·1860	0·9865	0	−0·217612	0	0·750786	−1·71917
0·280	1·3990	1·05165	0	−0·376647	0	0·817871	−1·84022

7.7.1. The efficiency of B.W.O.s

GROW and WATKINS[30] have investigated the efficiency of these devices, using the more or less arbitrary assumption (which is known, however, to be near the truth in klystrons and T.W.A.s) that the maximum r.f. current magnitude is equal to the d.c. current I_0. Then, since the output power is taken from the gun end of the circuit

$$\eta = \frac{P(O)}{I_0 V_0} = \frac{|E(O)|^2}{V_0{}^2} \frac{1}{8\beta^2 C^3} \tag{89}$$

where we have just introduced the definition of C^3. The efficiency is now expressed in terms of the current at the output end of the circuit. If we write the voltage equivalent of Eq. (32) evaluated at exit from the circuit we have

$$\frac{V_1(L)}{\delta_1{}^2} + \frac{V_2(L)}{\delta_2{}^2} + \frac{V_3(L)}{\delta_3{}^2} = -2\frac{V_0 C^2}{I_0} i_1(L) \tag{90}$$

But $V_1(L)/\delta_1{}^2$ etc., are given by Eqs. (83) and (84) as

$$\frac{V_1(L)}{\delta_1{}^2} = \exp(-j2\pi N)\left[\frac{V(O)\exp(2\pi CN\delta_1)}{(\delta_1 - \delta_2)(\delta_1 - \delta_3)}\right] \tag{91}$$

if we allow $4QC \to 0$. If we put $E(O) = \Gamma V(O) \doteq -j\beta_e V(O)$ we finally obtain

$$i_1(L) = -j\frac{I_0 G}{2V_0 C^2 \beta_e}E(O) \tag{92}$$

where

$$G = \exp(-j2\pi N)$$

$$\times \left[\frac{\exp(2\pi CN\delta_1)}{(\delta_1 - \delta_2)(\delta_1 - \delta_3)} + \frac{\exp(2\pi CN\delta_2)}{(\delta_2 - \delta_1)(\delta_2 - \delta_3)} + \frac{\exp(2\pi CN\delta_3)}{(\delta_3 - \delta_1)(\delta_3 - \delta_2)}\right] \tag{93}$$

or, using Eq. (92) in Eq. (89) and putting $i_1(L)_{\max} = I_0$,

$$\eta_0 = \frac{C}{2|G|^2} \tag{94}$$

This is the desired relation for η_0. Equation (93) can be evaluated using the δ's of the last section. When this is done it turns out that the efficiencies obtained from Eq. (94) are much smaller than those measured. However, when QC is large the values tend to oscillate above and below the straight line

$$\frac{\eta}{C} = \sqrt{4QC} = \frac{F\omega_p}{C\omega} \tag{95}$$

In this case the measured efficiencies show a distinct tendency to group about the same line and Eq. (95) does give a reasonable estimate of the efficiency when $\sqrt{(4QC)} > 1\cdot5$. It is not difficult to show directly from Eq. (79) that the values of δ for large QC are as follows:

$$\delta_1 = -j\sqrt{4QC}\left[1 - \frac{1}{4(QC)^{3/4}}\right] \tag{96}$$

$$\delta_2 = j\sqrt{4QC} \tag{97}$$

$$\delta_3 = -j\sqrt{4QC}\left[1 + \frac{1}{4(QC)^{3/4}}\right] \tag{98}$$

and that these values lead to the efficiency value quoted. The details are given by Johnson.

In calculating the output efficiency, two effects not yet considered have to be included. These are the drop in output due to the distributed loss (if any) in the circuit and the effects due to the beam diameter. These points are discussed by Grow and Watkins. For large QC, it can be shown that the current and field at a plane z are given by

$$i(z) = i(L) \sin\frac{\pi z}{2L} \exp(-j\beta z)$$

$$E(z) = i(L) \cos\frac{\pi z}{2L} \exp(-j\beta z)$$

and therefore

$$P(z) = P(O) \cos^2\frac{\pi z}{2L} \tag{99}$$

and

$$\frac{dP(z)}{dz} = \frac{\pi}{2L}P(O) \sin\frac{\pi z}{L} \tag{100}$$

Equation (100) shows that the rate of power transfer is zero at $z = 0$ and $z = L$ and a maximum at $z = L/2$, so that the central region of the circuit is responsible for most of the power transfer. To calculate the reduction in power, the power elements are weighted according to Eq. (100) and the attenuation in traversing the distance $L - Z$ is calculated. The result is

$$F_1 = \exp\left(-0{\cdot}115L\right) \frac{\cosh\left(0{\cdot}115L\right)}{1 + \left(0{\cdot}230L/\pi\right)^2} \qquad (101)$$

where L = total circuit loss in dB. From the curve given in Fig. 15 it can be seen that the output is reduced to less than half if the circuit loss is more than 6 dB. In general, B.W.O. circuits are not made purposely lossy, except perhaps in the immediate vicinity of the collector where some added loss is often used to ease the matching problem. However, at the highest operating frequencies the inevitable circuit losses are quite important and contribute to the general lowering of efficiency.

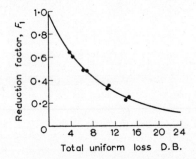

FIG. 15. Theoretical and experimental loss factor.

The variation with beam thickness follows from the same reasoning we have used in the case of the klystron. Current saturation first occurs on the edge of the electron beam where the electric field is strongest. However, in this case, the electric field may either vary as $I_0(\gamma r)$, as it does in a circuit which has a backward fundamental mode, or as $I_1(\gamma r)$ as in the more usual first space-harmonic structure. The efficiency may be considered to vary over the beam as

$$\frac{\eta r}{\eta_0} = \frac{Z_{c(r)}}{Z_{c\max}} \qquad (102)$$

and this, for a solid beam in a fundamental circuit gives a reduction factor F_2 of familiar form.

$$F_2 = \frac{I_0{}^2(\gamma b) - I_1{}^2(\gamma b)}{I_0{}^2(\gamma b)} \qquad (103)$$

This does not lead to a serious reduction if $\gamma b < 1$. The helix used in the first space harmonic mode gives rise to values of γa between 3·0 and 4·5 and the $I_1(\gamma a)$ field gives a reduction factor which varies more rapidly with argument than does Eq. (103). For this reason, helix circuit B.W.O.s are usually made with relatively thin hollow beams. Grow and Watkins give a useful approximation for this case, valid when $\gamma b \gg 1$. It is

$$F_2 = \frac{1 - \exp(-2\gamma t)}{2\gamma t}$$

where $\qquad\qquad t = \text{beam thickness} \qquad\qquad (104)$

This is plotted in Fig. 16 and we observe that the normalized beam thickness should be less than one-fifth to avoid undue loss in efficiency. Equation (104) is independent of whether the field varies as I_0 or I_1.

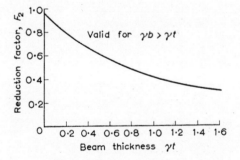

FIG. 16. Reduction factor for thin annular beam.

Backward-wave oscillators are particularly valuable as they have been shown to oscillate at extremely high frequencies, the work of KARP[31] being particularly noteworthy in this connexion. The special type of circuit used was briefly discussed in Chapter 3. Karp has used the Grow and Watkins efficiency expression of Eq. (95) to obtain a useful order of magnitude relation for the power output from a B.W.O. The electric field is assumed to drop off away from the circuit as $\exp(-\gamma y)$ where, as usual,

$$\gamma = \frac{2\pi}{(p/c)\lambda_0} \qquad\qquad (105)$$

[31] KARP; *Proc. I.R.E.*, 1955, **43**, 41; 1957, **45**, 496.

Since the square of the electric field is required, an effective beam width can be defined through

$$\frac{1}{2\beta} = \frac{p}{c} \cdot \frac{\lambda_0}{4\pi} \tag{106}$$

If the beam, supposed to be on either side of the ladder circuit, is of density J_0 and width $W/2$, the available power input is

$$\frac{J_0 V_0 W}{2\beta} = \frac{J_0 V_0 W \lambda_0 (p/c)}{4\pi} \text{ watts} \tag{107}$$

For very short wavelengths $F \to 1$, so substituting for ω_p, u_0 and ω we find

$$P_{\text{out}} \doteqdot 86 \cdot 5 J_0^{3/2} V_0^{5/4} (\lambda_0^2 W) \tag{108}$$

where the units are, power in milliwatts, current in A/cm², lengths in centimetres and kilowatts. Since W usually varies as $m\lambda_0$, we can replace the bracket by $m\lambda_0^3$, to show how rapidly the output falls off as the wavelength diminishes. The table shows results calculated for $m = \frac{1}{3}$, a basis which allows for the variations

TABLE 4

Calculated performance of B.W.O's at 100 and 200 kMc/s.

Wavelength	3 mm	1·5 mm
Voltage (kV)	1·0	2·5
Cathode density (A/cm²) ..	3·0	8·0
Circuit loss (dB)	30·0	58·0
Reduction factor (F_1) ..	0·1	0·025
Uncorrected output (mW) ..	3·5	6·0
Corrected output (mW) ..	0·35	0·15

of E_z with x as well as with y. The table immediately shows how important the circuit loss becomes at high frequencies. The observed output is reduced to one-tenth in one case and to one-fortieth in the other. The cathode current densities are computed on the basis of no gun convergence, which Karp considers to be required to prevent spiralling of the beam. It hardly needs to be said that the figures given are excessive for long life operation of even the best cathodes known. Karp also points out that under these conditions of high circuit loss, increasing the circuit length does not reduce the starting current. It is therefore necessary to design the circuit for minimum loss rather than for maximum Z_c and this leads to thicker lateral conductors, which are naturally desirable from the viewpoint of heat dissipation also.

7.8. REFERENCES ON PRACTICAL EMBODIMENTS OF B.W.O.s

In view of the interest of the subject it would seem appropriate to give some extra references on the actual state of B.W.O. development. These devices seem destined to have their major uses in equipment, such as laboratory signal generators and panoramic receivers, which is required to be readily tunable over a wide range of frequencies. Signal generators of this type are already in production. The references below give an accurate indication of the results achieved at the time of writing.

BIBLIOGRAPHY

1. WATKINS; *Traveling-Wave Tubes and Backward-Wave Tubes*, Symposium on Modern Advances in Microwave Techniques, Polytechnic Institute of Brooklyn, 1955.
2. PALLUEL; *Onde Élect.*, 1956, **36**, 962.
3. JOHNSON and WEGLEIN; *Trans. I.R.E.*, 1957, ED4, 180.
4. BARNES; *Le Vide*, 1957, **12**, 43.
5. PALLUEL and GOLDBERGER; *Proc. I.R.E.*, 1956, **44**, 333.

CROSSED FIELD DEVICES

IN THIS chapter we study the crossed field devices analogous to the T.W.A.s and B.W.O.s already discussed. It is convenient to use the French terminology and classify these as the "M" devices.

While the overall behaviour of "M" devices is very similar to that of the valves we have encountered before, it should be made clear, *ab initio*, that there is a major difference as far as the efficiency is concerned. The "M" devices should operate with much greater efficiencies than do the normal ones. The basic reason for this is simple: the drift velocity with which the electrons travel, is considerably smaller than the velocity corresponding with the d.c. potential applied to the valve. In Appendix 6 we see that in a planar magnetron the drift velocity is given by $u_z = V_0/B \cdot d$ or the equivalent drift voltage is $V_z = V_0^2/2\eta B^2 d^2$ which is generally small in comparison with V_0. Simple theories of "M" devices lead to electronic efficiencies of the form

$$\eta_e = 1 - \frac{mV_z}{V_0}$$

where m depends on the geometry, being unity for a planar device (linear electron trajectories) and equal to 4 for a cylindrical magnetron without space charge. The electrons have relatively small amounts of kinetic energy. The process of bunching in "M" devices leads to periodic variations of the width of the beam. The high-frequency field would reduce the longitudinal velocity were it not for the fact that the magnetic field forces the electrons outwards into a region of greater potential energy without, however, much altering the actual value of u_z. Thus, the potential energy which would normally have increased the electron velocity is directly transferred to the h.f. field. It is therefore sometimes said that crossed field devices transform potential energy into r.f. energy.

Existing "M" type amplifiers[1] have reasonably high values of

---

[1] WARNECKE, KLEEN, LERBS, DÖHLER and HUBER; *Proc. Inst. Radio Engrs. N.Y.*, 1950, **38**, 486.

efficiency but such small gains that their use is not particularly attractive. The "M" type B.W.O., hereafter termed the Carcinotron, is a much more useful device. It has the usual feature of B.W.O.s, a large tuning range obtained by merely altering the operating voltage, and it is not difficult to make valves giving moderate C.W. power.[2] The recorded efficiencies are rather disappointing.

8.1. THE CIRCUIT AND ELECTRONIC EQUATIONS FOR "M" DEVICES

The determinantal equations for the "M" devices have been given by several authors. The French literature includes the following: a simplified derivation by BROSSART and DOEHLER[3] which is subsequently improved and corrected by DOEHLER, BROSSART and MOURIER.[4] The extension to include space-charge effects is given by WARNECKE, DOEHLER and BOBOT.[5] In the United States the results of PIERCE[6] are used. The main difference is that Pierce's treatment retains the small term in the a.c. charge density and thus exhibits more solutions. Since the treatment is otherwise very reminiscent of that used in Chapter 4, we refer the reader to Pierce for details and quote the result, which is

$$(\Gamma^2 - \Gamma_0{}^2)(j\beta_e - \Gamma)[(j\beta_e - \Gamma)^2 + \beta_m{}^2]$$
$$= -j\beta_e\Gamma_0\Gamma^2\left[(j\beta_e - \Gamma) + 2j\frac{\alpha}{1+\alpha^2}\beta_m\right]H^2 \qquad (1)$$

$$H^2 = 2(1+\alpha^2)\phi^2C^3$$

Here Γ's are the hot propagation constants, Γ_0 is the circuit propagation constant

$$\beta_e = \frac{\omega}{u_z}, \qquad \beta_m = \frac{\omega_c}{u_z}$$

where $\omega_c = \eta B$, ϕ and α are dimensionless parameters depending on the transverse variation of the h.f. field.

Equation (1) is of the fifth degree in Γ, so there are five propagation constants, one more than in the "O" type T.W.A. If we include Γ_0 there are thus six possible waves, since Γ_0 will be observed

[2] WARNECKE; *Ann. Radioélectricité*, 1954, **9**, 108.
[3] BROSSART and DOEHLER; *Ann. Radioélec.*, 1948, **3**, 328.
[4] DOEHLER, BROSSART and MOURIER; *Ann. Radioélec.*, 1950, **5**, 293.
[5] WARNECKE, DOEHLER and BOBOT; *Ann. Radioélec.*, 1950, **5**, 279.
[6] PIERCE; *Traveling-Wave Tubes*, Chapter 15. Van Nostrand, 1950.

unperturbed when the device is far off interaction. We shall subsequently find that the six constants are formed by perturbation of the results found off synchronism, namely,

Two Γ's of value $j\beta_e$

Two Γ's of value $j(\beta_e \pm \beta_m)$

Two Γ's of value $\pm\Gamma_0$

We note that instead of space-charge waves with propagation constants $\beta_e \pm F\omega_p/u_0$ we have $\beta_e \pm \beta_m$. Numerically, β_m is much greater than $F\omega_p/u_0$.

Equation (1) is solved by the same technique we applied to the T.W.A., i.e., we put

$$\Gamma_0 = j\beta$$

$$\Gamma = j\beta(1 + p)$$

where p is very small. Putting these in Eq. (1) and neglecting p compared with unity, we find

$$p\left(\frac{\beta_e}{\beta} - 1 - p\right)\left[\left(\frac{\beta_e}{\beta} - 1 - p\right)^2 - \left(\frac{\beta_m}{\beta}\right)^2\right]$$

$$= \frac{-\beta_e}{2\beta}\left[\left(\frac{\beta_e}{\beta} - 1 - p\right) + \frac{2\alpha\beta_m}{(1 + \alpha^2)\beta}\right]H^2 \qquad (2)$$

The right-hand term is small, as it is not much different from C so that if either one of the left-hand terms is also small, then Eq. (2) will be satisfied.

Choosing $\beta_e \doteq \beta$ makes the first factor small and the solution for p becomes

$$p = \pm j\left[\frac{\alpha}{(1 + \alpha^2)}\right]^{1/2}\left(\frac{\beta}{\beta_m}\right)^{1/2}H \qquad (3)$$

Choosing $\beta_e \pm \beta_m \doteq \beta$ makes the second factor small and the solution for p becomes

$$p^2 = \pm\frac{1}{4}\frac{(1 \pm \alpha)^2}{1 + \alpha^2}\left(\frac{\beta}{\beta_m} \pm 1\right)H^2 \qquad (4)$$

From the definition of p, gain is only obtained when p is imaginary. From Eq. (3) this only happens when α is positive. In Eq. (4), p

is imaginary when $\beta_e + \beta_m = \beta$ and α is less than unity. This last condition comes from rewriting Eq. (4) as

$$p = \pm \frac{1}{2} \frac{1 - \alpha}{(1 + \alpha)^{1/2}} \left(\frac{\beta_e}{\beta_m}\right)^{1/2} H \tag{5}$$

The backward waves are investigated by putting $\Gamma = -j\beta(1 + p)$. The analogue of Eq. (2) then shows that roots are only possible for

$$\beta + \beta_e = \beta_m$$

when
$$p = \pm j\frac{1}{2} \frac{(1 + \alpha)}{(1 + \alpha^2)^{1/2}} \left(\frac{\beta_e}{\beta_m}\right)^{1/2} H \tag{6}$$

This gives rise to increasing backward waves for all values of α except $\alpha = -1$.

Since $H \propto C^{3/2}$, Eqs. (3), (5) and (6) show that the gain per unit length in "M" devices is lower than in "O" devices using similar circuits, because as C is small, $C^{3/2} < C$. By the same token, the gain per unit length $\propto I_0^{1/2}$, instead of $I_0^{1/3}$ a considerably faster variation with current.

In the form given above these results are not very easy to appreciate physically. An excellent discussion of the general behaviour has been given by MULLER[7] who separates the determinantal equation into two parts: a circuit equation for ρ/V and a ballistic equation for the same quantity. ρ/V is analogous to an admittance and the intersections of the two curves for the admittance determine the allowed propagation constants. The equations are normalized by writing $\Gamma = j\gamma$, $\Gamma_0 = j\beta$, $\delta = \gamma/\beta_e$ or, in other words, the solution is sought in terms of pure imaginaries.

The circuit equation gives

$$\frac{\rho}{V} = \frac{(\beta/\beta_e)^2 - \delta^2}{\omega\beta/\beta_e\phi Z_c} \tag{7}$$

while the corresponding ballistic equation is

$$\frac{\rho}{V} = \frac{-\eta I_0 \phi \delta^2}{u_0^3} \frac{[(1 + \alpha^2)(1 - \delta) + 2\alpha m]}{(1 - \delta)(m^2 - (1 - \delta)^2)} \tag{8}$$

where $m = \beta_m/\beta_e$.

[7] MULLER; Proc. Inst. Radio Engrs. N.Y., 1954, 42, 1651.

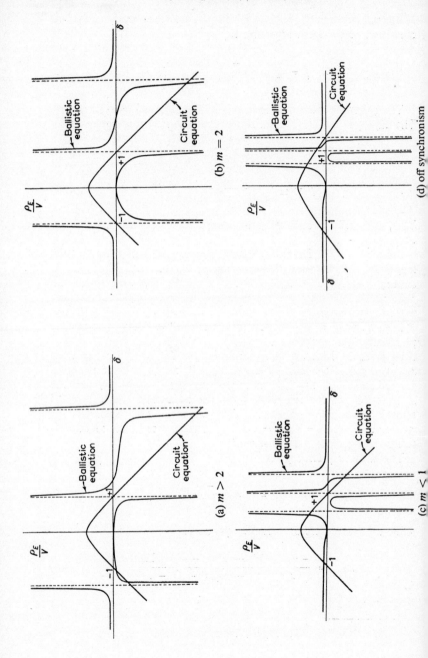

(a) $m > 2$

(b) $m = 2$

(c) $m < 1$

(d) off synchronism

The circuit equation is independent of m, which is clearly a parameter defining the magnetic field. Note that Eq. (8) has a simple pole at $\delta = 1$. It also has poles at $m = \pm(1 - \delta)$. The circuit equation is a parabola about the ρ/V axis. Figs. 1 show some plots of these equations for diminishing values of magnetic field. The first three are plotted for synchronous conditions, i.e., $\beta = \beta_e$. In Fig. 1(a) $m > 2$, so that the three poles of the ballistic equation are at $\delta = 1$, $\delta > 3$ and $\delta < -1$. The intersections giving rise to gain are, of course, complex and do not appear as cuts in the purely imaginary plot of Fig. 1(a). However, it is easy to visualize the complex roots which occur where the circuit and ballistic equations become close together near $\delta = +1$. For $m = 2$, Fig. 1(b), the poles are at $\delta = \pm 1$, $+3$ and, as m diminishes the poles move towards the axis from left to right until $m = 1$, below which value all the poles take on positive signs, leading to the situation of Fig. 1(c). Finally, Fig. 1(d) shows a situation for $m < 1$ and $\beta_e < \beta$, i.e., a non-synchronous beam. Clearly, this case also shows the possibility of complex roots and therefore gain. Fig. 1(d) is plotted, as has been said, for $\beta_e < \beta$. The fact that gain is still possible under these conditions is another difference between "M" and "O" devices, for, in the conventional T.W.A., gain is only possible when $\beta_e > \beta$. This can be seen, for instance, by deriving the analogues of Eqs. (7) and (8), i.e., by putting $\phi = 1$, α and $m = 0$. It is then found that if $\beta_e < \beta$ the equations have four purely imaginary roots and gain is therefore impossible.

We also note that the complex roots of Eqs. (7) and (8) correspond with values of ρ/V very close to zero. Since the r.f. voltage is certainly not infinite, ρ must therefore be small. This is a situation already encountered in other types of flow in magnetic fields, for instance, in Brillouin flow in "O" devices, as we saw in Chapter 4.

8.2. REMARKS ON CIRCUITS IN "M" DEVICES

So far we have characterized the circuit only through the dimensionless parameters ϕ and α which save much writing. In "M" devices as used today, the only circuit utilized is the interdigital line, although the first descriptions and experimental work related to the flattened helix, which was treated by DOEHLER, BROSSART and MOURIER.[4] Since we have discussed the interdigital line rather completely in Chapter 3, we need to say little here.

The quantities ϕ and α are defined by Pierce through the following relations. The voltage in the vicinity of the circuit is given by

$$V(x, y) = \phi V \qquad (9)$$

and, in deriving the circuit equation, it is assumed that

$$\phi = Ae^{-j\Gamma y} + Be^{j\Gamma y} \tag{10}$$

while

$$\alpha = \frac{Ae^{-j\Gamma y} - Be^{j\Gamma y}}{Ae^{-j\Gamma y} + Be^{j\Gamma y}} = \frac{-1}{\Gamma \phi} \frac{d\phi}{dy} \tag{11}$$

In an exact solution of the problem the adjustable constants should be derived from a solution to the field problem when the beam is present, but this procedure is, in general, too difficult. Equations (10) and (11) are usually therefore applied to the cold-circuit fields. In the immediate vicinity of the delay line these fields are simply those already determined in Chapter 3 and, apart from the actual computations, no difficulty arises. However, one must remember that, especially for the space harmonic fields, the delay line fields fall off rapidly as the distance from the conductor increases and that between the beam and the cathode plane or sole, fields derived from

$$E_z = jA \cosh (\Gamma_0 y) \tag{12}$$

can exist (see Fig. 2).

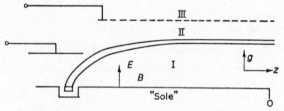

Fig. 2. Notation for "M" type injection system.

One, then, has to solve the following rather complicated boundary value problem. The fields and current at the lower edge of the beam have to be matched to the fields derived from Eq. (12). Similarly, the fields and current at the upper edge of the beam have to be matched to the field between the delay line and the beam, region II in Fig. 2. Finally, the fields in region II have to be matched to those in the delay line (region III) at their common boundary. Sometimes the last two steps will coincide if the beam is made to travel sufficiently near to the delay line. The results of such a procedure are very complicated and the reader is referred to the writings of Warnecke *et al.* for examples.

8.3. THE INITIAL CONDITIONS

The initial conditions are just the same as those in a travelling-wave amplifier. The sum of the fields at the input has to be equal to the externally applied field, the sum of the r.f. currents at input is zero and the sum of the r.f. voltages at input is zero. As we have seen, there are in reality five waves required to satisfy the secular equation and therefore the sums should be taken over five waves. In ordinary circumstances, only two waves interact strongly with the circuit and we obtain conditions of the usual form

$$E_1 + E_2 = E_{im} \tag{13}$$

$$E_1/\delta_1 + E_2/\delta_2 = 0 \tag{14}$$

$$E_1/\delta_1{}^2 + E_2/\delta_2{}^2 = 0 \tag{15}$$

from which $$E_1 = \frac{E_{in}}{1 - \delta_2/\delta_1} = \frac{E_{in}}{2} \tag{16}$$

Equation (16) shows that the initial power loss in the case of the magnetron amplifier is only 6 dB. We can write the gain in dB as

$$G = 8 \cdot 66 Im(\Gamma_1)l - 6 \tag{17}$$

where Im means "imaginary part of".

The first published results of WARNECKE et al.[8] on "M" type amplifiers gave gains of only a few dB. This was partially due to the rather restricted values which it was possible to give to l. Increasing l by increasing the mean diameter of the circuit means increasing the area over which the magnetic field must be constant, either as l, in the linear case, or as l^2 in the cylindrical case. Also, especially at low voltages, the coupling impedance of the interdigital circuit compares unfavourably with that of the helix.

The cylindrical tubes of WARNECKE et al. used a cylindrical version of the type of gun described in Appendix 6, Section 3. Very recently the Raytheon Company have announced high-power pulsed amplifiers in which a double-ended delay line circuit is used in conjunction with a large cylindrical cathode, coated round its whole periphery. These tubes are called "Amplitrons." From a slightly different viewpoint they can be characterized as magnetrons in which the circuit is broken and input and output connexions made to the two ends. By increasing the circumference of the tube

---

[8] WARNECKE, KLEEN, LERBS, DOEHLER and HUBER; Proc. Inst. Radio Engrs. N.Y., 1950, 38, 486.

the circuit length is increased so as to obtain values of gain in excess of 10 dB. The properties of the amplitron are, then, high power output, rather low gain, high efficiency and a moderate bandwidth, of about 10% of the centre frequency. For example, the QK520 works over a 10% band around 1300 Mc/s. The anode voltage and current are 40 kV and 35A while a peak power output of 800 kW is obtained for an input of 80 kW. The efficiency is 55%.

8.4. THE "M" CARCINOTRON

A very much more useful device is the "M" analogue of the B.W.O. which is called by its inventors[9] the "Carcinotron." This device also exists in both linear and cylindrical forms. The delay line is terminated at the collector end by spraying attenuating material on to the surfaces of the conductors. The output is taken from the gun end of the delay line which is, in the valves at present commercially available, an interdigital line. Clearly, in this case the electron drift velocity has to be in synchronism with a backward-space harmonic. We investigate this case in more detail. As in the case of "O" devices, the only modification in the secular equation is a change of sign in the circuit equation. If this change is made in Eq. (1) and if, following Muller, we write

$$\Gamma_0 = j\beta$$

$$\Gamma = jk + \epsilon$$

we obtain for the Carcinotron, on eliminating negligible terms,

$$[\beta^2 - k^2 + 2jk\epsilon][j(\beta_e - k) - \epsilon][\beta_m^2 - (\beta_e - k)^2 - 2j(\beta_e - k)\epsilon]$$
$$= j\beta\beta_e k^2 \left\{\beta_e - k + \frac{2\alpha}{1+\alpha^2}\beta_m\right\}H^2 \qquad (18)$$

We next look for a solution of this equation near to synchronism, by putting $\beta = \beta_e$ and $\beta_e - k = \beta_e b'$, where b' is a small number so that terms like b'^2 and $b'\epsilon$ may be neglected. This yields

$$2\epsilon(j\beta_e b' - \epsilon) = \beta\beta_e k\left\{\frac{b'}{\beta_m^2} + \frac{2\alpha}{1+\alpha^2}\frac{1}{\beta_m}\right\}H^2 \qquad (19)$$

$$\doteq \beta_e k\frac{2\alpha}{1+\alpha^2}\cdot\frac{\beta}{\beta_m}\cdot H^2 \qquad (20)$$

[9] WARNECKE, GUÉNARD, DOEHLER and EPSZTEIN; Proc. Inst. Radio Engrs. N.Y., 1955, 43, 413.

or, if we write
$$D^2 = \frac{\alpha}{1 + \alpha^2} \frac{\beta}{\beta_m} \cdot H^2 \qquad (21)$$

$$\epsilon = \beta_e D\delta, \qquad b' = bD$$

$$\delta(\delta - jb) = -1 \qquad (22)$$

In this degree of approximation we have reduced the number of waves to two, with propagation constants given by

$$\Gamma_1 = j(\beta_e + b) + \beta_e D\delta_1 \qquad (23)$$

$$\Gamma_2 = j(\beta_e + b) + \beta_e D\delta_2 \qquad (24)$$

where the δ's are the roots of Eq. (22).

An interesting point is that when $b = 0$, ϵ is a pure imaginary and there is no exponential gain. As in the case of the B.W.O. the oscillation is due to an interference phenomenon and not to increasing waves.

We can now write down the condition for oscillation from Eqs. (13)–(15). These show that $V_1(O) = V(O)/(1 - \delta_2/\delta_1)$ with a similar expression for $V_2(O)$.

Then
$$V(L) = V_1(O) \exp(-\Gamma_1 L) + V_2(O) \exp(-\Gamma_2 L)$$

$$= V(O) \left[\frac{\delta_1 \exp(-\Gamma_1 L) - \delta_2 \exp(-\Gamma_2 L)}{\delta_1 - \delta_2} \right] \qquad (25)$$

The term in the square bracket is the inverse of the voltage gain of the device. Oscillation takes place when this is zero, i.e., when

$$\delta_1 \exp(-\beta_e D\delta_1 L) = \delta_2 \exp(-\beta_e D\delta_2 L) \qquad (26)$$

or
$$\delta_1/\delta_2 = \exp[-\beta_e DL(\delta_2 - \delta_1)] \qquad (27)$$

But, from Eq. (22)
$$\delta_1/\delta_2 = \frac{b - \sqrt{b^2 + 4}}{b + \sqrt{b^2 + 4}} \qquad (28)$$

$$\delta_2 - \delta_1 = j\sqrt{b^2 + 4}$$

Thus
$$\delta_1/\delta_2 = \exp(-j\beta_e DL\sqrt{b^2 + 4}) \qquad (29)$$

Equations (28) and (29) can only be satisfied simultaneously if $b = 0$ and

$$2\beta_e DL = (2n + 1)\pi \qquad (30)$$

making $\delta_1 = -\delta_2$. If we introduce N, as usual defined through $\beta_e L = 2\pi N$, the oscillation condition becomes

$$DN = \frac{2n+1}{4} \tag{31}$$

D has been defined in a somewhat roundabout way. Simplified, it becomes $D^2 = 2\alpha\beta_e/\beta_m\phi^2 C^3$ but this still contains α and ϕ. WARNECKE et al.[9] give an explicit form to these quantities by using a simplified expression for the circuit field. This is

$$V(z, y, l) = V(l) \frac{\sinh j\Gamma y}{\sinh j\Gamma y_0} \exp(j\omega t - \Gamma z)$$

where y_0 is the co-ordinate of the delay line-beam boundary. Comparing this with Eqs. (9) and (10) we see that

$$A = B = 1$$

so that

$$\phi = \frac{\sinh(j\Gamma y)}{\sinh(j\Gamma y_0)}$$

$$\alpha = \coth(j\Gamma y)$$

Then, if we evaluate these quantities at the beam-circuit boundary,

$$y = y_0$$

$$\alpha\phi^2 = \coth(j\Gamma y_0) \tag{32}$$

and

$$D^2 = 2\beta_e/\beta_m C^3 \coth(\beta_e y_0) \tag{33}$$

Then, Eqs. (31) and (33) contain the information necessary for calculating the start oscillation condition. We note that in this approximation the electron velocity must be in exact synchronism with the unperturbed wave, as $b = 0$.

In the above work the effects of space charge have been neglected and the beam has been considered to be very thin. When the space-charge forces are important, this assumption becomes unrealistic and one must go over to the real, thick beam. Linear trajectories along the circuit can now only be obtained in rather special circumstances. One set of these is that a unipotential cathode is used and the plasma frequency is made equal to the cyclotron frequency (Brillouin condition). This involves a velocity variation across the beam of the form $u_z + \omega_c y$. If the cathode is made non-unipotential, the velocity range is reduced to $\omega_p/\omega \cdot \omega_c y$, a useful reduction.

WARNECKE, DOEHLER and BOBOT[9] have calculated the space-charge corrections by a perturbation method, based on rather different assumptions from those of Pierce. A shortened account of this work is given elsewhere.[10] The modifications introduced by the space-charge bring the theory into much closer agreement

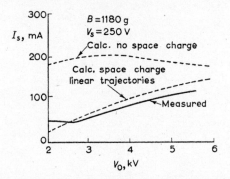

B = 1180 g
V_s = 250 V
Calc. no space charge
Calc. space charge linear trajectories
Measured

I_s, mA
V_0, kV

FIG. 3. Starting current vs. voltage. Experimental and theoretical values.

with measurements, as is shown in Fig. 3. It is, perhaps, somewhat strange that the inclusion of space-charge effects reduces the calculated starting currents. The result is

$$\Gamma_{1,2} = \Gamma_m \pm j\left\{\Gamma_d{}^2 + \gamma_m{}^2\left(1 - \frac{\alpha}{\Gamma_d \mp j\sqrt{\Gamma_d{}^2 + \gamma_m{}^2}}\right)\right\}^{1/2} \quad (34)$$

where

$$\Gamma_m = \frac{\Gamma_0 + j\beta_e}{2} \quad (35)$$

$$\Gamma_d = \frac{j\beta_e - \Gamma_0}{2} \quad (36)$$

$$\alpha = \frac{\omega_p{}^2 \Delta}{u_0{}^2} \quad (37)$$

$$\gamma_m{}^2 = -\frac{\Gamma_0{}^2 \beta_e I_0 Z_c}{E_0} \coth(\beta_e y_0) \equiv \beta_e{}^2 D^2 \quad (38)$$

$\Delta = \frac{1}{2}$ beam width

[10] WARNECKE, GUÉNARD and DOEHLER; Onde Élect., 1954, 34, 323.

The corresponding starting condition is

$$\Gamma_d = \frac{\alpha}{2} \tag{39}$$

$$\gamma_m L \left(1 + \frac{3\alpha^2}{8\gamma_m{}^2} \right) = \frac{\pi}{2} + 2n\pi \tag{40}$$

Equation (40) shows that the starting current is lowered by space-charge, as we stated above, since $\gamma_m{}^2$ is positive when $\Gamma_0 \doteq j\beta_e$. One of the disadvantages of the "M" Carcinotron turns out to be that, for low operating voltages, the start oscillation current for $n = 1$ is but little greater than for $n = 0$, so that moding constitutes a problem.

We next turn to the efficiency. This has already been mentioned in the introduction. Experimentally, it is found from current distribution measurements that only about 80% of the electrons reach the line and are collected there. The remainder go to the "sole" even when this is quite highly negative. The efficiency will be reduced to

$$\eta_e = 0.8 \left(1 - \frac{mV_z}{V_0} \right) \tag{41}$$

$$= 0.8 \left\{ 1 - \frac{m}{4} \left(\frac{B_c}{B} \right)^2 \right\} \tag{42}$$

where B_c is the cut-off field in a planar magnetron under the same conditions. The overall efficiency is, as usual, obtained by multiplying η_e by η_c, the circuit efficiency. This latter can be approximated by

$$\eta_c = \exp\left(-\gamma_a L \right) \tag{43}$$

where γ_a is the line attenuation in nepers/cm, if small-signal results for the distribution of power along the line are used. (Compare with the same calculation for the B.W.O.). Then

$$\eta_0 = 0.8 \exp\left(-\gamma_a L \right) \left(1 - \frac{mV_z}{V_0} \right) \tag{44}$$

For a tube tuning from 2·5–4·0 kMc/s, Warnecke and his co-workers obtained efficiencies ranging from 30–45%.

8.5. THE "RISING SUN" EFFECT

The analysis given so far has tacitly assumed that only the main space harmonic couples to the beam. However, WILLSHAW, MOURIER and GUILBAUD[11] have considered what happens when, in addition, another space harmonic couples to the beam wave with propagation constant $j(\beta_e - \beta_m)$. The condition for this to occur is

$$\Gamma_0 - \Gamma'_0 = j\beta_m \qquad (45)$$

If we use the substitution $\Gamma_0 - \Gamma'_0 = 2\pi/l$ where l is the period of the circuit, we find

$$\beta_m = 2\pi/l \qquad (46)$$

Other unwanted couplings can be ignored because of the rapid decrease in the coupling impedance as the order of the harmonic increases.

In the interdigital line, used in most Carcinotrons, both symmetrical and asymmetrical space harmonics exist, as was shown in Chapter III. Since the first symmetrical space harmonic is normally the desired one, unwanted interaction may occur with the first asymmetrical space harmonic, if, from Eq. (46),

$$\lambda B = \frac{10,700\pi}{\beta} \qquad (47)$$

where β is the phase-angle. The effect is to cause a dip in the efficiency curve. This was observed under similar conditions in "rising sun" magnetrons when they were first studied during the war, hence the name.

8.6. THE DIOCOTRON

It is found that, in crossed electric and magnetic fields, a type of electron motion can be set up which gives rise to exponentially increasing waves even in the absence of a circuit. The classical system which exhibits this behaviour is the Brillouin beam, in which, as we have said

$$u_z = u_0 + \frac{\omega_p^2}{\omega_c} \cdot y \qquad (48)$$

and

$$\omega_p = \omega_c \qquad (49)$$

---

[11] WILLSHAW, MOURIER and GUILBAUD; C. R. Acad. Sci., Paris, 1955, **240**, 283.

The velocity therefore increases across the beam. Under the influence of r.f. forces the boundaries of the beam become scalloped so that the beam exhibits two surface currents which propagate with mean velocities different from one another by $2\omega_p \,.\, \varDelta$. The Diocotron effect is then the result of double stream amplification between the two surface currents.

The theory of this effect was first indicated by BUNEMANN[12] then given by MACFARLANE and HAY in full detail,[13] and experimental results were obtained by GUÉNARD and HUBER.[14] The analysis is too long for inclusion here. The gain per cm length is proportional to

$$\frac{\omega_p{}^2}{\omega \,.\, \omega_c} = \frac{\omega_p}{\omega} \tag{50}$$

and GUÉNARD and HUBER were able to obtain good agreement with this figure. However, the Diocotron has not been put to practical use, presumably because of the high noise level. The main interest of the effect is that it probably has a bearing on various unexplained details of the observed phenomena in crossed-field devices. Among these phenomena we may instance the "sole" current† and the relatively low values of efficiency observed. Some of these points are briefly discussed by DOEHLER.[15]

An effect very similar to the Diocotron effect is observed in thin annular beams of high perveance, which are focused by magnetic fields, especially when such beams travel at considerable distance from any surrounding conductor. Here, instabilities are set up, perhaps at the cathode, by charge excess or deficiency and manifest themselves by the break-up of the beam into a number of comet-shaped patterns. The phenomenon has been studied by KYHL and WEBSTER[16] and a theory has been given by PIERCE.[17] A paper by CUTLER[18] should also be consulted.

---

† Sole current is the current flowing to the electrode, called in French "sole," which is opposite to the delay line anode. The sole may be either at cathode potential or, more usually, quite strongly negative. Even in the latter case current is observed in the sole lead. The precise reasons for this current are not well understood.

[12] BUNEMANN; *Nature, Lond.*, 1950, **165**, 474.
[13] MACFARLANE and HAY; *Proc. Phys. Soc.*, 1950, **63B**, 409.
[14] GUÉNARD and HUBER; *Ann. Radioélec.*, 1952, **7**, 252.
[15] DOEHLER; *Symposium on modern advances in Microwave techniques*, Polytechnic Institute of Brooklyn, 1955.
[16] KYHL and WEBSTER; *Trans. I.R.E.*, 1956, ED–3, 172.
[17] PIERCE; *Trans. I.R.E.*, 1956, ED–3, 183.
[18] CUTLER; *J. Appl. Phys.*, 1956, **27**, 1028.

8.7. THE CARMATRON

The Carmatron[19] is a magnetron in which the resonators have
been replaced by a slow-wave structure. Over a small-bandwidth
the beam now sees a purely resistive load and oscillation depends
on the angular velocity of the electron stream. Thus, the device
is voltage tunable over a range of frequencies. This range is somewhat limited in the most obvious type of structure, by the very
rapid variation of power input with voltage, but in the work cited
a 10% bandwidth was obtained. It appears rather improbable
that the characteristics of this device represent any advance on those
of the "M" type Carcinotron.

---

[19] WARNECKE, NALOT, EPSZTEIN and DOEHLER; *C. R. Acad. Sci., Paris*, 1955, **241**,
     695.

9

SPECIAL SPACE-CHARGE WAVE DEVICES

IN THIS chapter we give a brief account of the method of operation of the less well-known and therefore, perhaps, less useful space-charge wave devices. Most of these have been qualitatively described in Chapter 1. Starting with the simplest devices, we consider the family which consists of the velocity jump amplifier, the rippled wall or space-jump amplifier and the rippled beam tube.

9.1. AMPLIFICATION BY CHANGES OF SPACE-WAVE IMPEDANCE

We have essentially treated the single-mode theory of velocity and space jumps in Chapter 4, Section 4.8, where we showed that the r.f. current beyond a plane where there was a sudden discontinuity in the space-charge wave impedance was given by

$$\frac{i_3}{i_1} = \frac{V_{01} \cdot F_1 \cdot \omega_{p1}}{V_{02} \cdot F_2 \cdot \omega_{p2}} \tag{1}$$

It must be remembered that F_1 and F_2 are implicit functions of the d.c. voltages V_{01}, V_{02} and that ω_{p1}, ω_{p2} vary as $(V_{01})^{-1/4}$, $(V_{02})^{-1/4}$.

Thus
$$\frac{i_3}{i_1} \propto \frac{F_1}{F_2} \left(\frac{V_{01}}{V_{02}}\right)^{3/4} \tag{2}$$

To obtain this condition, the discontinuity had to be located where the r.f. current wave went through an instantaneous zero.

Equation (2) relates to the pure velocity jump amplifier with the beam proceeding through a cylindrical tunnel of uniform diameter. In this case if $V_{01} > V_{02}$, $F_1 < F_2$ so that some of the velocity jump gain is lost by the change in F. It is clear that a better performance can be obtained if the tunnel diameter in the high voltage region V_{01} is made greater than in the low voltage region, for F will then be reduced. It turns out that F_1 can be made greater than F_2 so that gain is possible even when $V_{01} = V_{02}$ and we have the space-jump amplifier with the considerable practical advantage of requiring only a single voltage. Returning to Eq. (1) we see that there is a third way in which gain can be obtained. If we change the beam diameter, we can obtain gain by the variation in ω_p. For practical reasons, it is difficult to do this suddenly at the required points, so what is usually done is to encourage the tendency of the

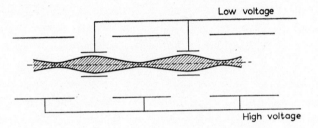

FIG. 1. The most general space-charge wave amplifier.

beam to follow a scalloped path. In Fig. 1 we illustrate the most general amplifier of this type which, as far as I know, has never been built, on purpose.

If the relevant beam diameters are b_1 and b_2, we can rewrite Eq. (1) as

$$\frac{i_3}{i_1} = \left(\frac{V_{01}}{V_{02}}\right)^{3/4}\left(\frac{F_1}{F_2}\right)\left(\frac{b_2}{b_1}\right) = \alpha \tag{3}$$

If n sections each consisting of one high voltage and one low voltage region are used in cascade, the overall gain is just α^n. It is interesting to see what gain can be obtained from a given length of beam.[1] The average space-charge wavelength can be defined by

$$\langle\lambda_s\rangle = \tfrac{1}{2}\{\lambda_{s1} + \lambda_{s2}\} \tag{4}$$

The current gain in a length l is then $\alpha^{2l/\langle\lambda_s\rangle}$ or the power gain is

$$\frac{40l}{\langle\lambda_s\rangle}\log_{10}\alpha \ \mathrm{d}B \tag{5}$$

Equation (5) shows that the gain per unit length depends on $I_0^{1/2}$, through λ_s, whereas the stage gain is independent of beam current.

Velocity-jump amplification has been experimentally studied by

FIELD, TIEN and WATKINS[1] and by TIEN and FIELD.[2] Space-jump amplification was experimentally obtained by BIRDSALL,[3] and MIH-RAN[4] has shown rippled stream amplification to exist, and in addition considers the modifications to be made in the theory when the beam exhibits a sinusoidal ripple, which is the usual case in magnetic fields. In all these cases the gain observed was a good deal less than the calculated values. This is, of course, consistent with the neglect of higher order modes. These alter the calculations in two ways: first, the calculated lengths are based on the assumption that r.f. current maxima coincide with r.f. velocity minima or, con-cretely, r.f. velocity zeros. In fact, as we have seen in Chapter 5, if the beam fills the tunnel, the behaviour is not nearly so simple and there are, in fact, no r.f. current zeros. To obtain current zeros one must work with the beam not filling the tunnel. The use of the correct boundary conditions reduces the calculated gain or, if one uses single-mode calculations, the drift lengths are not optimized. Secondly, if one works with beams considerably smaller than the tunnel diameters, which are readily calculable, then the observed gains will be low anyway. It would be straightforward, but laborious, to calculate the multi-mode gain, but at present it does not seem worthwhile to do this. It may happen, for example, at very high frequencies, that amplifiers of this type prove to have useful pro-perties in view of their simplicity, but they are not now competitors with T.W.A.s or klystrons.

9.2. THE EASITRON

Not much has been printed about the Easitron, which is the name given by the Bell Telephone Laboratories to an amplifier, invented by L. R. Walker, in which an electron beam acts in co-operation with a circuit which alone cannot support a propagating slow-wave. Two examples of such circuits are a row of half-wave resonant wires placed along the centre line of a waveguide and a chain of pill-box cavities traversed by the beam, the dimensions of the centre hole being chosen so that coupling in the absence of the beam is negligible. The first system is apparently that tried by the inventor, but no results have been reported. The second system can be regarded as the limiting case of a multicavity klystron with the cavities stacked as closely as possible along the beam.

[1] FIELD, TIEN and WATKINS; *Proc. I.R.E.*, 1951, **39**, 194.
[2] TIEN and FIELD; *Proc. I.R.E.*, 1952, **40**, 694.
[3] BIRDSALL; *Proc. I.R.E.*, 1954, **42**, 1628.
[4] MIHRAN; *Trans. I.R.E.*, 1956, ED–3, 32.

The theory of this device can be approached from two different viewpoints, that of the klystron or that of an amplifier with a special type of boundary wall admittance, in this case a purely inductive boundary wall. Here, we adopt the latter procedure as has been done by BIRDSALL and WHINNERY.[5] We consider, for simplicity, that the beam fills the tunnel in a cylindrical system. In Eq. (44) of Chapter 5 we then let $a = b$, and put the wall admittance $Y_s = -jB_W$, corresponding with a pure inductance. This results in

$$\frac{(\gamma_r b)J_1(\gamma_r b)}{J_0(\gamma_r b)} = -\frac{(\beta_e b)^2 . B_{\vec{W}}}{\omega \epsilon_0 b} \tag{6}$$

Equation (6) has solutions for $\gamma_r b$ real when $\gamma_r b$ is greater than 2·405 which is the first pole of the function on the L.H.S. Such solutions, however, correspond with higher order space-charge waves as they give rise to fields with radial nodes. Are there any other possible solutions? The answer is that there is another solution when $\gamma_r b$ is purely imaginary, for Eq. (6) becomes, putting $\gamma_r = j\beta_r$

$$\frac{\beta_r b I_1(\beta_r b)}{I_0(\beta_r b)} = \frac{(\beta_e b)^2}{\omega \epsilon_0 b} . B_W \tag{7}$$

which obviously has a single real root. From Eqs. (28) and (30) of Chapter 4, we now find for the longitudinal propagation constants

$$\gamma_l = \frac{\omega}{u_0} \pm \frac{\omega_p}{u_0} \left\{ 1 - \left(\frac{\beta_r b}{\beta_e b}\right)^2 \right\}^{-1/2} \tag{8}$$

This differs from the usual form by the minus sign in the final bracket. We consider three cases:

9.2.1 $\beta_r b < \beta_e b$

Here β_e is purely real, there is therefore no gain or attenuation, except of a klystron-like character.

9.2.2 $\beta_r b > \beta_e b$

In this case β_e is complex and there is gain due to exponentially growing waves. The longitudinal phase velocity is equal to the electron velocity u_0. The amplification constant increases as $\beta_r b$ reduces towards $\beta_e b$ until we reach the singularity.

9.2.3 $\beta_r b = \beta_e b$

Here, the amplification constant becomes infinite and with it the

---

[5] BIRDSALL and WHINNERY; *J. Appl. Phys.*, 1953, **24**, 314.

gain. In view of this observation it becomes interesting to find the relevant value of B_W. From Eq. (7) $B_W = (\omega \epsilon_0 b / \beta_e b)[I_1(\beta_e b)/I_0(\beta_e b)]$.

In view of the lack of experimental data on this device there is no more usefully to be said. *A priori*, it would seem to be a useful device and it is strange that its properties have not been more extensively investigated.

To complete this section, we consider what happens when the wall admittance is made capacitative. The sign of the R.H.S. in Eq. (6) will be changed and we simply obtain a perfectly normal spectrum of space-charge waves. Such a wall, therefore, will support klystron-like gain but will have no new or interesting properties.

9.3. THE TWO-BEAM TUBE AND RELATED DEVICES

In view of the fact that no recent experimental, or for that matter theoretical, progress on these valves has been reported, we can be very brief. Appropriate references have been given in Chapter 1. The main question of interest is whether a beam of electrons whose potential is depressed by space-charge so that the velocity distribution varies monotonically over a specified limited range, can or cannot give rise to propagation constants corresponding with exponentially growing waves. This question has been partially discussed in the sections on plasmas in Chapter 4. These treatments may not be convincing to all readers and an alternative treatment, due to BEAM[6] is interesting. He considers a ribbon beam in a rectangular co-ordinate system and treats in detail a case in which the velocity increases linearly with the transverse distance from the axis. For this case it can be shown that

$$u_0(x) = u_{00} + \frac{du_0}{dx} \cdot x \qquad (9)$$

and moreover

$$\frac{du_0}{dx} = \omega_p \qquad (10)$$

We consider that the beam is infinitely wide in the y direction so that $\partial E_z / \partial y = 0$ and obtain from Eq. (14) of Chapter 4, neglecting k^2 in comparison with β^2

$$\frac{d^2 E_z}{dx^2} - \beta^2 \left(1 - \frac{\omega_p{}^2}{\{\omega - \beta(u_{00} + du_0/dx \cdot x)\}^2}\right) E_z = 0 \qquad (11)$$

---

[6] BEAM; *Proc. I.R.E.*, 1955, **43**, 454.

Putting $u = (\omega - \beta u_0)/(du_0/dx) = (\omega - \beta u_0)/\omega_p$ into Eq. (11) we find

$$\frac{d^2 E_z}{dx^2} - \left(1 - \frac{1}{u^2}\right) E_z = 0 \qquad (12)$$

It is obvious from Eq. (12) that the only interesting solutions are those for which $1/u^2 \gg 1$, i.e., the solutions of

$$\frac{d^2 E_z}{dx^2} + \frac{E_z}{u^2} = 0 \qquad (13)$$

This has the solutions $\sqrt{(u)} \sin [\sqrt{(3)}/2 \ln . u]$, $\sqrt{(u)} \cos [\sqrt{(3)}/2 \ln . u]$. The discussion which proves that complex values of β do not arise is too lengthy to reproduce here; we merely note that if β is real, u is real and ordinary space-charge wave solutions follow. We may therefore reason that if a set of perturbed space-charge modes can be deduced from the modes of the univelocity beam such a set should be complete and no complex modes are possible.

The problem remains of explaining the observations both of Haeff and of Beam himself who observed gain in an experiment designed to check his theory. When Beam's tube was operated with a collector voltage below the drift tube voltages, gain was observed due to regeneration set up by secondary electrons from the collector returning to the input region. In the other conditions no experimental gain was observed, though the device showed klystron gain. Beam considers that his experiments were more carefully conducted from the point of view of avoiding rippled beam and velocity-jump gain than were those of Haeff, conducted before these phenomena were recognized. He therefore concludes that secondary emission phenomena, perhaps aided by contributions from the other sources, gave rise to the observed results. Whatever the explanation of Haeff's results, it seems certain that the space potential depression type of tube does not give rise to exponential gain in the way originally postulated.

As a matter of fact, another mechanism exists which could give rise to exponential gain in this tube. We saw, in Chapter 4, that if a cylindrical beam is focused by a non-infinite magnetic field, some of the r.f. current is propagated in the form of ripples on the periphery of the beam. The major part of the current is, however, the body current carried by the density modulation of the beam. When a considerable velocity depression is evident at the axis of the beam it is not at all unreasonable to picture these currents

T

travelling with different mean velocities so that two-beam amplification results. Viewed in this way the effect is the analogue of the Diocotron effect. It is not to be expected that this mechanism would give rise to important values of gain as the interaction conditions would be unfavourable.

9.4.   BACKWARD-WAVE AMPLIFIERS

From the theory developed in Chapter 7, it will be clear that the backward-wave oscillator tube may be used as an amplifier if the circuit is provided with an input connexion at the collector end and if the beam current is adjusted so as to be somewhat below the value for maintained oscillations. This simple system turns out to have limited application because the gain is low unless the current is very close to the start-oscillation value and it is difficult to obtain reliable operation under these conditions. The idea is important as it is the basis of some much more useful devices described in the next section.

The behaviour of the amplifier was studied by HEFFNER[7] who found that the following first order approximation gives an excellent estimate of the gain:

$$\text{Power gain ratio} = \left[\frac{k}{I_0 - I_s}\right]^2 \qquad (14)$$

where k is a constant, very nearly equal to unity and I_s is the starting

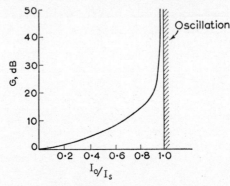

FIG. 2. Gain of B.W.O. below starting current.

current of the oscillation. Fig. 2 shows a sketch of this relation, which indicates that the gain increases sharply when I_0 exceeds

[7] HEFFNER; *Proc. I.R.E.*, 1954, **42**, 930.

$0.9I_s$. The gain is confined to a narrow band of frequencies, since backward-wave circuits are fundamentally highly dispersive, and Heffner finds, in the same approximation, that the gain frequency characteristic is represented by:

$$\text{Power gain ratio} = \left[\frac{a}{1 + b(f - f_0)^2}\right]^2 \qquad (15)$$

where $a^2 =$ gain at $f = f_0$, and b is an adjustable constant. Heffner quotes, to give an idea of the magnitudes involved, the case of a tube tuning from 3–9 kMc/s which, used as an amplifier, had an equivalent Q greater than 2000.

9.5. CASCADE BACKWARD-WAVE AMPLIFIERS

This device, of which several variants are possible, was invented by WHINNERY and CURRIE.[8] As shown in Fig. 3 it consists of two backward-wave circuits coupled successively to the same electron

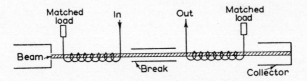

FIG. 3. Cascade backward wave amplifier.

beam and separated by a drift tube. The input signal is amplified in the first circuit and produces a strong r.f. current modulation on the beam, which persists through the transformation represented by the drift tube. The second helix is then excited by the r.f. currents and kinetic voltages on the beam and an output signal can be derived from the end of the second circuit which is nearer to the gun. At this point it has to be admitted that it is not clear what advantages, if any, the device possesses. These only emerge as a result of an analysis, but it is convenient to summarize them now. They are:

1. Considerable gain with current of only 50–70% of the oscillation current.

2. One end of each circuit is terminated in a matched load. The operating characteristics vary smoothly with frequency when

[8] WHINNERY and CURRIE; *Proc. I.R.E.*, 1955, **43**, 1617.

well-designed loads are used and the gain can be made constant over a wide frequency range.

3. Since there is no direct connexion between input and output terminals, but only through the medium of the beam, only signal frequencies which are in synchronism with the beam velocity are amplified. Other frequencies are completely suppressed instead of being only attenuated by the cold circuit loss, as is the case in the amplifier of the last section.

The device can thus be described as an electronically tunable (by circuit voltage variation) filter amplifier. The bandwidth can be increased by operating the two circuits at slightly different voltages but this advantage is at the cost of a considerable reduction in gain.

The theory of the tube has been fully described by the inventors so that it is not proposed to include this work here as it is a straightforward extension of ideas we have fully covered. Moreover, there are a whole family of similar devices which may be studied and which may have useful properties. For example, one might use the first circuit as a forward-wave amplifier and there are many permutations. We do, however, outline the steps of the theory so that interested readers can deduce the results.

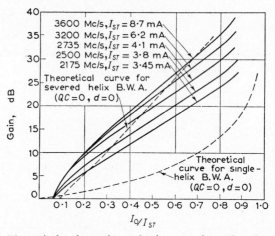

FIG. 4. Theoretical and experimental gain curves for various frequencies.

The theory starts from Eqs. (30), (31) and (32) of Chapter 7 without using the small C approximation used to simplify the forms given there. This allows the output quantities $E(L)$, $i(L)$

and $u(L)$ to be expressed in terms of the corresponding input quantities, $E(O)$, etc., the δ's also given in Chapter 7 and the tube parameters. The r.f. current and velocity waves on the beam at output are calculated and transformed through the space-charge wave matrix which represents the drift tube. These quantities, evaluated at exit from the drift tube, form the initial values $i(O_2)$, $u(O_2)$ for the second circuit. The final expressions for the output parameters can then be calculated. Fig. 4 shows a comparison between theoretical results for the single circuit B.W.A. and the severed circuit B.W.A. together with experimental results obtained at different frequencies. While the theory shows the general tendency of the experimental results, agreement is not particularly close. The cascade B.W.A., however, remains a very useful device for use in specialized fields.

9.6. TRANSVERSE CURRENT T.W.A.

We next describe an even more specialized tube. This tube, as its name implies, operates with the current flowing transversely across a flat type of forward-wave circuit, for example, a flattened helix. The distinguishing feature of this device is that once the saturation power level is reached, further increase in input power produces very little change in the output power. A characteristic of this type is of value in F.M. transmitters. The theory of the tube is given in detail by DUNN et al.[9] and an experimental model is described by DUNN and HARMAN.[10]

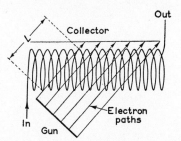

FIG. 5. Transverse current travelling wave amplifier.

The form of tube tested is sketched in Fig. 5. The circuit is a flat helix and the long linear electron gun is skewed with respect

---

[9] DUNN, HARMAN, FIELD and KINO; *Proc. I.R.E.*, 1956, **44**, 879.
[10] DUNN and HARMAN; *Proc. I.R.E.*, 1956, **44**, 888.

to the circuit so that the electrons interact with the circuit only over a predetermined length which is considerably less than the total length of the circuit. It is clear on qualitative grounds that saturation sets in when the current elements from the extreme right-hand end of the gun are fully bunched. As the r.f. input is increased still further, current elements successively farther to the left saturate but the power output remains substantially unchanged.

The theory of this system is interesting in that the circuit equation is identical to that of a normal T.W.A. but the electronic equation is different. The electronic equation is established from an integral equation, which is the univelocity analogue of Eq. (189) of Chapter 4, written down in Eq. (190).

$$i_{(z)} = j\frac{I_0}{2V_0} \int_0^z E(\zeta)\beta_e(z - \zeta) \exp -j\beta_e(z - \zeta) \, d\zeta \qquad (16)$$

where the beam current interacts with the circuit over the distance $\zeta = 0$ to $\zeta = z$. For the present case we consider a current element $J_0 \, d\xi$, J_0 = current per unit length at ξ. The a.c. current due to this element is

$$di(z, \xi) = j\frac{I_0 \, d\xi}{2V_0} \int_\xi^z E(\zeta)\beta_e(z - \zeta) \exp \{-j\beta_e(z - \zeta)\} \, d\zeta \qquad (17)$$

The total current is found by integrating over the range $\xi = z - L$ to $\xi = z$, where L is the length of travel of any electron over the circuit (Fig. 5). Then,

$$i_{(z)} = j\frac{I_0}{2V_0} \int_{z-L}^z \int_\xi^z E(\zeta)\beta_e(z - \zeta) \exp \{-j\beta_e(z - \zeta)\} \, d\zeta \qquad (18)$$

The electronic equation is obtained by differentiating Eq. (18) and is

$$\frac{d^3i}{dz^3} + 3j\beta_e \frac{d^2i}{dz^2} - 3\beta_e^2 \frac{di}{dz} - j\beta_e^3 i = j\frac{\beta_e J_0}{2V_0} \left\{ L \frac{dE_{(z)}}{dz} + (j\beta_e L - 2)E_z + \right.$$

$$\left. + \left[L \frac{dE_{(z-L)}}{dz} + (j\beta_e L + 2)E_{(z-L)} \right] \exp(-j\beta_e L) \right\} \qquad (19)$$

In the reference cited, the pair of equations represented by Eq. (19) and the circuit equation are solved by Laplace transform methods, which is probably the best procedure in view of the introduction of the boundary conditions. It is, however, interesting to write Eq. (19) with our standard form $\partial/\partial z = -\Gamma$. We obtain

$$(j\beta_e - \Gamma)^3 = j\frac{\beta_e J_0}{2V_0}\{L\Gamma E_{(z)} + (j\beta_e L - 2)E_z +$$

$$+ [L\Gamma + j\beta_e L + 2]E_{(z-L)} \cdot \exp(-j\beta_e L)\} \quad (20)$$

Equation (20) immediately shows that, with the circuit equation, we have acquired another root, five in all. It is not possible to give the details of the solution here, but the analysis quoted shows that three forward waves growing in amplitude are set up, instead of one in the conventional T.W.A. One of these varies exponentially with distance along the circuit, one linearly and one as the square of the distance. However, when the value of CN is large enough, (>0.4) the exponential wave accounts for nearly all the gain. In this tube C has to be redefined by

$$C^3 = \frac{J_0 L Z_c}{4V_0} \quad (21)$$

and another parameter,

$$M = \frac{\beta_e L}{2\pi} \quad (22)$$

which contains the interaction length, is also important; in fact it turns out that B in the Pierce form of gain expression

$$G = A + BCN$$

is given by

$$B \doteqdot \frac{54 \cdot 5(\beta_e C L)^5}{72} = (5 \cdot 94 CM)^5 \quad (23)$$

The experimental tube described elsewhere[10] showed two unexpected types of behaviour. The first of these was that the range of voltage for which the tube gave zero output (Kompfner dip) was very broad instead of being narrow. The other is the behaviour observed when the tube is excited by two signal generators at different frequencies. If the power input at one frequency ($2 \cdot 27$ kMc/s in the experiments) was held constant while a second power input at $1 \cdot 98$ kMc/s was steadily increased, the power output at the higher frequency decreased above a certain level until the lower frequency output saturated, after which point it remained constant at a new, low level. Fig. 6 illustrates the results observed.

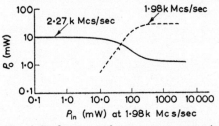

FIG. 6. Performance of transverse current tube.

The tube gave outputs of the order 30 mW for inputs of about 3·3 W. The gain vs. frequency characteristic was very irregular, but reached maximum values of about 24 dB, which were lower than calculated. The main difference between the theoretical curves and those observed was that the experimental curves were shifted to lower frequencies and compressed. The maximum of the smoothed experimental gain curve was around 1·7 kMc/s as against 3·0 kMc/s calculated without allowance for space-charge.

On the whole it would seem not unfair to conclude that the useful limiting feature in this tube is obtained at the cost of too big an increase in complexity for it to become generally used.

9.7. "E" TYPE DEVICES

Some thought has been given to the possibility of realizing higher efficiencies by the use of devices in which the potential energy of the electrons is turned into r.f. energy rather than kinetic energy. All devices in which kinetic energy is converted are subject to the basic difficulty that the electrons fall progressively out of phase with the wave as their kinetic energy is lost. In devices with extended fields this inevitably means that eventually they fall so far behind the phase front that they start to take energy back from the field. In the last chapter we saw that crossed field devices act differently in this respect because, as an electron moves through the interaction space its velocity normal to the electric field, which is by far the greatest contribution to the kinetic energy, remains unchanged. The potential energy is, however, reduced as the electron moves outwards towards the circuit. A "magnetless" magnetron exhibiting the same behaviour has been described by VERSNEL and JONKER.[11]

[11] VERSNEL and JONKER; *Philips Res. Rep.*, 1954, **9**, 458.

This is sketched in Fig. 7. An electron gun injects a beam tangentially into the space between the circuit, bent into cylindrical form, and

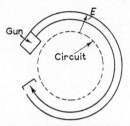

FIG. 7. "E" type device.

an outer cylindrical electrode held at a lower potential. The beam is held in equilibrium by the radial electric force and the centrifugal force acting in opposition. If now the r.f. forces act in such a way as to move the electron nearer to the circuit, it will lose potential energy but will maintain the same angular velocity. The efficiency should be comparable with that of "M" type devices. In fact, however, this is not the case because the current injected into the system is limited to values well below those obtained in the "M" devices.

It has been shown by HEFFNER and WATKINS[12] that the number of electronic wavelengths in the circuit is limited to around $N = \sqrt{2}$, whereas in "O" and "M" devices $N = 8\text{--}40$. This calculation is based on requiring that a given lateral or radial velocity produces an equivalent lateral or radial displacement in all three types of tube. They suggest some ways of overcoming this by giving the beam an extra initial drift velocity into the paper in Fig. 7 so that the beam spirals along the circuit which now extends to considerable length. An ordinary or a bifilar helix would serve the purpose. Little experimental work appears to have been done in this field, but a Russian tube, the "Spiratron"[13] is of interest in this connection.

9.8.   MICROWAVE DETECTION

To conclude this chapter we give a brief description of some methods for using microwave amplifiers as detectors. The principle used in such devices is that of velocity sorting and there are several possible ways in which this can be carried out. The best known is the use of some form of triode structure at the collector end of a

[12] HEFFNER and WATKINS; *Proc. I.R.E.*, 1955, **43**, 1007.
[13] CHERNOV; *Paris Microwave Tube Conference*, 1956.

T.W.A. as illustrated in Fig. 8. The grid is biased approximately
to cathode potential so that, when no r.f. power is applied to the
helix, all the electrons are brought to rest in the vicinity of the
grid. Under these conditions an anode characteristic of the form
shown in Fig. 9, is obtained. The steepness of the curve depends
on the quality of the grid, etc. Now consider that V_a is adjusted to,
usually, the lower bend of the characteristic. Then, when r.f. is
applied to the circuit, electrons which have velocities higher than
the mean value u_0 will reach the anode and ordinary anode bend
rectification will be observed.

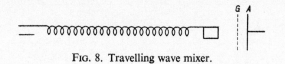

Fig. 8. Travelling wave mixer.

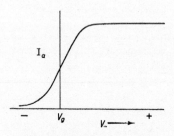

Fig. 9. Mixer characteristic.

An ingenious modification of this scheme is due to MENDEL[14]
who replaced the triode section by a periodic magnetic focusing

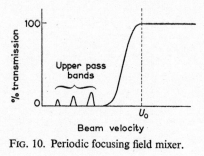

Fig. 10. Periodic focusing field mixer.

[14] MENDEL; *Proc. I.R.E.*, 1956, 44, 503.

field region (see Appendix 6). This has a characteristic of the type sketched in Fig. 10. The periodic focusing system is designed so that the normal operating voltage brings the d.c. beam velocity to the knee of the main pass-band. When r.f. is applied to the helix some electrons lose energy and are therefore deflected to the walls of the periodic section and cannot reach the collector. The collector current therefore drops when the signal is applied. Using a Taylor expansion

$$I_{(u_0+u_1)} = I_{(u_0)} + \frac{\delta I}{\delta u} \cdot u_1 + \frac{1}{2!}\frac{\delta^2 I}{\delta u^2} \cdot u_1{}^2 \text{ etc.} \tag{24}$$

But, from the theory of the T.W.A.,

$$u_1 = \frac{\eta E_{(L)}}{u_0 \beta_e C \delta_1} \tag{25}$$

or

$$\frac{u_1}{u_0} = \left(\frac{2P_0C}{I_0V_0}\right)^{1/2} \tag{26}$$

Since the change in mean collector current is due to the square-law term in Eq. (24) we see from Eq. (26) that the rectified output is proportional to the power output P_0, from the T.W.A. helix, while the sensitivity depends on $\delta^2 I/\delta u^2$ and the helix parameters. In Mendel's experiments, outputs of 100 μA/mW output were obtained, which are a factor of 10 worse than the best crystals. However, it must be remembered that this device exhibits gain while the crystal gives a loss, and therefore might prove better than the crystal on the basis of input power. Mendel makes the general comment that the noise figure cannot be better than that of the T.W.A. section as an amplifier, but gives no experimental figures. It would seem probable that the noise figure is actually a good deal worse than the limiting value.

Microwave detector valves have not been widely used. Their great advantage over crystals is freedom from burn-out when subjected to excessive r.f. inputs. Against this must count the large size, expensive power supplies and weight. These factors have been decisive in the past.

10

NOISE PHENOMENA
IN SPACE-CHARGE WAVE DEVICES

In communication theory all unwanted signals are spoken of as "noise." Here we are concerned with the much more restricted field of electrical fluctuation noise in microwave valves. Even so there are several different sources of such noise including:

1. Shot noise, essentially due to the fact that the smooth current is actually due to a continuously fluctuating rate of particle flow.

2. Noise due to gas ionization.

3. Noise due to poor contacts and vibration.

4. Flicker noise, a phenomenon observable only at very low frequencies.

5. Partition noise, due to the element of randomness in the paths taken by the electrons in passing through the device.

Of these sources, (1) and (3) can be eliminated by care in manufacture; (4) is of no concern in the present work, and (1) and (5) have to be considered in detail. Partition noise is often sub-divided into two categories; classical partition noise which is noise due to random division of current between two or more positive electrodes, e.g., the screen and suppressor grids of a pentode; and induced current noise. The latter is only observed at fairly high frequencies as it is due to variation in the current induced in an electrode, such as a negative grid, which is not necessarily collecting any finite electron convection current. Taking the grid as an example, it is possible that all the electrons passing through the grid plane in a specified short time interval t move on paths which bring them very close to the actual conductors of the grid while, in some subsequent equal time interval t, all the electrons pass through at the centres of the apertures. The total induced current, which at low frequencies is identically zero, becomes finite at higher frequencies and on the above reasoning, is subject to statistical fluctuations. It seems logical to regard these as two aspects of the same phenomenon, i.e., randomness in the precise paths taken.

Shot noise is the major phenomenon and it will be the centre of our attention. We shall find that space-charge wave theory is very well adapted to describe the changes undergone by noise currents and kinetic voltages as an observer moves along a long beam, but that it is much more difficult to ascribe correct initial values to the noise parameters, which arise essentially in the region of the space-charge minimum just outside the cathode from which the beam current is drawn. Noise theory has made very marked progress in the last decade but the results obtained depend very much on the initial assumptions made and these have not always been either clearly stated or the best set available. We have thus lived through a period in which it was thought that microwave amplifiers with noise figures down to 2 dB could be made, a second period in which the minimum was thought to be 6·3 dB, and into a third period in which very elaborate machine calculations begin to give real information as to the precise behaviour of the diode region and show that, if it is correctly designed, figures of 2–3 dB can really be obtained. At the same time, practical valves show minimum figures of 4·5 dB. The precise nature of the various assumptions is discussed in more detail below, but first it is necessary to give a résumé of the behaviour of a simple system, the space-charge limited diode.

10.1. SHOT NOISE IN DIODES

It is assumed that the reader has a general knowledge of fluctuation phenomena in valves, such as that given by BECK,[1] but some of the major points are reiterated here.

10.1.1. Shot noise in a temperature-limited diode

Here, the current is independent of the electrode voltages but fluctuates due to the statistical variation in the number of electrons reaching the emitting surface from the interior of the cathode, in unit time. By considering the variation in number of electrons per very short time unit Δt from the expected number, which is $(I/e)\Delta t$, we can show that the mean square fluctuation current is

$$\langle i^2 \rangle = 2eI\Delta f \tag{1}$$

where Δf is a frequency interval, defined by the bandwidth of the measuring instrument. Equation (1) is only valid at very low frequencies. The complete frequency-dependent expression is, however, very easily calculated for a planar diode, the most direct

---

[1] BECK; *Thermionic Valves*, Chapter 8, Cambridge University Press, 1953.

method being to determine the Fourier spectrum of the induced current pulse due to the passage of a single electron. The result is

$$\langle i^2 \rangle = 2eI\Delta f \cdot F(\theta) \tag{2}$$

where
$$F(\theta) = \frac{4}{\theta^4} [\theta^2 + 2(1 - \cos\theta - \theta\sin\theta)] \tag{3}$$

and $\theta = \omega\tau =$ the d.c. transit angle through the valve. $F(\theta)$ is a slowly diminishing function of θ which drops from 1 to $\frac{1}{2}$ for $\theta \doteq \pi$. The temperature limited diode is therefore a fairly simple device.

10.1.2. The space-charge limited diode

This is, unfortunately, far more complicated. We recall some of the simple experimental facts.

(a) The current through the diode depends on the electrode voltages.

(b) The current through the diode does not depend on changes of the cathode work function, but only of the anode work function.

(c) If the saturated emission from the cathode is increased by changes in temperature, a small but finite change in anode current is observed.

(d) The electrons are emitted with a Maxwellian electron velocity distribution.† This last fact is important in several different ways. That all the electrons have initial velocities > 0 causes the formation of the potential minimum while the form of the velocity distribution gives rise to a particular shape of potential curve round the minimum.

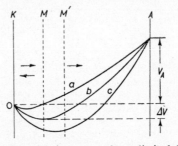

FIG. 1. Potentials in a space-charge limited diode.

---

† This is rigorously correct only for pure metal emitters; oxide cathodes can be proved experimentally to give rise to excessive numbers of high energy electrons and to a spectrum with definite lines. The causes of these phenomena are partially understood and we here treat them as controllable and therefore outside the range of our theory. In any case, there are good emitters which do not show these effects.

In Fig. 1 we show a very exaggerated potential diagram for a space-charge limited diode. Three potential profiles for three different values of saturated emission at a definite anode voltage are shown, c being that for the biggest emission. We now discuss the physics of the fluctuation problem by assuming that profile b represents the state of affairs when the ideal constant mean current I_0 is flowing. Consider a sudden increase in the saturated emission, i.e., the emission of a packet of electrons in excess of the mean number. For a short time (somewhat less than the transit time) the potential profile is modified to c. Profile a shows what happens when we inject a deficiency of electrons. Two things happen; first, the field acting on all the electrons in the space M'A is increased and their velocities are therefore increased. If the depth of the minimum profile c is $\Delta V'$ volts, the slowest electron which just passes the minimum reaches the anode with an energy of $V_A + \Delta V'$ $> V_A + \Delta V$ electron volts; secondly, some of the slower electrons previously emitted which are still in the space KM but which would have eventually reached the anode, if the b profile had been maintained, are turned back to the cathode. Their number, at least partially, offsets the increased number of charges reaching the anode. Whether the offsetting is complete or partial depends on the precise nature of the fluctuation, whether it is in number or in energy. To be more precise, we need to know whether the velocities of the electrons in the excess packet are distributed in normal form or whether they have some other distribution; for instance, they might all have energies above the average. If the number fluctuates but the instantaneous velocity distribution does not, we expect the current to behave as though the cathode work function changed, i.e., there will be no change in anode current measured just to the right of the minimum. If the instantaneous velocity distribution is modified, the change is similar to a change of cathode temperature and the anode current, measured as before, shows a small fluctuation. Clearly, both types of fluctuation must be allowed and they are normally assumed to be uncorrelated, that is, the probability of one type of fluctuation taking place in a specified interval is completely independent of whether the other type is, or is not, observed.

The final state of affairs, to the right of M', is then as follows. The number of electrons injected into the anode space exhibits a statistical fluctuation. This fluctuation is smaller than the fluctuation in number of the electrons injected at the cathode by a factor which depends partly on the smoothing action of the minimum and partly on transit time phenomena in the space KM. Also, the electron stream reaching the anode is velocity-modulated by the voltage fluctuation $\Delta V' - \Delta V$ and if the transit time from minimum to anode is made sufficiently great, the velocity modulation is transformed, by drift action, into current modulation.

The next step is to assume that the potential minimum is the origin of noise space-charge waves, one of r.f. current and the other of a.c. velocity. These are assumed to be uncorrelated. If we can determine the initial amplitudes it is rather easy to calculate the subsequent noise behaviour of the beam. We next take up the question of calculating the initial parameters for the noise waves. It turns out to be much easier to obtain an expression for the velocity wave than for the current waves, and it is the last step which has required machine techniques.

Before discussing the initial values, we should note that our first historical stage of arbitrarily low noise corresponds to complete neglect of the initial current fluctuation. Stage two corresponds to the assumption that the current fluctuation is just the mean square shot noise in the mean current I_0 as given by Eq. (1). This assumption, therefore, over-estimates the current noise by a factor which turns out to depend on the diode geometry and the frequency. The last stage has not yet been reduced to an analytical form, but more or less informed guesses at the reduction factor have been made.

The derivation of the velocity modulation, in the form originally due to RACK,[2] is given in considerable detail in BECK[1] and it is not necessary to give more than the result here. It is

$$\langle u_n{}^2 \rangle = \frac{4kT}{I_0} \eta \left(1 - \frac{\pi}{4} \right) \Delta f \qquad (4)$$

The new symbols are Boltzmann's constant k and the cathode temperature T. kT is the mean energy of a thermal electron and there are I_0/e electrons, and Eq. (4) is clearly closely related to the properties of the Maxwellian distribution.

For the initial current fluctuation we write

$$\langle i_n{}^2 \rangle = \gamma \,.\, 2eI_0 \Delta f \qquad (5)$$

where γ is a smoothing factor which we cannot, as yet, calculate. This notation is adopted by analogy with the space-charge smoothing factor Γ^2 which is always used in the l.f. case and which can be calculated by well-known means. γ is a function of geometry and frequency.

---

[2] RACK; *Bell Syst. Tech. J.*, 1938, **17**, 592.

10.2. SPACE-CHARGE WAVES IN THE DIODE GUN

Equations (4) and (5) give the initial velocity and current fluctuations at the plane of the potential minimum in front of the cathode. To be useful we have first to derive values for the space-charge waves set up in a cylindrical beam in a cylindrical tunnel. Perhaps the simplest way of doing this is to assume that the gun region can be replaced by an infinite planar diode with an aperture in the anode through which the desired beam flows. The situation is sketched in Fig. 2. The application of this model to real valves

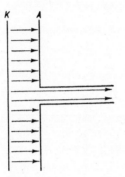

FIG. 2. Section of infinite planar flow.

seems a little more plausible if we remember that in Pierce guns, care is taken to make the potential at the beam edge the same as it would be in Fig. 2. However, the simple model is certainly not correct in detail and ways of improving on this model will be mentioned later. Returning to the infinite planar model, it is now easy to use the Llewellyn electronic equations to determine the values of the current and voltage waves at the anode plane. This approach is adopted for the following reasons: First, Llewellyn equations are not restricted by the small-signal assumption, they only assume that the much less stringent condition of no overtaking is obeyed. The space-charge wave treatment of Smullin, Chapter 4, Section 11, needs more justification than we wish to give if it is to be applied just to the right of the minimum. Secondly, it is easy to deal with the space-charge limited diode in this formalism and third, since we know that only the computer approach gives really satisfactory results, it is better for the moment to keep the treatment simple. It should be clearly understood that the least satisfactory aspect of the use of Llewellyn's equations is that they do not, nor are they

u*

claimed to, apply to the cathode-potential minimum region where electrons move in both directions. To use them we must assume an artificial cathode located at the plane of the minimum, injecting a velocity-modulated electron stream with the mean square variation given by Eq. (4). The Llewellyn coefficients, in the form used here, are given in Appendix 12. The I's and q's are current *densities* in these equations, which are

$$\begin{vmatrix} I \\ q_b \\ u_b \end{vmatrix} = ||b_{ik}|| \begin{vmatrix} V_b - V_a \\ q_a \\ u_a \end{vmatrix} \tag{6}$$

where suffix b relates to the anode plane, a to the (fictitious) cathode plane.

We take the cathode as the zero of potential, so that the initial mean velocity u_a is zero and consider that the cathode-anode capacitance is large enough to short-circuit the diode for r.f., thus making $V_b - V_a = 0$. Reference to Appendix 12 shows that for complete space-charge $\zeta = 1$ and $u_a = 0$, b_{12}, b_{22}, b_{32} all become zero, which shows that the results in this treatment are independent of q_a. Equations (6) then yield

$$q_b = b_{23} \cdot u_a \tag{7}$$

$$u_b = b_{33} \cdot u_a \tag{8}$$

or, inserting the coefficients,

$$q_b = \frac{I_0}{u_b} \left\{ \beta e^{-\beta} + \frac{3\phi_3{}^2(\beta)}{\phi_6(\beta)} \right\} u_a \tag{9}$$

$$u_b = - \left\{ e^{-\beta} - \frac{\phi_3(\beta)\phi_4(\beta)}{\phi_6(\beta)} \right\} u_a \tag{10}$$

The behaviour of the transit angle functions in the brackets is well-known[3,4], and for transit angles a to b greater than 3π, we can put, to a very good degree of approximation,

$$q_b = j\frac{u_a \cdot I_0\omega\tau_1}{u_b} \exp(-j\omega\tau_1) \tag{11}$$

$$u_b = -u_a \exp(-j\omega\tau_1) \tag{12}$$

where τ_1 is the transit time from a to b. Equations (11) and (12) are

---

[3] BAKKER and DE VRIES; *Physica*, 1935, **2**, 683.
[4] GUNDLACH; *F.T.Z.*, 1949, **2**, 319.

the desired results for the convection current and velocity modulations present on the electron beam at the anode plane. We see that, as was to be expected, the drift action has acted in such a manner that the initial v.m. has given rise to both velocity and current waves. The next step is to consider the propagation of space-charge waves along the circuit using Eqs. (11) and (12) as the initial amplitudes for the space-charge waves. Before taking up this question, however, we must derive expressions for the effect of the injected current fluctuations. Since the assumption $u_a \to 0$ eliminates any possibility of considering them, we must find an acceptable value of $u_a \neq 0$. One obvious choice is to make u_a equal to the mean velocity of the Maxwellian distribution, i.e., to put

$$u_a = \langle u \rangle = \sqrt{\frac{\pi k T}{2m}} \qquad (13)$$

We might equally well take the r.m.s. value,

$$\langle u_a{}^2 \rangle^{1/2} = \sqrt{\frac{2kT}{m}} \qquad (13a)$$

The three coefficients b_{12}, b_{22}, b_{32} are now $\neq 0$, but only b_{22} is finite for large transit angles so that there is an extra term in the current wave but not in the velocity wave. It is given by

$$q'(b) = -\frac{u_a}{u_b} q_a \exp(-j\omega\tau_1) \qquad (14)$$

where q_a is given by Eq. (5). In subsequent work we assume that the current waves of Eqs. (14) and (11) are uncorrelated.† We therefore add the mean square contributions from each pair of waves to obtain the total noise current or velocity at any plane.

Since u_a/u_b is, obviously, a small number, we might think that the introduction of Eq. (14) would make no appreciable difference to the noise behaviour. In fact this is far from the case, for it turns out that noise theories based on Eqs. (11) and (12) alone predict noise space-charge waves which go to zero at certain values of z so that, apart from partition noise, perfect valves could be made. Experiments on the noise space-charge waves show that the minima are not nearly so pronounced as would be expected on this basis.

---

† This assumption may well seem much too drastic. It has been discussed in the literature (*A.E.U.*, 1954, 7, 5), but the reasoning justifying particular values of correlation constant does not seem very strong. Again, the results of the computer attack give the most acceptable answers.

Retention of Eq. (14) predicts that, even in the absence of partition noise, the minimum noise figure should be finite, i.e., if $\gamma \to 1$, the value is about 6 dB, and this is in much better agreement with measurements. We therefore conclude that Eq. (14) must be retained, but that $\gamma < 1$ for frequencies up to several thousand megacycles per second.

We now return to the question of calculating the space-charge waves set up in the tunnel of Fig. 3. It is necessary to match the known values at entry to the tunnel to the space-charge waves.

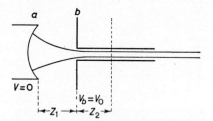

FIG. 3. Flow in a Pierce-type gun.

To do this we assume that the velocity wave in the tunnel has a maximum at z_2 behind the anode plane (Fig. 3). From now on, it will be convenient to work in mean square values as these are directly additive. We are thus dealing with products of the form $b_{ik}\, b_{ik}{}^* \, \delta_{ik}$; the suffix 2 denotes values measured at the new origin z_2.

Then
$$\langle u_b{}^2 \rangle = \langle u_2{}^2 \rangle \cos^2 Z_2$$

$$\langle q_b{}^2 \rangle = \left(\frac{I_0}{u_0}\right)^2 \left(\frac{\omega}{F\omega_p}\right)^2 \langle u_2{}^2 \rangle \sin^2 Z_2$$

or, using values from Eqs. (11) and (12)

$$\cos^2 Z_2 = \frac{1}{1 + \theta_1{}^2 (F\omega_p/\omega)^2} \tag{15}$$

$$\langle u_2{}^2 \rangle = \left\{ 1 + \theta_1{}^2 \left(\frac{F\omega_p}{\omega}\right)^2 \right\} \langle u_a{}^2 \rangle \tag{16}$$

Here $Z_2 = F\omega_p z_2/u_0$, $\theta_1 = \omega\tau_1$, $\langle u_a{}^2 \rangle = 4\eta kT/I_0\,(1 - \pi/4)\varDelta f$.

We then have for the space-charge waves at any plane z distant from the anode plane b

$$\langle u^2 \rangle = \langle u_a{}^2 \rangle \left\{ 1 + \theta_1{}^2 \left(\frac{F\omega_p}{\omega} \right)^2 \right\} \cos^2 (Z - Z_2) \qquad (17)$$

$$\langle i^2 \rangle = \langle u_a{}^2 \rangle \left\{ \left(\frac{\omega}{F\omega_p} \right)^2 + \theta_1{}^2 \right\} \frac{I_0{}^2}{2\eta V_0} \sin^2 (Z - Z_2) \qquad (18)$$

When the same process is applied to the waves originating from Eq. (14) we easily find that

$$\langle u^2 \rangle = \langle q_a{}^2 \rangle \frac{2\eta V_0}{I_0{}^2} \left(\frac{F\omega_p}{\omega} \right)^2 \cos^2 [(Z - Z_2) + \psi] \qquad (19)$$

$$\langle i^2 \rangle = \langle q_a{}^2 \rangle \sin^2 [(Z - Z_2) + \psi] \qquad (20)$$

where $\psi = Z_2 + (2n + 1)\pi/2$, $\langle q_a{}^2 \rangle = \pi k T / 2 V_0 \cdot \gamma I_0 \cdot \Delta f$.

It is at once obvious that if we choose z so that either Eq. (17) or Eq. (18) vanishes, then the corresponding one of Eq. (19) or Eq. (20) will be finite. It therefore follows that it is impossible to choose a location for zero noise but, at best, it is possible to find one for a finite minimum.

Before proceeding further we introduce a little extra notation, to eliminate θ_1. In a space-charge limited diode $\tau_1{}^2 = (3z_1/u_b)^2$. Using the relation between the current and z, it is easy to show that

$$\theta_1{}^2 = (\omega \tau_1)^2 = \frac{2\omega^2}{\omega_p{}^2}$$

or

$$\left\{ 1 + \theta_1{}^2 \left(\frac{F\omega_p}{\omega} \right)^2 \right\} = 1 + 2F^2 \qquad (21)$$

In this form it is clear that Eq. (21) can only range from 1 to 3, which is far from obvious in the other relation.

10.3.   NOISE FACTOR FOR VALVES WITH INPUT RESONATORS

We are now in a position to consider the noise figures for some simple tube configurations. The easiest is a resonant input circuit. We consider such a resonator matched to an aerial. The loaded cavity conductance, including beam loading, is put equal to G. Then the mean square noise voltage from the aerial and the input resonator is[5]

$$\langle V_{na}^2 \rangle = \frac{4kT_a}{G} \Delta f \tag{22}$$

and this causes a mean square velocity modulation on the beam equal to

$$\langle u_{na}^2 \rangle = \frac{2\eta k T_a M^2}{G V_0} \Delta f \tag{23}$$

Now, if we are willing to assume that the gain of the first amplifying stage is high enough for us to ignore noise contributions from the second stage, we can work on the basis of noise quantities at the input alone. We shall look at the gain question later. The effects to be considered are:

(a) Current fluctuations in the beam induce voltages on the resonator which reinduce velocity fluctuations in the beam.

(b) Velocity fluctuations at input are transformed by the amplifying action of the device into current fluctuations at the output. However, at low levels, the transconductance of the tube is independent of amplitude so signal and noise wave have the same gain and the conditions at the output are those at input multiplied by the gain constant.

The noise current in the beam induces a noise voltage given by

$$\langle V_{nb}^2 \rangle = \frac{M^2}{G^2} \langle i^2 \rangle \tag{24}$$

The noise figure of the amplifier is now given by

$$\text{N.F.} = 1 + \frac{\langle V_{nb}^2 \rangle}{\langle V_{na}^2 \rangle} + \frac{\langle u_{nb}^2 \rangle}{\langle u_{na}^2 \rangle} \tag{25}$$

where $\langle V_{nb}^2 \rangle$ denotes Eq. (24) using the sum of the $\langle i^2 \rangle$ from Eqs. (18) and (20) while $\langle u_{nb}^2 \rangle$ denotes the sum of Eqs. (17) and (19). All quantities are, of course, to be evaluated at the plane of the gap centre. We see that any one of the four noise waves may be chosen to be identically zero at this plane.

---

[5] BECK; *Thermionic Valves*, pp. 221–222, Cambridge University Press, 1953.

10.3.1. $\sin (Z - Z_2) = 0$.

This choice eliminates what used to be termed the "amplified shot noise" of the electron beam. We find immediately that

$$\cos^2 (Z - Z_2) = 1$$

$$\sin^2 [(Z - Z_2) + \psi] = \cos^2 Z_2 = (1 + 2F^2)^{-1}$$

$$\cos^2 [(Z - Z_2) + \psi] = \sin^2 Z = 1 - (1 + 2F^2)^{-1}$$

Therefore

$$\text{N.F.} = 1 + \frac{\langle q_a^2\rangle M^2/G^2(1/1 + 2F^2)}{\langle V_{na}^2\rangle} +$$

$$+ \frac{\langle q_a^2\rangle 2\eta V_0/I_0^2(F\omega_p/\omega)^2[1 - 1/1 + 2F^2] + \langle u_a^2\rangle[1 + 2F^2]}{\langle u_{na}^2\rangle}$$

If we put in the values $\langle q_a^2\rangle$, $\langle u_a^2\rangle$, $\langle V_{na}^2\rangle$ and $\langle u_{na}^2\rangle$ and introduce the klystron parameter P, which in the present notation is equal to $2V_0G/I_0M^2$, we easily find

$$\text{N.F.} = 1 + \frac{PT}{T_a}\left[\left(1 - \frac{\pi}{4}\right)(1 + 2F^2) + \frac{\pi}{4}\gamma\frac{F^2\omega_p^2}{\omega^2}\left(\frac{2F^2}{1 + 2F^2}\right)\right] +$$

$$+ \frac{\pi}{4}\cdot\frac{T}{T_a}\cdot\frac{\gamma}{P}\left[\frac{1}{1 + 2F^2}\right] \quad (26)$$

If the current fluctuation at the minimum had been ignored, which amounts to putting $\gamma = 0$, then only the first and second terms remain. In this approximation the equation says that P should be small for low N.F. But small P is just what is required for a high-power klystron and it is clearly unlikely that such a valve will exhibit a low N.F. Equation (26), on the other hand, shows that the last term becomes significant if P is small and the more accurate theory therefore shows that there is some optimum value of P. The third term of Eq. (26) is negligible compared with the second, because of the factor $F^2\omega_p^2/\omega^2$ which is of the order 10^{-2} or less. If we do neglect this term and put $\gamma = 1$, Eq. (26) can be written

$$\text{N.F.} = 1 + \left(1 - \frac{\pi}{4}\right)T\frac{Y}{T_a} + \frac{\pi}{4}\frac{T}{T_aY} \quad (27)$$

where $Y = (1 + 2F^2)P$.

Equation (27) has a minimum when $Y = \sqrt{[\pi/(4 - \pi)]} = 1\cdot90$. The value is

$$\text{N.F.} = 1 + \frac{T}{T_a}\sqrt{\frac{5\pi}{4}\left(1 - \frac{\pi}{4}\right)}$$

If $T/T_a = 3\cdot5$, N.F.$_{(\text{min})} = 4\cdot2$ or $6\cdot2$ dB. This is the well-known minimum N.F. predicted by this theory. We observe that the optimum value of P is between $1\cdot90$ and $0\cdot63$ depending on the value of F^2. These values still correspond with very high perveance guns, i.e., with high-powered valves, which one is very unlikely to encounter in input stages.

10.3.2. $\cos(Z - Z_2) = 0$

If we now make the velocity modulation due to the original velocity fluctuations zero, the reader can easily verify that

$$\text{N.F.} = 1 + \frac{1}{P}\frac{T}{T_a}\left[\left(1 - \frac{\pi}{4}\right)\frac{\omega^2}{F^2\omega_p{}^2}\left(1 + \frac{2F^2\omega_p{}^2}{\omega^2}\right) + \frac{\pi}{4\gamma}\left(\frac{2F^2}{1 + 2F^2}\right)\right] +$$

$$+ \frac{\pi}{4}\frac{T}{T_a}\cdot P\gamma\frac{F^2\omega_p{}^2/\omega^2}{1 + 2F^2} \qquad (28)$$

If we put $Y_1 = P(F^2\omega_p{}^2/\omega^2)(1 + 2F^2)$ and $\gamma = 1$, we now find the same minimum N.F. of $6\cdot2$ dB for $Y_1 = 0\cdot524$. However, this means that $P(1 + 2F^2)$ is required to be quite large, e.g., $52\cdot4$, so that this choice certainly leads to low-powered valves. The difficulty here is that the resultant large value of P leads to a valve with very little gain.

When these results were first worked out, it seemed very surprising that both approaches should lead to the same value of minimum noise figure. We now know that these are both examples of a general noise theorem due to PIERCE[6] which states that "if measurements are made in a bandwidth Δf around ω_0 of the maxima and minima of the noise current standing waves in a beam, carrying current I_0 at a potential V_0 with respect to the cathode, of temperature T, then

$$\langle i_{\text{min}} \rangle \langle i_{\text{max}} \rangle = \sqrt{\pi(4 - \pi)}\,\frac{\omega}{F\omega_p}\cdot\frac{kT}{eV_0}\cdot eI_0\Delta f\,\text{"} \qquad (29)$$

---

[6] PIERCE; *J. Appl. Phys.*, 1954, **25**, 931.

This holds for any part of a beam no matter what system of accelerating and decelerating fields is applied to it. This theorem is basic to the modern developments of noise theory. It is also another facet of the behaviour of space-charge waves; the fluctuation energy is given to the beam at its origin at the cathode and unless this energy is removed from the beam, by some process different from the linear processes so far studied, it propagates along the beam as a system of standing waves.

10.4. NOISE FIGURE OF T.W.A.s

Before embarking on the more generalized theory of noise we wish to discuss the noise behaviour of the T.W.A. if only because these amplifiers are actually used as low noise input stages. The theory used here is based on a rather simplified version of the T.W.A. but this is legitimate in view of the fact that low-noise tubes operate with low beam currents and small signals. The procedure is to drop the assumption, made in Section 7.3.4, that the initial amplitudes of the r.f. current and velocity are zero, by putting in the amplitudes of the noise space-charge waves at the plane where the helix begins. The relations for the initial fields then become:

$$E_1 + E_2 + E_3 = E_i \tag{30}$$

$$\frac{E_1}{\delta_1} + \frac{E_2}{\delta_2} + \frac{E_3}{\delta_3} = -\frac{\beta_e C u_0}{\eta} u_1 \tag{31}$$

$$\frac{E_1}{\delta_1{}^2} + \frac{E_2}{\delta_2{}^2} + \frac{E_3}{\delta_3{}^2} = -j\frac{2V_0 C^2}{I_0} i_1 \tag{32}$$

where E_i is now due to the Johnson noise in the input circuit. The solution† is (see Appendix 9)

$$E_1 = \frac{E_i + (\beta_e u_0 C/\eta)(\delta_2 + \delta_3)u_1 - j\beta_e (2V_0 C^2/I_0) \delta_2 \delta_3 i_1}{(1 - \delta_2/\delta_1)(1 - \delta_3/\delta_1)} \tag{33}$$

The input noise power is

$$P_n = kT_a \Delta f \tag{34}$$

---

† The results of this section are due to PIERCE; *Traveling-Wave Tubes*, Chapters 9 and 10; WATKINS; *Proc. I.R.E.*, 1952, **40**, 65; and PIERCE and DANIELSON; *J. Appl. Phys.*, 1954, **25**, 1163.

We know that the parameter C^3 is defined by

$$C^3 = \frac{E^2}{2\beta_e{}^2 P} \cdot \frac{I_0}{4V_0} \tag{35}$$

where E is the peak value of the field. The mean square value of E_t is thus given by

$$\langle E_{t_A}{}^2 \rangle = \frac{4\beta_e{}^2 V_0 C^3 P_n}{I_0} \tag{36}$$

The noise factor is given by

$$\text{N.F.} = \frac{|E_{1A}{}^2| + |E_{1N}{}^2|}{|E_{1A}{}^2|} \tag{37}$$

Here E_{1A} is obtained by putting Eq. (36) into Eq. (33) for E_t and taking $u_1 = 0 = i_1$, while E_{1N} is taken from Eq. (33) when u_1 and i_1 are given their appropriate noise wave values and $E_t = 0$. Equation (37) yields

$$\text{N.F.} = 1 + \frac{I_0}{2\eta k T_a C \Delta f} \left| (\delta_2 + \delta_3) u_1 - j \frac{u_0 C}{I_0} (\delta_2 \delta_3) i_1 \right|^2 \tag{38}$$

If space-charge is taken into account by Pierce's method, we obtain $(\delta_2 \delta_3 - 4QC) i_1$, instead of $\delta_2 \delta_3 \cdot i_1$. Using Eqs. (17) and (18) we may now write down an expression for the noise figure. It is

$$\text{N.F.} = 1 + \frac{\langle u_a{}^2 \rangle I_0 \{1 + 2F^2\}}{2\eta k T_a C \Delta f}$$

$$\times \left| (\delta_2 + \delta_3) \cos (Z - Z_2) - \frac{(\delta_2 \delta_3 - 4QC)}{(4QC)^{1/2}} \sin (Z - Z_2) \right|^2 \tag{39}$$

where we have used the fact that $F\omega_p = 2\omega C \sqrt{(QC)}$ (Eq. 7.2.2.). If we now use the value of $\langle u_a{}^2 \rangle$ the result is

$$\text{N.F.} = 1 + \frac{(4 - \pi)T}{2T_a} \frac{\{1 + 2F^2\}}{C}$$

$$\times \left| (\delta_2 + \delta_3) \cos (Z - Z_2) - \frac{(\delta_2 \delta_3 - 4QC)}{(4QC)^{1/2}} \sin (Z - Z_2) \right|^2 \tag{40}$$

Equation (40) is due to Watkins and is fully discussed by him in the reference cited. Here, we merely note that if we ignore the Q term and use the first approximation to the δ's, i.e., $\delta_2 = -\sqrt{(3/2)} - j/2$, $\delta_3 = j$, the square of the modulus becomes

$$\cos^2{(Z - Z_2)} + \left(\frac{\omega}{F\omega_p}\right)^2 C^2 \sin^2{(Z - Z_2)} \tag{41}$$

Since $\omega^2 C^2 / F^2 \omega_p^2$ is of the order 0·1, this function oscillates with the periodicity of the space-charge waves between 1·0 and 0·1, so that an improvement of N.F. by about 10 dB should be possible by correct choice of the distance between gun anode and the start of the helix. Moreover, Watkins shows that the noise factor can be made as small as one likes by the use of velocity jumps in the region between gun anode and helix. However, this is not the case when the initial current fluctuations are included, as we now show. This is done by the use of Pierce's theorem, which we first transform into a velocity expression. This is done using the wave impedance and kinetic voltage relations to obtain

$$u_1 = \frac{2F\omega_p}{\omega} \cdot \frac{\eta}{u_0} \cdot \frac{V_0}{I_0} \cdot i_1 \tag{42}$$

and yields
$$\langle u_{\max} \rangle \langle u_{\min} \rangle = \langle u_a^2 \rangle \frac{\sqrt{\pi}}{\sqrt{4 - \pi}} \frac{F\omega_p}{\omega} \tag{43}$$

with $\langle u_a^2 \rangle = (4 - \pi)\,\eta k T_c / I_0 \cdot \Delta f$, as before.

If we had chosen the mean square velocity as our initial condition, instead of the square of the mean velocity, Eq. (43) would read

$$\langle u_{\max} \rangle \langle u_{\min} \rangle = \langle u_a^2 \rangle \frac{2}{\sqrt{4 - \pi}} \frac{F\omega_p}{\omega} \tag{44}$$

Pierce prefers to write these expressions as $2\alpha/4 - \pi \cdot F\omega_p/\omega$ so that α is either $\frac{1}{2}\sqrt{[(4 - \pi)\pi]}$ or $\sqrt{[4 - \pi]}$, i.e., is nearly unity in either case. We now write

$$\frac{\langle u_{m1}^2 \rangle \langle u_{m2}^2 \rangle}{\langle u_a^2 \rangle^2} = \frac{4\epsilon^2(F\omega_p/\omega)}{\sin^2{\theta_d}} = \frac{(4\epsilon^2)(4QC^3)}{\sin^2{\theta_d}} \tag{45}$$

where now $\epsilon = \alpha/4 - \pi = 1\cdot165\alpha \doteq 1$.

Pierce's Q has been used instead of $F\omega_p$ and θ_d is the phase angle between the planes of the velocity maxima of the two standing waves. Now, assume that at entry to the helix one standing wave has its maximum at an angle $(2\theta + \theta_d)/2$ away from the entry and therefore the other maximum is at $(2\theta - \theta_d)/2$. We have already noted that the modulus in Eq. (40) varies sinusoidally with $(Z - Z_2)$ and we can now write for the modified noise figure

$$\text{N.F.} = 1 + \frac{(4 - \pi)T}{2T_a}\frac{f_{\min}}{C(1 - \beta)}$$

$$\times \left[r\{1 - \beta \cos(2\theta + \theta_d)\} + \frac{1}{r}\frac{(4\epsilon^2)(4QC^3)}{\sin^2\theta_d} \cdot \{1 - \beta \cos(2\theta - \theta_d)\}\right] \tag{46}$$

where $f_{\min}$ is the minimum, with respect to $\delta z = Z - Z_2$, of the squared modulus in Eq. (40) and

$$\beta = \frac{f_{\max} - f_{\min}}{f_{\max} + f_{\min}} \tag{47}$$

$$r = (1 + 2F^2) \tag{48}$$

If we minimize N.F. with respect to r we find

$$r = 2\epsilon(4QC^3)^{1/2}\left[\frac{1 - \beta \cos(2\theta - \theta_d)}{\sin^2\theta_d\,[1 - \beta \cos(2\theta + \theta_d)]}\right]^{1/2} \tag{49}$$

Using Eq. (49), Eq. (46) becomes

$$\text{N.F.} = 1 + 4(4 - \pi)\frac{\epsilon T}{T_a}(QC)^{1/2}f_{\min}$$

$$\times \left[\frac{1 - 2\beta \cos 2\theta \cos \theta_d - \beta^2 + \beta^2 \cos^2 2\theta + \beta^2 \cos^2 \theta_d}{(1 - \beta)^2 \sin^2 \theta_d}\right]^{1/2} \tag{50}$$

Differentiating with respect to θ:—

$$\sin 2\theta(\cos \theta_d - \beta \cos 2\theta) = 0 \tag{51}$$

so that for N.F.$_{\min}$, either

$$\cos 2\theta = 1 \tag{52}$$

or

$$\cos 2\theta = \frac{\cos \theta_d}{\beta} \tag{53}$$

Both choices actually lead to the same minimum noise figure.

Using Eq. (53) in Eq. (50)

$$\text{N.F.}_{\text{min}} = 1 + \frac{\epsilon T}{T_a} 4(4 - \pi) Q C^{1/2} f_{\text{min}} \left(\frac{1 + \beta}{1 - \beta}\right)^{1/2} \qquad (54)$$

Equation (54) is independent of θ_d, so it must hold for $\beta = \theta_d$ which leads back to Eq. (52), showing that Eq. (54) does include both cases. From Eq. (47)

$$\frac{f_{\text{max}}}{f_{\text{min}}} = \frac{1 + \beta}{1 - \beta} \qquad (55)$$

and Eq. (54) then becomes

$$\text{N.F.}_{\text{min}} = 1 + \frac{\epsilon T}{T_a} 4(4 - \pi) Q C^{1/2} (f_{\text{max}} \cdot f_{\text{min}})^{1/2} \qquad (56)$$

Equation (56) may be further investigated by introducing values for $f_{\text{max}} \cdot f_{\text{min}}$; deduced for particular values of the δ's depending on the parameters and operating voltage of the T.W.A. In particular, for the case of no circuit attenuation, Pierce shows that

$$\text{N.F.}_{\text{min}} = 1 + \frac{\epsilon T}{T_a} (4 - \pi) \qquad (57)$$

which, for $\epsilon T/T_a = 3 \cdot 5$. leads to the value $6 \cdot 0$ dB. Increasing the circuit loss increases the noisiness of the tube and for a given loss greater than zero, increasing QC increases the noisiness. This is shown in Fig. 4.

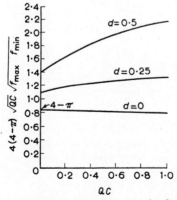

Fig. 4. Effect of circuit loss on noise figure.

We observe once more that there are two optimum conditions for the location of the beginning of the helix. Both lead to the same N.F. which it is not possible to improve upon. Since this is what we found in the case of the klystron, it is reasonable to suppose that the behaviour of all microwave amplifiers is similar. That this is the case has been proved in general terms by HAUS and ROBINSON[7] and we now give an account of their work.

10.5. GENERAL THEORY

The general theory of noise in beams is based on the general theorems on power flow in space-charge waves already dealt with in Section 4.9. As in Chapter 6 we write U for the kinetic voltage. Here we consider the fast and slow space-charge waves separately. Equation (116) of Chapter 4 shows that the total kinetic power, the sum of the powers in both waves, is

$$P_k = \frac{Z}{2}[i_1 i_1^* - i_2 i_2^*] \tag{58}$$

where suffix 1 relates to the fast wave and suffix 2 to the slow wave. Z is given its positive value, $|Z|$. Haus and Robinson prefer to introduce the normalized amplitudes $a_1 = (\frac{1}{2}Z)^{1/2}i_1$, $a_2 = (\frac{1}{2}Z)^{1/2}i_2$, so that Eq. (58) simplifies to

$$P_k = a_1 a_1^* - a_2 a_2^* \tag{59}$$

In the same way the matrix relation

$$\begin{vmatrix} U_2 \\ i_2 \end{vmatrix} = \begin{vmatrix} A & B \\ C & D \end{vmatrix} \begin{vmatrix} U_1 \\ i_1 \end{vmatrix}$$

is generalized to

$$\begin{vmatrix} b_1 \\ b_2 \end{vmatrix} = |M| \begin{vmatrix} a_1 \\ a_2 \end{vmatrix} \tag{60}$$

The coefficients M are readily determined. We now develop some very general relations based on the matrix foundation, following HAUS and ROBINSON.[8] We consider a system with many beam

---

[7] HAUS and ROBINSON; *Proc. I.R.E.*, 1955, **43**, 981.

[8] ROBINSON and HAUS; *J. Electronics*, 1956, **1**, 373.

modes, e.g., due to higher order space-charge waves. Equation (59) can be generalized to

$$W = \sum_{j=1}^{m} p_j a_j a_j^*$$

where p_j is the parity of the jth mode and is ± 1 depending on whether this mode is the fast one or the slow one of a pair. Furthermore Eq. (60) can be written as

$$b_i = \sum_{j=1}^{m} M_{ij} a_j \qquad (61)$$

so that M_{ij} is the matrix representing the transformation between planes a and b. The matrix equation equivalent to Eq. (61) is

$$b = Ma \qquad (62)$$

where M is a square matrix. Moreover, if the path a–b is lossless, i.e., no power is extracted from the beam along this path, the power available at a must equal that available at b or

$$\sum_{j=1}^{m} p_j a_j a_j^* = \sum_{i=1}^{m} p_i b_i b_i^* \qquad (63)$$

If corresponding modes are given the same suffix we can introduce a parity matrix P which is a diagonal matrix, i.e., it might be of the form

$$P = \begin{vmatrix} 1 & 0 & 0 & 0 \\ 0 & -1 & 0 & 0 \\ 0 & 0 & 1 & 0 \\ 0 & 0 & 0 & -1 \end{vmatrix}$$

for two space-charge modes. Equation (63) may then be written, introducing the Hermitian conjugate matrix,† b^+,

$$b^+ P b = a^+ P a \qquad (64)$$

or, using Eq. (62),

$$a^+ M^+ P M a = a^+ P a$$

or

$$M^+ P M = P \qquad (65)$$

---

† Matrix theory is discussed in MARGENAU and MURPHY; *Mathematics of Physics and Chemistry*, 1st Ed., Chapter 10, Van Nostrand, 1943; and FRAZER, DUNCAN and COLLAR; *Elementary Matrices*, Cambridge University Press, 1938. The Hermitian conjugate is defined by $(A^+)_{ij} = A_{ji}^*$, i.e., the elements are reflected in the diagonal and the complex conjugate taken. Such conjugates have the property $(AB)^+ = B^+ A^+$.

Equation (65) must be satisfied by any lossless transformation matrix.

We now consider a system in which a beam interacts with a circuit. We can regard this as a "black box" into which the beam

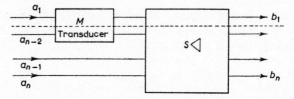

FIG. 5. A general noise circuit.

modes and circuit modes are introduced. (Fig. 5.) If the circuit modes are normalized, we need make no special distinction between them and the beam modes and we can write the scattering matrix[9]

$$b = Sa \qquad (66)$$

If there are no ohmic losses, Eq. (66) can be shown to be equivalent to

$$S^+PS = P \qquad (67)$$

while, if there are losses, from Eq. (64)

$$b^+Pb = a^+Pa$$

therefore

$$S^+PS = P - L \qquad (68)$$

where L is the dissipation matrix. The R.H.S. of Eq. (67) can be transformed by multiplying it from the right by SP and from the left by $(PS)^{-1}$, obtaining

$$SPS^+PS(PS)^{-1} = SPP(PS)^{-1}$$

Now $PP = I$, the unit matrix

therefore

$$P^{-1} = P$$

and

$$(PS)^{-1} = S^{-1}P^{-1}$$

therefore

$$SPS^+ = P \qquad (69)$$

[9] M.I.T. Series, Vol. 8, 1946.

Similarly, Eq. (68) gives

$$SPS^+ = P - K \qquad (70)$$

These results all go over into those of ordinary circuit theory if P is replaced by I, since all the circuit modes carry positive powers.

We next have to set up a matrix description of the noise. This is done by departing somewhat from usual ideas. Suppose that N measurements are made of the noise current, using an instrument with bandwidth Δf at f_0, each measurement lasting τ seconds such that $\omega_0\tau \gg 1$, $\tau\Delta f \ll 1$. Each time we observe a sine wave of definite amplitude, phase and frequency. Let i_k be the complex amplitude of the kth observed current. Then the mean square sum is

$$\langle i^2 \rangle = \frac{1}{2N} \sum_{k=1}^{N} i_k \cdot i_k{}^* \qquad (71)$$

As $N \to \infty$, this result tends to the usual shot noise expression.† If there are several, n, noise modes and the amplitude in the ith mode is a_i and N measurements are made simultaneously on the n modes, we form the averages

$$\langle a_i \cdot a_j{}^* \rangle = \lim_{N \to \infty} \frac{1}{N} \sum_{k=1}^{N} a_{ik} a_{jk}{}^* \qquad (72)$$

When $i = j$, the self power of a mode is in question; when $i \neq j$ the cross power between modes is involved. If the noise modes are uncorrelated, no cross power terms appear. Equation (72) can be written in the form

$$\langle a_i \cdot a_j{}^* \rangle = 4\pi\Delta f A_{ij} \qquad (73)$$

where A_{ij} = cross power density spectrum of modes i and j. A_{ij} is a square matrix, subsequently called the noise matrix, and from Eq. (72) this matrix is Hermitian, i.e.,

$$A_{ji} = A_{ij}{}^*$$

We now set up the transformation relation for matrices of noise type. We write

$$4\pi\Delta f B_{ij} = \langle b_i \cdot b_j{}^* \rangle$$

† See, for example, the argument leading to Eq. (23) of chapter 8 in *Thermionic Valves*.

x

or, using (66)

$$4\pi\Delta f B_{ij} = \langle \sum_r S_{ir} \cdot a_r \sum_s S_{js}{}^* \cdot a_s \rangle$$

$$= 4\pi\Delta f\,(SAS^+)_{ij}$$

Therefore the relation is

$$B = SAS^+ \tag{74}$$

Robinson and Haus proceed to demonstrate that Eq. (74) leads to certain noise invariants, which turn out to be those used in Pierce's theorem and in an earlier paper by HAUS.[10] This simply demonstrates that the matrix method leads to standard results and we omit the proof.

The next question is the calculation of the elements of the matrix B. M satisfies

$$MAM^+ = B$$

$$MPM^+ = P$$

therefore $\qquad MAP = BPM \tag{75}$

B and P are both diagonal, therefore so is BP. Equation (75) is then an eigenvalue problem and the elements of BP are the λ's in

$$\det(AP - \lambda I) = 0 \tag{76}$$

We note that the sign of λ has to equal the parity of the mode. The λs all taken positive are the diagonal elements of B, those which were positive in BP having parity $+1$, those negative of parity -1.

This demonstrates that any noise process in n modes can be regarded as the effect of at most n independent sources, one per input mode, modified by a lossless transducer. The relations given allow us to assign values to each process. As an example, consider Fig. 5. The circuit modes are a_n and a_{n-1} which are operated on by the amplifier to become b_n and b_{n-1}. The remaining modes are noise modes in the beam which are also operated by the amplifier but, before this, by a lossless transducer M which is supposed to minimize the noise. The incident noise matrix A is an $n-2 \times n-2$ matrix whose elements are known, from Eq. (76).

[10] HAUS; *J. Appl. Phys.*, 1955, **26**, 560.

The system matrix is now

$$G = S \begin{vmatrix} M & 0 & 0 \\ 0 & 1 & 0 \\ 0 & 0 & 1 \end{vmatrix} \qquad (77)$$

The output noise power is now

$$N = \langle \sum_r G_{nr} . b_r \sum_s G_{ns} . b_s \rangle$$

Or, since the b's are uncorrelated

$$N = \sum G_{nr} . G_{nr}{}^* \langle b_r b_r{}^* \rangle$$
$$= 4\pi \varDelta f \sum G_{nr} . G_{nr}{}^* B_{rr} \qquad (78)$$

But, in view of Eq. (70)

$$\sum_r p_r G_{nr} . G_{nr}{}^* = p_n - K_{nn} = 1 - K_{nn} \qquad (79)$$

Now the overall gain $G_{nn}G_{nn}{}^*$ can only be large if at least one of the coefficients G_{nr} belonging to a mode of negative parity $p_r = -1$ is also large. For a given gain N is least when all the G_{nr} are zero except G_{nn}, giving the gain, and the particular G_{nr} corresponding with the mode of negative parity which has the smallest element B_{rr}. In this case

$$N = 4\pi \varDelta f(G_{nn} . G_{nn}{}^* . B_{rn} + G_{nr} . G_{nr}{}^* . B_{rr})$$

From (79) $G_{nr} . G_{nr}{}^* = G_{nn}G_{nn} - 1 + K_{nn}{}^*$

Then, using the definition of N.F. and $B_{nn} = kT/4\pi$

$$\text{N.F.} = 1 + \frac{4\pi B_{rr}}{kT}\left(1 - \frac{1 - K_{nn}}{G_{nn} . G_{nn}{}^*}\right) \qquad (80)$$

Equation (80) assumes that the output is matched. It proves that the least N.F. is obtained with an amplifier (i) which is either lossless or has $K_{nn} = 0$, (ii) which couples the output only to the negative beam mode with the least noise. We conclude that in general the inclusion of higher order modes on the beam will worsen the N.F.

10.6 PARTITION NOISE

We first study low frequency partition noise due to current division between n electrodes. NORTH[11] shows that when an electron current divides between several electrodes, the mean square noise component of the nth current is

$$\langle i_n^2 \rangle = \langle i^2 \rangle \frac{[1 - I_n/I(1 - \Gamma^2)]}{\Gamma^2} \frac{I_n}{I} \qquad (81)$$

where I = total cathode current

I_n = electron current to nth electrode

Γ^2 = low frequency smoothing factor

$\langle i^2 \rangle = 2eI\Gamma^2 \cdot \Delta f$, the l.f. shot noise component of I.

It follows that $\langle i_n^2 \rangle$ is always less than the full shot noise in I_n, but approaches this value when I_n is a very small proportion of I. When $I_n \rightarrow I$,

$$\frac{\langle i_n^2 \rangle}{\langle i^2 \rangle} \rightarrow \frac{I_n}{I}$$

Explicitly if $I_n/I = 1 - \epsilon$

$$\frac{\langle i_n^2 \rangle}{\langle i^2 \rangle} \rightarrow \left(1 + \frac{\epsilon}{\Gamma^2}\right) \frac{I_n}{I}$$

Γ^2 is usually a number of the order $0 \cdot 1$ so that ϵ must be very small if the effective smoothing is not to be considerably reduced. For this reason, very considerable pains are taken in the design of guns for low noise T.W.A.s to ensure that the beam efficiency is better than 99%. The beam current is then very little more noisy than the ideal beam of the same current.

The second type of noise, usually called induced current noise, is, as we have already said, observed even when there is no convection current flowing in an electrode lead. An instance is the noise induced in the grid cathode circuit of a negative grid triode. In this case the induced grid noise is the major noise component at frequencies above about 20–30 Mc/s. Part of this noise is simply the induced shot noise from the electron stream but part is known, from experiment, to be uncorrelated with this. Various sources

---

[11] NORTH; *R.C.A. Rev.*, 1940, 244. See BECK; *Thermionic Valves*, Section 8.5.

of uncorrelated noise have been considered and one of them is induced partition noise, due to the fluctuations in the electron trajectories, i.e., fluctuation in the average transit angle in the case of the triode. In passing, we should note that TALPEY and MACNEE[12] have shown that, in the case of the triode, the observed large value of uncorrelated noise is most likely due to electrons reflected from the anode and the effect of induced partition noise is small. However, our main interest is in low noise tubes using beams in which the coupling between the field and the beam varies fairly considerably over the beam diameter. In such circumstances induced partition noise may well be more important. Relatively little work has been done on this matter, the only direct calculations being those of BELL[13] on the negative grid triode. However, owing to the complexity of the electron-optical problem in this case, Bell was not able to complete his analysis and only draws qualitative conclusions.

ROBINSON and KOMPFNER[14] have made a calculation of the effect in a T.W.A. basing their argument on an extension of the low-frequency case, in which it is considered that the phenomenon of noise reduction in a space-charge limited device is due to a "compensating" current flow. The details of the l.f. argument are as follows. Let the cathode current be I_0 and the current which reaches the collector be I_a, the intercepted current then being $I_0 - I_a$. The fluctuation in the cathode current is then $S^2 \cdot 2eI_0 \cdot \Delta f$ where we have written S^2 instead of the usual Γ^2 to include possible differences of definition. The noise components of the divided current are:

(i) Shot noise in I_a of magnitude

$$\sqrt{2eI_a\Delta f} \tag{82}$$

(ii) "Compensating" current distributed over the whole beam

$$\sqrt{2eI_a\Delta f}(1 - S) \tag{83}$$

(iii) Shot noise in the intercepted current

$$\sqrt{2e(I_0 - I_a)\Delta f} \tag{84}$$

(iv) "Compensating" current distribution over the whole beam

$$\sqrt{2e(I_0 - I_a)\Delta f} \cdot (1 - S) \tag{85}$$

---

[12] TALPEY and MACNEE; *Proc. I.R.E.*, 1955, **43**, 449.
[13] BELL; *Wireless Engr.*, 1948, **25**, 294.
[14] ROBINSON and KOMPFNER; *Proc. I.R.E.*, 1951, **39**, 918.

The first two components are fully correlated but opposite in sense, i.e., the correlation coefficient is minus one. The same remark applies to the second pair. We can now write down the total noise in I_a using Eq. (82) plus I_a/I_0 times Eq. (83) and Eq. (85), the latter being uncorrelated. The result is

$$I_n{}^2 = \left\{ \left[I_a{}^{1/2} - \frac{I_a}{I_0} I_a{}^{1/2}(1 - S) \right]^2 + \left[\frac{I_a}{I_0} (1 - S)(I_0 - I_a)^{1/2} \right]^2 \right\}$$

(86)

If contributions (i) and (ii) had not been correlated we should merely have summed the three separate squares. When this result, Eq. (86) is evaluated, the expression given at the start of this section results.

The extension to the case of no interception in the case of the helix is dealt with by Robinson and Kompfner by putting $I_a = I_0$ so that items (iii) and (iv) vanish. Item (ii) is coupled to the circuit by the coupling factor averaged over the beam, but item (i) is coupled by the coupling factor evaluated at the radius under consideration. Below, we apply their method to a V.M. gap.

We consider the current in an annulus of width Δr at r. The current density is J_0. Then the noise current associated with this annulus is

$$I_\Delta = \left(\frac{2r\Delta r}{b^2} \right)^{1/2} (2_e I_0 \Delta f)^{1/2}$$

(87)

and the noise current induced in the gap is $M_r \cdot I$. The compensating current induced in the gap is

$$-\langle M \rangle (1 - S) I_\Delta$$

(88)

where $\langle M \rangle$ is the coupling factor averaged over the beam. Thus the mean square induced noise current is

$$\langle I_n{}^2 \rangle = \frac{2}{b^2} \cdot 2_e I_0 \Delta f \int_0^b (M_r - (1 - S)\langle M \rangle)^2 r \, dr$$

Putting in the standard expression for M_r and evaluating

$$\langle M \rangle = \frac{2}{b^2} \frac{I_0(A)}{J_0(L/2)} \int_0^b I_0(R) r \, dr = \frac{2 J_0(L/2) I_1(B)}{B I_0(A)}$$

we find on evaluating the integral, that

$$\langle I_n{}^2 \rangle = 2 e I_0 \Delta f \langle M^2 \rangle \left[S^2 + \frac{B^2}{4} \left\{ \frac{I_0{}^2(B)}{I_1{}^2(B)} - 1 \right\} - 1 \right]$$

(89)

If we had paid no attention to the variation with B, we should simply have had

$$\langle I_n^2 \rangle = 2eI_0 \Delta f \langle M^2 \rangle S^2 \tag{90}$$

There is thus an additive correction term

$$\frac{B^2}{4} \left\{ \frac{I_0^2(B)}{I_1^2(B)} - 1 \right\} - 1 \tag{91}$$

which expresses the effect due to induced partition noise. This term is equal to $(\frac{1}{2}B)^2$ for small B but increases more slowly for larger B.

The result obtained by ROBINSON and KOMPFNER for the helix is exactly the same as Eq. (89) if $\langle M^2 \rangle$ is replaced by the value $2E^2(0)[I_1(B)/B]$, where $E(0)$ is the electric field on the axis of the helix. These authors give a plot of Eq. (91) which is shown in Fig. 6. From this we see that, if S is given the simple-minded l.f. meaning Γ^2, which is of the order 0·1, induced partition noise should *less than double the noise* observed in practical valves, for which $0.5 < B < 1.5$. This effect should hardly be experimentally observable, but I have been unable to find any results bearing on the question.

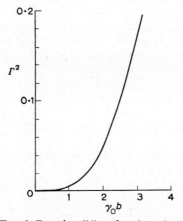

FIG. 6. Equation (91) as function of $\gamma_0 b$.

It should be stated that the development above is, in fact, distinctly suspect. We now realize that the concept of compensating current has no physical validity and the whole question requires the application of more powerful statistical tools.

10.7 THE PRACTICAL ATTAINMENT OF
LOW NOISE FIGURES

The practical aspects of obtaining low noise figures have been dealt with in great detail by the R.C.A. workers, in an interesting series of papers.[15] Our discussion here can therefore be brief.

Obvious general requirements are that the beam current should be kept as low as is consistent with the requirement of obtaining enough gain to make the overall N.F. of the receiver independent of the N.F. of the second stage. If G is the gain of the first stage, F_1 and F_2 the N.F.s of the first and second stages respectively, we have

$$F = F_1 + \frac{F_2}{G} \qquad (92)$$

so that F_2/G must be made small in comparison with F_1 if the second stage is not to lower the performance. In existing low noise tubes G is around 20 dB. Next, the electron optics must be good to keep down partition noise. The vacuum must be good to discourage ionic noise and it has been found empirically that uniform cathode emission, i.e., freedom from patchiness, is desirable. For this reason and because of the high current densities used, great care in the manufacture and processing of the cathode is necessary.

The major theoretical requirement is that the correct disposition of the noise space-charge waves should be attained at entry to the helix. This means that we have to carry out physically the operations corresponding to the mathematical operations which lead from Eq. (46) to Eq. (56). Two separate operations are required. We have to adjust the conditions in the gun so that we obtain the best relation between the noise quantities at the place where the beam reaches its final diameter and velocity, and we have to adjust the position of the start of the helix correctly with respect to this plane.

The first operation corresponds to Eq. (49) into which we now put condition (52) obtaining

$$r_{\text{opt}} = \frac{2\epsilon(4QC^3)^{1/2}}{\sin \theta_d} \qquad (93)$$

The quantities on the R.H.S. all belong to the helix region, while

---

[15] BLOOM and PETER; *R.C.A. Rev.*, 1954, **15**, 252.
BLOOM; *R.C.A. Rev.*, 1955, **16**, 179.
KNECHTLI and BEAM; *R.C.A. Rev.*, 1956, **17**, 410.

Eq. (48) defines r from the gun side. The gun parameters then have to be adjusted so that Eq. (93) is obeyed. The second operation corresponds to obtaining the correct relation (53) between θ, θ_d and β. Fig. 7 shows curves prepared by Watkins which facilitate

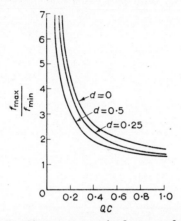

FIG. 7. The ratio of best to worst noise figure as a function of QC.

the computation of β, which has to be known. It is of some interest to evaluate the maximum N.F. which results from a poor choice of quantities in this relation. It is easy to show that N.F.$_{\text{max}}$ occurs when the numerator of the square bracket in Eq. (50) equals unity. Then,

$$\text{N.F.}_{\text{max}} = 1 + \frac{\epsilon T}{T_a} 4(4 - \pi) QC^{1/2} \frac{f_{\text{min}}}{1 - \beta}$$

$$= 1 + \frac{\epsilon T}{T_a} 2(4 - \pi) QC^{1/2}\{f_{\text{min}} + f_{\text{max}}\} \quad (94)$$

or
$$\frac{\text{N.F.}_{\text{max}} - 1}{\text{N.F.}_{\text{min}} - 1} = \frac{f_{\text{min}} + f_{\text{max}}}{2(f_{\text{min}} \cdot f_{\text{max}})^{1/2}} = \frac{1}{(1 - \beta^2)^{1/2}} \quad (95)$$

The plane of maximum noise figure is spaced a quarter space-charge wavelength away from the plane of the minimum.

For full details of possible matching procedures the reader should consult the references mentioned at the beginning of this section.

Several types of gun have been described for this purpose. That due to Watkins includes various regions of velocity jump. The most successful, however, is due to Peter and consists of a series of apertured disks, an example being shown in Fig. 8, from Knechtli and Beam. The potentials used are: $V_{a1} = 50$ V, $V_{a2} = 275$ V, $V_{a3} = 650$ V; the beam current is 300 μA and the confining magnetic field 825 g, a very high figure for such a small current. The idea underlying this gun is to simulate an exponential transformation

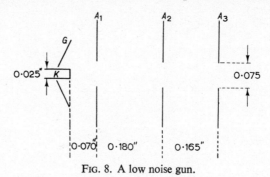

FIG. 8. A low noise gun.

between the cathode and the start of the helix. By adjusting the electrode potentials the current matching condition can be obtained. The advantage of the system is that there are no sudden discontinuities of potential, which although desirable on a single space-charge wave theory, probably set up undesirable higher order modes when more sophisticated investigations are made. It will be noted that the beam diameter is made considerably smaller than the apertures and this is also a situation which favours the gravest space-charge mode against the higher order modes.

The results obtained with this gun are excellent, noise figures of 4·8 dB having been obtained at 4500 Mc/s. Somewhat worse results are obtained from completely encapsulated tubes plus coupling devices but these tubes demonstrate that valves with noise figures better than the 6·3 dB limit can in fact be made and therefore demonstrate that the theory on which this limit is based is itself inadequate.

10.8. THE SMOOTHING OF CURRENT FLUCTUATIONS NEAR THE POTENTIAL MINIMUM

We now discuss rather briefly the recent work on improving the theory. In the introductory part of this chapter we stressed the unsatisfactory nature of our knowledge of current smoothing at the potential minimum, and in Eq. (5), we included a smoothing factor γ, which was put equal to unity in the earlier theories. The present section deals with work designed to assign values to γ, values which turn out to depend on the frequency.

Before starting to describe this work, it is better to clarify the major difficulty in calculating the current fluctuation. Basically, this is due to the flatness of the potential minimum which gives rise to a situation in which electrons emitted with energies just sufficient to reach the minimum region are trapped there and exhibit exceedingly long or infinite transit times. Therefore, quite apart from the difficulty of writing down a multi-velocity theory, there is a separate difficulty in that some of the important integrands become infinite in the very regions of interest. Various authors have studied the problem, a useful survey of two possible approaches being given by WHINNERY.[16] WATKINS[17] has given a theory based on simple premises, which probably leads to results of the correct order of magnitude at the low frequency end of the spectrum. However, as has been said before, the most profitable approach is the computer approach of TIEN and MOSHMAN.[18] For details the reader should consult their paper. A specific diode configuration was studied and the time was divided into a large number of short $(2 \times 10^{-12} \text{ sec})$ intervals. On the average about 8 electrons should leave the cathode in each interval. For the statistical problem, random numbers were generated to prescribe the number to be injected during each interval. The emitted electrons are also given random initial velocities, distributed according to a Maxwellian distribution. All the electrons in a time interval are injected at the same time, but at initial distances from the cathode surface appropriate to their initial velocities. The computer is then used to compute the a.c. velocities and currents at the plane of the potential minimum starting from the space-charge limited condition. The final results, derived for 3000 of the chosen time intervals, are presented first in the form of auto-correlation functions for the current and velocity. The power spectrum is then derived from these functions, as usual, i.e.,

$$A(s) = \frac{1}{2T} \int_{-T}^{+T} i_1(t) i_1(t + s) \, \mathrm{d}t \qquad (96)$$

$$W(f) = 2 \int_{-\infty}^{+\infty} A(s) \cos 2\pi f s \, \mathrm{d}s \qquad (97)$$

where $i_1(t)$ = a.c. current at time t

$i_1(t + s)$ = a.c. current at a later time $t + s$, $T \gg s$

[16] WHINNERY; *Trans. I.R.E., PGED* 1 No. 4, 1954, 221.
[17] WATKINS; *J. Appl. Phys.*, 1955, **26**, 622.
[18] TIEN and MOSHMAN; *J. Appl. Phys.*, 1956, **27**, 1067

Fig. 9 shows the result obtained for $W(f)$ which is equivalent to γ^2. If the factor γ were included in the results for the minimum noise figure, we should obtain

$$F_{\min} = 1 + \tfrac{1}{2}[\pi(4 - \pi)]^{1/2} \gamma \frac{T}{T_a} \qquad (98)$$

where we have chosen the mean velocity criterion of Eq. (43). Fig. 10 shows a plot of Eq. (98) for $T/T_a \doteq 4 \cdot 0$. The N.F. has a distinct minimum at 2500 Mc/s and rises to a slight maximum at

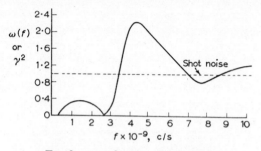

FIG. 9. γ as a function of frequency.

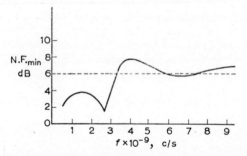

FIG. 10. The minimum noise figure as function of frequency.

4000 Mc/s, above which frequency the smoothing is absent and the full shot noise result prevails. An interesting point is that the plasma-frequency at the potential minimum is $\doteq 3800$ Mc/s. It appears likely, therefore, that the smoothing effect disappears when the operating frequency reaches the plasma frequency. The possibility of oscillatory phenomena in the potential minimum has already been remarked upon by Whinnery and this observation would seem to indicate the actual existence of such phenomena.

The conclusion is that either practical valves for really low noise figures can only be designed for a band in the vicinity of 2500 Mc/s, or that, to get good results at higher frequencies, the plasma frequency must be increased, a matter of some difficulty as these results already relate to a cathode density of 1·5 A/cm².

As regards the velocity function, the computations show that it has a sharp peak at $s = 0$ and fluctuates slightly elsewhere, thus confirming that the low frequency calculations are valid. The cross-correlation between current and velocity fluctuations has been calculated but it turns out to be smaller than is significant. in relation to the round-off error 0·006. Thus cross-correlation, if present, is less than 0·006.

These results are of the highest importance and it is to be hoped that the very considerable labour involved will not prevent their extension to other gun arrangements. This would give better information on the precise influence of the plasma theory.

In view of the influence of partition noise, ionic noise and variations in cathode state, it must be acknowledged that the achievement of N.F.s as low as 4·8 dB in the R.C.A. tubes is a very fine one.

BIBLIOGRAPHY

1. SIEGMAN and WATKINS; Potential-minimum noise in the micro-wave diode, *Trans. I.R.E.*, 1957 *ED*–4 82.

APPENDIX 1

POWER FLOW IN A CIRCULAR GUIDE

Detailed calculation. T.E.$_{11}$ Mode

$$P = \int_0^a \int_0^{2\pi} S_z r \, d\theta \, dr$$

$$= \tfrac{1}{2} Re \int_0^a \int_0^{2\pi} (E_r H_\theta^* - E_\theta H_r^*) r \, d\theta \, dr$$

but $H_\theta = E_r/Z_H$, $H_r = - E_\theta/Z_H$

Therefore

$$P = \frac{1}{2Z_H} \int_0^a \int_0^{2\pi} \{|E_r|^2 + |E_\theta|^2\} r \, d\theta \, dr$$

and

$$|E_r|^2 = A^2 \frac{\omega^2 \mu^2}{k_c^4 r^2} \frac{\cos^2}{\sin^2} \theta J_1^2(k_c r)$$

$$|E_\theta|^2 = A^2 \frac{\omega^2 \mu^2}{k_c^2} \frac{\cos^2}{\sin^2} \theta {J'}_1^2(k_c r)$$

Therefore

$$P = \frac{A^2 \omega^2 \mu^2}{2Z_H k_c^2} \int_0^a \int_0^{2\pi} r \left\{ {J'}_1^2(k_c r) + \frac{1}{k_c^2 r^2} J_1^2(k_c r) \right\} \frac{\cos^2}{\sin^2} \theta \, d\theta \, dr$$

$$= \frac{A^2 \omega^2 \mu^2 \pi}{2Z_H k_c} \int_0^a r \left\{ {J'}_1^2(k_c r) + \frac{1}{k_c^2 r^2} J_1^2(k_c r) \right\} dr$$

But

$${J'}_1(k_c r) = \tfrac{1}{2}(J_0(k_c r) - J_2(k_c r))$$

$$\frac{J_1(k_c r)}{k_c r} = \tfrac{1}{2}(J_0(k_c r) + J_2(k_c r))$$

The integral therefore becomes $\frac{1}{2}\int_0^a \{J_0{}^2(k_cr) + J_2{}^2(k_cr)\}r\,\mathrm{d}r$

$$\int_0^a rJ_0{}^2(k_cr)\,\mathrm{d}r = \frac{a^2}{2}[J_0{}^2(k_ca) + J_1{}^2(k_ca)]$$

$$\int_0^a rJ_2{}^2(k_cr)\,\mathrm{d}r = \frac{a^2}{2}[J_2{}^2(k_ca) - J_1(k_ca)J_3(k_ca)]$$

Now $J'_1(k_ca) = 0$, from the boundary condition

$\therefore$ $J_2(k_ca) = J_0(k_ca) = J_1(k_ca)/(k_ca)$

and $J_3(k_ca) = \dfrac{4}{k_ca}J_2 - J_1$

so that $J_1J_3 = \dfrac{4}{k_c{}^2a^2}J_1{}^2 - J_1{}^2$

and the integral is

$$\frac{a^2}{4}\left[\frac{2J_1{}^2}{(k_ca)^2} + J_1{}^2 - \frac{4J_1{}^2}{(k_ca)^2} + J_1{}^2\right] = \frac{a^2}{2}\left[1 - \frac{1}{(k_ca)^2}\right]J_1{}^2(k_ca)$$

Therefore $P = A^2\dfrac{\pi^2a^2\omega^2\mu^2}{4\pi Z_Hk_c{}^2}\left[1 - \dfrac{1}{(k_ca)^2}\right]J_1{}^2(k_ca)$

$$= A^2\frac{\pi^2\omega^2\mu^2}{4\pi Z_Hk_c{}^4}[(k_ca)^2 - 1]J_1{}^2(k_ca)$$

Now $\dfrac{\omega^2\mu^2}{Z_H} = Z_H\beta^2 = \dfrac{4\pi^2Z_H}{\lambda_g{}^2} = \dfrac{4\pi^2}{\lambda_g\lambda}\zeta$

and $k_c{}^4 = \dfrac{16\pi^4}{\lambda_c{}^4}$

Therefore $P = \dfrac{A^2\lambda_c{}^4}{16\pi\lambda\lambda_g}\zeta[(k_ca)^2 - 1]J_1{}^2(k_ca)$

$$= \frac{A^2\lambda_c{}^4}{16\pi\lambda\lambda_g}\zeta[(q'_{11})^2 - 1]J_1{}^2(q'_{11})$$

Montgomery (see bibliography) has twice this value. The above calculation only takes either the sine or the cosine mode into account. Both carry equal powers, therefore if both are used, we get a factor of 2.

APPENDIX 2

INTEGRALS OF PRODUCTS OF BESSEL FUNCTIONS

$Z_p(R)$ is used as an abbreviation for the general cylinder function. $\overline{Z}_p(R)$ is used for a second similar function. Note that $J_p(R)$, $Y_p(R)$, $aJ_p(R) + bY_p(R)$ are all cylinder functions but $I_p(R)$ and $K_p(R)$ are not.

The integral formulae we shall need are:

$$\int r Z_p{}^2(kr)\,dr = \frac{r^2}{2}\{Z_p{}^2(kr) - Z_{p-1}(kr)Z_{p+1}(kr)\}$$

$$\int r Z_p(k_1 r)\overline{Z}_p(k_2 r)\,dr = \frac{1}{k_1{}^2 - k_2{}^2}$$

$$\times \{(k_2 r)Z_p(k_1 r)\overline{Z}_{p-1}(k_2 r) - (k_1 r)Z_{p-1}(k_1 r)\overline{Z}_p(k_2 r)\}$$

When $p = 0$, these take on particularly simple forms

$$\int r Z_0{}^2(kr)\,dr = \frac{r^2}{2}\{Z_0{}^2(kr) + Z_1{}^2(kr)\}$$

$$\int r Z_0(k_1 r)Z_0(k_2 r)\,dr = \frac{1}{k_2{}^2 - k_1{}^2}$$

$$\times \{(k_2 r)Z_0(k_1 r)\overline{Z}_1(k_2 r) - (k_1 r)Z_1(k_1 r)\overline{Z}_0(k_2 r)\}$$

The integral we had to evaluate in Eq. (85) of Chapter 2 was

$$\int_0^a r J_n\left(q'_{m1}\frac{r}{a}\right) J_n\left(q'_{m2}\frac{r}{a}\right) dr$$

with the condition that $J'_n(q'_{m1}) = 0 = J'_n(q'_{m2})$

The integral is

$$\frac{a^2}{q'_{m1}{}^2 - q'_{m2}{}^2}\{q'_{m2}J_n(q'_{m1})J_{n-1}(q'_{m2}) - q'_{m1}J_{n-1}(q'_m)J_n(q'_{m2})\}$$

Now, the derivatives of cylinder functions are given by

$$\frac{dZ_p(R)}{dR} = \frac{p}{R}Z_p(R) - Z_{p+1}(R)$$

$$= -\frac{p}{R}Z_p(R) + Z_{p-1}(R)$$

so that, at the top limit of integration, $r = a$, we have

$$J_{p-1}(q'_{m1}) = J_{p+1}(q'_{m1}) = \frac{p}{q'_{m1}}J_p(q'_{m1})$$

$$J_{p-1}(q'_{m2}) = J_{p+1}(q'_{m2}) = \frac{p}{q'_{m2}}J_p(q'_{m2})$$

The integral therefore vanishes. This completes the proof that

$$\int_0^a rJ_n\left(q'_{m1}\frac{r}{a}\right)J_n\left(q'_{m2}\frac{r}{a}\right)\,dr = 0, \qquad m_1 \neq m_2$$

If $m_1 = m_2$, we have

$$\int_0^a rJ_n^2\left(q'_m\frac{r}{a}\right)\,dr = \frac{a^2}{2}\left(1 + \frac{n^2}{q'_m{}^2}\right)J_n^2(q'_m) \neq 0$$

When the boundary condition is of the other type $J_n(q_m) = 0$ or $E_z = 0$ at $r = a$, it is immediately obvious that the integral vanishes. Thus, for both the boundary conditions encountered the cross-product terms contribute nothing to the power flow.

Two points should be emphasized with regard to the above treatment. These are:

(i) the importance of the boundary conditions;

(ii) the necessity of including a weight factor r, without which the Bessel functions are not orthogonal. The function of the boundary conditions is somewhat disguised in Fourier expansions but a moment's thought shows that in practical problems the boundary conditions fix the range over which the expansion is valid and therefore appear in the argument of the eigenfunctions.

Y

APPENDIX 3

THE TAPE HELIX

3.1. THE FIELD COMPONENTS

The field components can be written down from the Hertzian vectors, using the equations developed in Chapter 2, specifically Eqs. (114) to (119). The wave functions are those derived from the symmetry conditions, discussed in Section 3.7.2.:—

$$\pi_z^{i,e} = \exp\left(-j\beta_0 z\right) \sum_m A_m^{i,e} \frac{I_n}{K_n}\left(\eta_m^{i,e} \frac{r}{a}\right) \exp -jm\left(\frac{2\pi z}{t} - \theta\right)$$

$$(1)$$

$$\pi_z^{*i,e} = \exp\left(-j\beta_0 z\right) \sum_m B_m^{i,e} \frac{I_n}{K_n}\left(\eta_m^{i,e} \frac{r}{a}\right) \exp -jm\left(\frac{2\pi z}{t} - \theta\right)$$

$$(2)$$

Equations (1) and (2) differ slightly from Eqs. (90) and (91) of Chapter 3 in that we have introduced $\eta_m^{i,e}$ to take care of dielectric outside the helix.† We define

$$\eta_m^i = \{(\beta_m^2 - k_0^2)a^2\}^{1/2} \tag{3}$$

$$k_0^2 = \omega^2 \epsilon_0 \mu_0 = \frac{\omega^2}{c^2}$$

$$\eta_m^e = \{(\beta_m^2 - k_e^2)a^2\}^{1/2} \tag{4}$$

$$k_e^2 = \omega^2 \mu_0 \epsilon$$

where ϵ is the dielectric constant of the material outside the helix. The explicit expressions for the field components are now:
Outside the helix

$$E_{zm}^e = (-\beta_m^2 + k_e^2)A_m^e K_m\left(\eta_m^e \frac{r}{a}\right) \tag{5}$$

---

† We thus follow TIEN.

326

$$H_{zm}{}^e = (-\beta_m{}^2 + k_e{}^2)B_m{}^e K_m\left(\eta_m{}^e \frac{r}{a}\right) \tag{6}$$

$$E_{rm}{}^e = -j\frac{\beta_m\eta_m{}^e}{a} A_m{}^e K'_m\left(\eta_m{}^e \frac{r}{a}\right) + \frac{m\omega\mu}{r} B_m{}^e K_m\left(\eta_m{}^e \frac{r}{a}\right) \tag{7}$$

$$E_{\theta m}{}^e = \frac{m\beta_m}{r} A_m{}^e K_m\left(\eta_m{}^e \frac{r}{a}\right) + j\frac{\omega\mu}{a} \eta_m{}^e B_m{}^e K'_m\left(\eta_m{}^e \frac{r}{a}\right) \tag{8}$$

$$H_{rm}{}^e = -\frac{m\omega\epsilon}{r} A_m{}^e K_m\left(\eta_m{}^e \frac{r}{a}\right) - j\frac{\beta_m\eta_m{}^e}{a} B_m{}^e K'_m\left(\eta_m{}^e \frac{r}{a}\right) \tag{9}$$

$$H_{\theta m}{}^e = -j\frac{\omega\epsilon}{a} \eta_m{}^e A_m{}^e K'_m\left(\eta_m{}^e \frac{r}{a}\right) + \frac{m\beta_m}{r} B_m{}^e K_m\left(\eta_m{}^e \frac{r}{a}\right) \tag{10}$$

Inside the helix we simply replace k_e by k_0, $\eta_m{}^e$ by $\eta_m{}^i$ and ϵ by ϵ_0, $A_m{}^e$, $B_m{}^e$ by $A_m{}^i$, $B_m{}^i$, and finally K_m by I_m, obtaining

$$E_{zm}{}^i = (-\beta_m{}^2 + k_0{}^2)A_m{}^i I_m\left(\eta_m{}^i \frac{r}{a}\right) \tag{11}$$

$$H_{zm}{}^i = (-\beta_m{}^2 + k_0{}^2)B_m{}^i I_m\left(\eta_m{}^i \frac{r}{a}\right) \tag{12}$$

$$E_{rm}{}^i = -j\frac{\beta_m\eta_m{}^i}{a} A_m{}^i I'_m\left(\eta_m{}^i \frac{r}{a}\right) + \frac{m\omega\mu}{r} B_m{}^i I_m\left(\eta_m{}^i \frac{r}{a}\right) \tag{13}$$

$$E_{\theta m}{}^i = \frac{m\beta_m}{r} A_m{}^i I_m\left(\eta_m{}^i \frac{r}{a}\right) + j\frac{\omega\mu}{a} \eta_m{}^i B_m{}^i I'_m\left(\eta_m{}^i \frac{r}{a}\right) \tag{14}$$

$$H_{rm}{}^i = -\frac{m\omega\epsilon_0}{r} A_m{}^i I_m\left(\eta_m{}^i \frac{r}{a}\right) - j\frac{\beta_m\eta_m{}^i}{a} B_m{}^i I'_m\left(\eta_m{}^i \frac{r}{a}\right) \tag{15}$$

$$H_{\theta m}{}^i = -j\frac{\omega\epsilon_0}{a} \eta_m{}^i A_m{}^i I'_m\left(\eta_m{}^i \frac{r}{a}\right) + \frac{m\beta_m}{r} B_m{}^i I_m\left(\eta_m{}^i \frac{r}{a}\right) \tag{16}$$

The phase factor $\exp\{-jm([2\pi z/t] - \theta)\}$ has been omitted from all these equations and its presence is taken as understood. The complete field is to be found as a sum over the infinite series of values of $m = 0, \pm1, \pm2 \rightarrow \pm\infty$.

Now the current on the tape is the source of the electromagnetic field and, in particular, it is the source of the magnetic field components H_z and H_θ which are parallel to the surfaces of the conductor. The current flow on the tape is constrained to be in the

ψ direction, and according to the Sensiper treatment, is of constant magnitude over the tape width. Then, denoting current densities by κ we have

$$\kappa_{\|m} = \kappa_{zm} \sin \psi + \kappa_{\theta m} \cos \psi \tag{17}$$

$$\kappa_{\perp m} = \kappa_{zm} \cos \psi - \kappa_{\theta m} \sin \psi = 0 \tag{18}$$

where $\kappa_{\|m}$ = current density along the direction of the helix

$\kappa_{\perp m}$ = current density perpendicular to this direction.

The total current is obtained by summing, e.g.,

$$\kappa_{\|} = \exp\left(-j\beta_0 z\right) \sum_m \kappa_{\|m} \exp - jm\left(\frac{2\pi z}{t} - \theta\right) \tag{19}$$

Then, from the Fourier analysis of a rectangular current distribution which is finite over δ and zero over the remainder of the pitch t,

$$|\kappa_{11m}| = \left|\kappa_{110} \frac{\sin m\,\pi\delta/t}{m\pi\delta/t}\right| \tag{20}$$

where κ_{110} = component in the fundamental mode.
The boundary conditions at $r = a$ are

$$E_z{}^i, E_\theta{}^i = E_z{}^e, E_\theta{}^e \tag{21}$$

$$\kappa_\theta = H_z{}^i - H_z{}^e \tag{22}$$

$$\kappa_z = H_\theta{}^e - H_\theta{}^i \tag{23}$$

It is now a matter of straightforward, but lengthy, algebra to obtain the A_m's and B_m's in terms of the κ's. We find:

$$j\frac{A_m{}^i}{\omega\mu a} = \frac{a^2 \kappa_{11m} \sin \psi}{I_m(\eta m)} M_m \tag{24}$$

where

$$M_m \doteq \frac{\eta m^2 - m\beta a \cot \psi}{\eta m^3 \{k_0{}^2 a^2 [I'_m(\eta m)/I_m(\eta m)] - k_e{}^2 a^2 [K'_m(\eta m)/K_m(\eta m)]\}} \tag{25}$$

$$j\frac{A_m{}^e}{\omega\mu a} \doteq \frac{a^2\kappa_{11m}\sin\psi}{K_m(\eta_m)} M_m \tag{26}$$

$$B_m{}^i = \frac{a^2\kappa_{11m}\sin\psi}{I_m(\eta_m)} Q_m \tag{27}$$

$$Q_m \doteq \frac{1}{\eta m} I_m(\eta_m)K'_m(\eta_m)\cot\psi \tag{28}$$

$$B_m{}^e = \frac{a^2\kappa_{11m}\sin\psi}{K_m(\eta_m)} S_m \tag{29}$$

$$S_m \doteq \frac{1}{\eta m} I'_m(\eta_m)K_m(\eta_m)\cot\psi \tag{30}$$

Here the approximation $\eta_m = \eta_m{}^i = \eta_m{}^e$ is used throughout.

Using the Wronskian relation for the I, K functions we can easily show that

$$S_m - Q_m = \frac{\cot\psi}{\eta m^2} \tag{31}$$

which somewhat simplifies the computations.

3.2. THE POWER FLOW

We can now set up the Poynting vector for each mode. It is convenient to do this separately for the regions inside and outside the helix. For the mth mode we then have $P_m = P_m{}^i + P_m{}^e$ where

$$P_m{}^i = \frac{R_e}{2}\left[\int_0^{2\pi}\!\!d\theta\int_0^a (E_{rm}{}^i H_\theta m^{*i} - E_\theta m^i H_{rm}{}^{*i})r\,dr\right] \tag{32}$$

$$P_m{}^e = \frac{R_e}{2}\left[\int_0^{2\pi}\!\!d\theta\int_0^a (E_{rm}{}^e H_\theta m^{*e} - E_\theta m^e H_{rm}{}^{*e})r\,dr\right] \tag{33}$$

For $m \neq 0$, we find

$$P_m{}^i = \pi a^2\omega\mu a \sin^2\psi\, T_m{}^i \tag{34}$$

where

$$T_m{}^i = |\kappa_{11m}|^2\{\beta_m a(k_0{}^2 a^2 M_m{}^2 + Q_m{}^2)$$
$$\times \left(\eta_m{}^i \frac{I'_m(\eta_m{}^i)}{I_m(\eta_m{}^i)} + \frac{\eta_m{}^i}{2}\frac{I'_m{}^2(\eta_m{}^i)}{I_m{}^2(\eta_m{}^i)} - \tfrac{1}{2}(\eta_m{}^i + m^2)\right) -$$
$$- m M_m Q_m(\beta_m{}^2 a^2 + k_0{}^2 a^2)\} \quad (35$$

$$P_m{}^e = \pi a^2 \omega \mu a \sin^2 \psi T_m{}^e \quad (36)$$

where

$$T_m{}^e = |\kappa_{11m}|^2\{\beta_m a(k_e{}^2 a^2 M_m{}^2 + S_m{}^2)$$
$$\times \left(-\eta_m{}^e \frac{K'_m(\eta_m{}^e)}{K_m(\eta_m{}^e)} - \frac{\eta_m{}^e}{2}\frac{K'_m{}^2(\eta_m{}^e)}{K_m{}^2(\eta_{me})} + \tfrac{1}{2}(\eta_m{}^e + m^2)\right)$$
$$+ m M_m S_m(\beta_m{}^2 a^2 + k_e{}^2 a^2)\} \quad (37)$$

For $m = 0$, the fundamental component, we find

$$T_0{}^i = |\kappa_{110}|^2 \beta_0 a(k_0{}^2 a^2 M_0{}^2 + Q_0{}^2)$$
$$\times \left(\frac{\eta_0{}^{i2}}{2}[I_1{}^2(\eta_0{}^i) - I_2{}^2(\eta_0{}^i)] - \eta_0{}^i I_1(\eta_0{}^i)I_2(\eta_0{}^i)\right)\frac{1}{I_0{}^2(\eta_0{}^i)} \quad (38)$$

$$T_0{}^e = |\kappa_{110}|^2 \beta_0 a(k_e{}^2 a^2 M_0{}^2 + Q_0{}^2)$$
$$\times \left(\frac{\eta_0{}^{e2}}{2}[K_2{}^2(\eta_0{}^e) - K_1{}^2(\eta_0{}^e)] - \eta_0{}^e K_1(\eta_0{}^e)K_2(\eta_0{}^e)\right)\frac{1}{K_0{}^2(\eta_0{}^e)} \quad (39)$$

$P_0{}^i$ and $P_0{}^e$ may also be expressed in terms of the axial value of E_z, i.e., $E_z(0)$ as

$$P_0{}^i = \tfrac{1}{2}a^2\pi\beta_0 a\omega\epsilon_0 U_0{}^i E_z{}^2(0) \quad (40)$$

where

$$U_0{}^i = \left[\frac{1}{\eta_0{}^{i2}} + \frac{I_0{}^2(\eta_0{}^i)}{\cot^2\psi\, k_0{}^2 a^2 I_1{}^2(\eta_0{}^i)}\right][I_1{}^2(\eta_0{}^i) - I_0(\eta_0{}^i)I_2(\eta_0{}^i)] \quad (41)$$

$$P_0{}^e = \tfrac{1}{2}a^2\pi\beta_0 a\omega\epsilon_0 U_0{}^e E_z{}^2(0) \quad (42)$$

where

$$U_0{}^e = \frac{\epsilon}{\epsilon_0}\left[\frac{1}{\eta_0{}^{e2}} - \frac{K_0{}^2(\eta_0{}^e)}{\cot^2\psi\, k_e{}^2 a^2 K_1{}^2(\eta_0{}^e)}\right]$$

$$\times\, [K_2(\eta_0{}^e)K_0(\eta_0{}^e) - K_1{}^2(\eta_0{}^e)]\frac{I_0{}^2(\eta_0{}^i)}{K_0{}^2(\eta_0{}^e)} \qquad (43)$$

We can now write down the coupling impedance

$$Z_c = \frac{E_z{}^2(0)}{2\beta_0{}^2\sum\limits_{m=-\infty}^{+\infty} P_m} = \frac{E_z{}^2(0)}{P_0}\cdot\frac{P_0}{\sum P_m}$$

$$= \frac{T_0{}^i + T_0{}^e}{\pi\beta_0{}^3 a^3\omega\epsilon_0 a(U_0{}^i + U_0{}^e)\sum(T_m{}^i + T_m{}^e)} \qquad (44)$$

To use Eq. (44) the value of β_0 is required. In Tien's treatment this is obtained from the sheath helix theory, the equivalence between the two theories being confirmed by experiment. In the Sensiper treatment, the determinantal equation for β_0 (Eq. (97) of Chapter 3), is a consequence of the requirement that $E_{\parallel}{}^e$ should be zero at the centre of the tape.

If Eq. (44) is compared with Eq. (83) of Chapter 3 we find that

$$Z_{ct} = Z_{cs}\,.\,F \qquad (45)$$

where

$$F = \frac{(\gamma a)^2 F_1(\gamma a)}{U_0{}^i + U_0{}^e}\frac{(T_0{}^i + T_0{}^e)}{\sum(T_m{}^i + T_m{}^e)} \qquad (46)$$

It is clear from Eq. (46) that as more power goes into the space harmonics, i.e., as either the T_m's become greater or more of them have to be included to obtain a convergent expression, the smaller F becomes.

APPENDIX 4

VARIATIONAL METHODS

VARIATIONAL methods of several types are useful in the solution of electromagnetic problems in the theory of cavities and slow-wave structures. One of the simplest is the Rayleigh–Ritz approximation method, which in the form required in our work, depends on the orthogonal nature of different solutions of the scalar and vector wave equations. We first demonstrate this orthogonal property, which has been observed in particular cases in earlier Appendices.

Suppose that two solutions ψ_1, ψ_2 of the scalar wave equation $\nabla^2\psi + k^2\psi = 0$, are known. Then, by cross-multiplication and subtraction

$$\psi_2\nabla^2\psi_1 - \psi_1\nabla^2\psi_2 = (k_2{}^2 - k_1{}^2)\psi_1\psi_2 \tag{1}$$

Integrating over the volume concerned

$$\int_v (\psi_2\nabla^2\psi_1 - \psi_1\nabla^2\psi_2)\,\mathrm{d}V = (k_2{}^2 - k_1{}^2)\int_v \psi_1\psi_2\,\mathrm{d}V$$
$$= \int_v \nabla\,.\,(\psi_2\nabla\psi_1 - \psi_1\nabla\psi_2)\,\mathrm{d}V \tag{2}$$

The last expression is transformed, using Green's identity, to a surface integral to become

$$\int_s (\psi_2\nabla\psi_1 - \psi_1\nabla\psi_2)\,\mathrm{d}s \tag{3}$$

But, if for example ψ represents the transverse motion of a string, the boundary condition on the surface is $\psi_1 = \psi_2 = 0$ so that the integral (3) is zero. From Eq. (2), since in general $k_1 \neq k_2$ we see that

$$\int_v \psi_1\psi_2\,\mathrm{d}V = 0 \tag{4}$$

Equation (4) proves that ψ_1, ψ_2 are orthogonal over the volume. We have already seen in Chapter 2 how a knowledge of one field component determines the other fields in any given mode. The complete set of allowed modes is known as the set of normal modes of the enclosure and since arbitrary functions can be expanded in complete sets of orthogonal functions, any vibration, no matter how complex, can be expanded in a series whose eigenfunctions are the normal modes.

If we now return to the wave equation and form the equation analogous to Eq. (2), but for a single mode, we find

$$k_n{}^2 = -\frac{\int_v \psi_n \nabla^2 \psi_n \, \mathrm{d}V}{\int_v \psi_n{}^2 \, \mathrm{d}V} \tag{5}$$

Equation (5) shows that if ψ_n is known, k_n may be calculated. This is the basis of the Rayleigh–Ritz method which we now consider.

To use this method we guess a trial function

$$\phi = \sum_n a_n \psi_n$$

where ϕ does not satisfy the wave equation. Then it is easy to show that

$$k_0{}^2 \leqslant -\frac{\int_v \phi \nabla^2 \phi \, \mathrm{d}V}{\int_v \phi^2 \, \mathrm{d}V} \tag{6}$$

Equation (6) is proved as follows:

$$\phi = a_0 \psi_0 + a_1 \psi_1, \text{ etc.}$$

$$\nabla^2 \phi = a_0 \nabla^2 \psi_0 + a_1 \nabla^2 \psi_1, \text{ etc.}$$

$$= a_0 k_0{}^2 \psi_0 + a_1 k_1{}^2 \psi_1, \text{ etc.}$$

From this and the orthogonal property of the ψ's

$$\frac{\int_v \phi \nabla^2 \phi \, \mathrm{d}V}{\int_v \phi^2 \, \mathrm{d}V} = \frac{a_0 k_0{}^2 + a_1{}^2 k_1{}^2 + a_2{}^2 k_2{}^2, \text{ etc.}}{a_0{}^2 + a_1{}^2 + a_2{}^2, \text{ etc.}}$$

$$= \frac{k_0{}^2[1 + (a_1 k_1/a_0 k_0)^2 + (a_2 k_2/a_0 k_0)^2, \text{ etc.}]}{1 + (a_1/a_0)^2 + (a_2/a_0)^2}$$

The inequality follows because each term of the top series is less than or equal to each term in the bottom one. It also follows that if several trial functions are used, the best is that which yields the lowest value of k_0. It can be shown that the errors are only of the second order.

Turning now to vector wave equations it can easily be shown that the analogous expression to Eq. (6) is

$$k_0{}^2 \leqslant -\frac{\int_v \mathbf{A}\nabla^2\mathbf{A}\,\mathrm{d}V}{\int_v \mathbf{A}\mathbf{A}\,\mathrm{d}V}$$

If we choose $\nabla \cdot \mathbf{A} = 0$ this becomes

$$k_0{}^2 \leqslant \frac{\int_v (\nabla \times \mathbf{A})(\nabla \times \mathbf{A})\,\mathrm{d}V}{\int_v \mathbf{A}\mathbf{A}\,\mathrm{d}V} \qquad (7)$$

If we now identify $\mathbf{A}$ with the electric field $\mathbf{E}$, Maxwell's equations show that Eq. (7) becomes

$$k_0{}^2 \leqslant \frac{\int_v \mathbf{B}^2\,\mathrm{d}V}{\int_v \mathbf{E}^2\,\mathrm{d}V} \qquad (8)$$

Many examples of the use of Eq. (8) are given in the literature.

It will be observed that this technique is only variational in the broad sense, that one is trying to guess functions which minimize a certain integral.

Variational methods in the more usual sense set out from the idea of integrating functions containing adjustable constants and using the techniques of the calculus of variations to ensure that the adjustable constants are chosen so that first order errors in the assumptions only lead to second order errors in the results. Such methods were extensively developed during the war by Schwinger at M.I.T. He has unfortunately not published a complete account of his work but the method is extensively used by Borgnis and Papas[1] although their applications are not of much interest in our field.

Variational procedures are based on two general approaches; one can either start out from functions which satisfy Maxwell's equations but not the boundary conditions, or vice versa. The choice between the two depends on the system under discussion;

---

[1] Borgnis and Papas; *Randwertprobleme der Mikrowellenphysik*, Springer, 1955.

if the geometry of the boundary is simple, i.e., straight lines or circles, one would normally choose to satisfy the boundary conditions, while in other cases, for example, an infinite array of half-wave wire resonators, the boundary conditions are far from simple but the field equations may be easily satisfied. An example of the latter type is the work of Chorodow and Chu, on the cross-wound helix, already referred to in the main text. The method is to vary the Lagrangian function, which is the difference $(T - V)$ between the kinetic energy T and the potential energy V of the system, i.e., the electromagnetic field. The variational equation is

$$\delta \int L \, d\tau = 0$$

integration being taken over the space and time co-ordinates. If there are no currents or free charges, the Lagrangian equation is

$$L = \tfrac{1}{2}(\mathbf{E} \cdot \mathbf{D} - \mathbf{H} \cdot \mathbf{B}) \tag{9}$$

and, using Maxwell's equations

$$\delta \int_v (\mathbf{E} \cdot \nabla \times \mathbf{H}^* + \mathbf{H}^* \cdot \nabla \times \mathbf{E}) \, dV = 0$$

But the integrand is simply $\nabla \cdot (\mathbf{E} \times \mathbf{H}^*)$

therefore
$$\delta \int_v \nabla \cdot (\mathbf{E} \times \mathbf{H}^*) \, dV = 0$$

and using Green's identity

$$\delta \int n \cdot (\mathbf{E} \times \mathbf{H}^*) \, dS = 0 \tag{10}$$

Equation (10) will be recognized as a variation of Poynting's vector. Thus, not only is the Poynting vector itself constant in a lossless region, but its first variation is also zero. We also note that if, as is natural, we choose a single period of the structure for the unit in the z direction, then the end walls can make no contribution and the integration does not have to be carried out.

The next requirement is to relate the field to the sources. Only the parallel components of $\mathbf{E}$ and $\mathbf{H}$ contribute to the integral and the parallel components of $\mathbf{E}$ will be continuous over the boundaries, where, however, there is a discontinuity in $H_\parallel$. In particular, at a metal surface, the discontinuity in $H_\parallel$ is equal to the surface current density and the integral reduces to

$$\delta \int_s \mathbf{E}_\parallel \cdot \mathbf{J} \, dS = 0 \tag{11}$$

Examination of Eq. (11) shows that two cases can be distinguished, those in which the rigorous solution would yield zero electric field and those in which the current is zero. The last case is that encountered by Chodorow and Chu, who use trial functions for the current and deduce $E_\parallel$. It is essential that not only the trial functions but also the variations of the trial functions used in the minimization do not give rise to currents, where, from the physics of the problem, no current can exist. This usually means that one must vary only the coefficients of a series of functions which obey the specified conditions.

The details of the procedures involved can hardly be grasped without actual practice. For example, the reader should consult Chorodow and Chu and CHU and HANSEN.[2] However, one should not imply that the calculations are not tedious and that professional computing effort will usually have to be applied to the extraction of sufficiently detailed results.

I am indebted to my colleague Dr. E. A. Ash for the ideas of the latter part of this Appendix.

---

[2] CHU and HANSEN; *J. Appl. Phys.*, 1947, **18**, 996; *J. Appl. Phys.*, 1949, **20**, 280.

APPENDIX 5

MEASUREMENTS ON
SLOW-WAVE STRUCTURES

IN VIEW of the importance of the subject it would seem very un-realistic not to say a little about slow-wave measurements in spite of the general restriction of our work to theoretical matters.

We may characterize such measurements under two broad headings:

(i) Cold tests, in which the circuit, or a model scaled to a more convenient frequency-band than that in which the particular circuit is desired to work, is tested in the absence of an electron beam by purely circuit techniques.

(ii) Hot tests, in which measurements are taken using an electron beam, not necessarily the beam with which the final valve will work, as a test device.

Hot testing is often much more informative than cold testing but it has the obvious major disadvantage that a tube of sorts has to be built before tests can be made, which, especially if new techniques are involved, may be a lengthy undertaking. Secondly, it is rarely the case that the beam dimensions and the location of the beam with respect to the circuit are known with sufficient accuracy to allow, for example, the circuit impedance to be unambiguously determined.

5.1. COLD TESTING

Cold testing usually comprises measurements on the phase-velocity as a function of frequency in the pass-band and the determination of impedance by perturbation techniques.

5.1.1. Measurement of phase velocity

The most direct method for obtaining the phase velocity is to measure the standing wave pattern in the slow-wave circuit as a function of frequency. This can be done either by building a section of circuit with a short-circuit fixed at one end and a mobile probe which indicates the standing-wave pattern, or by using a section of circuit with a mobile short-circuit and a fixed probe. In either case there are several practical difficulties. First, the short-circuit should not excite unwanted circuit modes. This is often observed in the helix which is difficult to short-circuit effectively[1] as a fast circuit mode is easily introduced. Such a mode perturbs the standing-wave pattern and makes interpretation difficult. Secondly, the introduction of the probe itself is much less easy than in, for example, a waveguide standing wave detector because, again, unwanted modes may be set up. Moreover the probe must come close to the conductors of the circuit because the space harmonic fields which it is desired to study fall off in magnitude away from the conductors. This makes it difficult to introduce a probe which can be considered as a small perturbation. Supposing these difficulties to be overcome the result is simple, the measurement gives the guide wavelength λ_g and p is determined from

$$\frac{c}{p} = \frac{\lambda_{\text{air}}}{\lambda_g} \tag{1}$$

The second of the difficulties mentioned above can be overcome by moving the short-circuit, for the probe can be located in a slotted line connected to the input of the circuit, though for this to be possible the input has to be well-matched. The best technique is to first locate the probe at the plane of a minimum then to move the short-circuit backwards or forwards over one period of the circuit. The distance d travelled by the probe to the new minimum gives the phase change directly through

$$\beta = 2\pi \frac{d}{\lambda_l} \tag{2}$$

where λ_l = wavelength in the slotted line, λ_{air} if it is an actual co-axial line, λ_g if it is a waveguide standing wave detector.

It has been suggested that the mobile short-circuit might be obtained by raising and lowering the circuit into a vessel of mercury.

Lastly, the phase velocity may be measured by determining the resonant frequencies of a short-circuited length of circuit. If this method is to give several points, the circuit must be made several periods long as there is one resonance per period. Here we have

$$\beta = \frac{m\pi}{n} \tag{3}$$

n = no. of periods of the circuit

$0 < m < n$

---

[1] See, for example, WATSON and WHINNERY; *Trans. I.R.E.*, 1955, *ED–3*, 34.

Thus, β can be determined for each of the n resonant frequencies. It is important that the Q be fairly high as, if one or more resonances are lost, the accuracy for all later measurements is very poor.

For more details the reader is referred elsewhere.[2,3]

5.1.2. Measurements of circuit impedance

By using perturbation techniques it is possible to make a direct measurement of the electric or magnetic field along a predetermined line through the circuit. The experimental method is to resonate a short length of the circuit, an integral number of periods in length. The perturbation is usually applied to the electric field, in which case the perturbing object is a small rod or sphere of some low-loss dielectric, such as synthetic sapphire, of known volume. In our work, T.M. modes are normally the centre of interest and for these E is strong on the axis of cylindrical systems and H there is zero, so that the perturbing object is moved along the axis.† The measurement consists in the determination of the change in resonant frequency as a function of position of the dielectric body. The difficulty is that the object must be small in comparison with the transverse dimensions of the circuit which, in turn, means that the frequency changes are small and correspondingly difficult to measure. In the apparatus used in our laboratory a crystal-controlled amplifier chain produces an output in the 4000 Mc/s band which can be shifted through 30 Mc/s by means of a standard signal generator of high accuracy. In this way frequency changes of about 1 part in 10^6 can be accurately measured, but an order of magnitude better than this would be desirable in some cases.

The theory of the perturbation method is given by SLATER.[4] The basic equation is

$$\frac{\Delta\lambda}{\lambda} = -\frac{\frac{1}{2}\int_{\Delta V}(\mu H^2 - \epsilon E^2)\,\mathrm{d}v}{\int_V(\mu H^2 + \epsilon E^2)\,\mathrm{d}v} \tag{4}$$

The upper integral is taken over the volume of the perturbing body ΔV while the lower is taken over the whole volume and is clearly the energy stored in the cavity, which we may assume constant during the perturbation. As the body is small the fields may be

---

† Provided H is in fact zero, a steel ball-bearing is equally good and provides an accurate volume.

[2] ALLEN and CLARKE, *I.E.E. Monograph* 151R, October, 1955.

[3] EPSZTEIN and MOURIER, *Ann. Radioélect.*, 1955, **10**, 64.

[4] SLATER; *Microwave Electronics*, pp. 80 *et seq.*, Van Nostrand, 1950.

considered as constant over its volume. If $H = 0$, from Eq. (4)

$$\frac{\Delta\lambda}{\lambda} = -\frac{1}{2}\frac{\epsilon_1 E^2 \Delta V}{W_T} \tag{5}$$

where W_T = total time average stored energy,

and therefore $\qquad\qquad E \propto \Delta\lambda^{1/2} \tag{6}$

We now have to determine a value for W_T to make this into an absolute measurement. A technique for doing this has been described by NALOS.[5] His cavity is shown in Fig. 1 where it will be

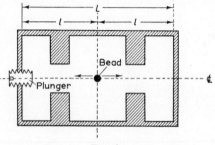

FIG. 1

seen to consist of two half periods short-circuited at planes of symmetry. It is furnished with a plunger in one end wall which is located on the axis of the circuit and which can be both moved into the cavity and withdrawn from it. The measurement consists of preparing a plot of frequency or wavelength change as the plunger is moved from a distance d behind the cavity wall to a distance d in front of it. The slope of this line at the plane of the cavity wall is then measured. We call this value $(\Delta\lambda/\Delta V_1)_{\Delta V_1=0}$ and it is half the value defined by Nalos. From Eq. (5), remembering that now $\epsilon = \epsilon_0$,

$$\frac{E_1^2}{W_T} = \frac{4}{\lambda\epsilon_0}\left(\frac{\Delta\lambda}{\Delta V_1}\right)_{\Delta V_1=0} \tag{7}$$

or $\qquad$ $$\frac{E_1^2 l^2}{cW_c} = 480\pi\frac{Ll^2}{\lambda}\left(\frac{\Delta\lambda}{\Delta V_1}\right)_{\Delta V_1=0} \tag{8}$$

[5] NALOS; *Proc. I.R.E.*, 1954, **42**, 1508.

But Eq. (8) gives the standing wave energy corresponding with two travelling waves. For each travelling wave

$$\frac{E_1^2 l^2}{cW_c} = 240\pi \frac{Ll^2}{\lambda}\left(\frac{\Delta\lambda}{\Delta V_1}\right)_{\Delta V_1 = 0} \tag{9}$$

Here $c =$ the velocity of light
$W_c =$ energy stored per unit length of cavity
$l =$ period of cavity
$L =$ total length of cavity
$W =$ energy stored per unit length of travelling wave.

We have seen that one definition of the circuit impedance is (Chapter 3) for the nth space harmonic

$$Z_c = \frac{E^2}{2\beta_n^2 \cdot g \cdot W} \tag{10}$$

$$= \frac{1}{2}\left[\frac{c}{g}\left(\frac{1}{\beta_n^2 l^2}\right)\right]\left[\frac{E^2}{E_1^2}\right]\left[\frac{E_1^2 l^2}{cW}\right] \tag{11}$$

Here the first bracket is found from the measured phase velocity, the second from a Fourier analysis of the measured relative field via Eq. (6) and the last bracket from Eq. (9). From the derivation of this result it should be clear that it is necessary to keep the radius of the tuning plunger small to obtain accurate results as one assumes both that H is zero and E is constant over the surface.

5.2. HOT TESTING

In one sense all measurements made on a complete valve contribute to the hot testing. However, to determine the circuit constants one can obtain better and more easily interpretable results by working with reduced beam currents so that, in T.W.A. terminology, C and QC both tend to zero. This may be done either by working the gun actually used in a valve at a much reduced current, e.g., by operating the gun temperature-limited or better, by the use of a special probe gun producing a low current beam of known properties.

One of the best-known techniques of making an accurate measurement of circuit parameters is due to KOMPFNER[6] and consists in operating a T.W.A. with the beam voltage and current adjusted so that the output is zero, i.e., the loss is infinite. Kompfner's

---

[6] KOMPFNER; *J. Brit. I.R.E.*, 1950, **10**, 283.

results have been extended by JOHNSON[7] to the case where QC is finite and the circuit may be short but $C \ll 1$. The result is obtained by writing down the output voltage in terms of the three component waves and requiring that it should be zero. Appendix 11 shows that, taking space-charge into account, a good approximation for the total circuit voltage at $z = l$ is

$$\frac{V_{c1} + V_{c2} + V_{c3}}{V} \exp{(j2\pi N)} = \frac{(\delta_1^2 + 4QC) \exp{(2\pi CN\delta_1)}}{(\delta_1 - \delta_2)(\delta_1 - \delta_3)} +$$

$$+ \frac{(\delta_2^2 + 4QC) \exp{(2\pi CN\delta_2)}}{(\delta_2 - \delta_3)(\delta_2 - \delta_1)} + \frac{(\delta_3^2 + 4QC) \exp{(2\pi CN\delta_3)}}{(\delta_3 - \delta_2)(\delta_3 - \delta_1)} \quad (12)$$

and this must equal zero for the Kompfner dip. Equation (12) is therefore equated to zero and the real roots CN and b determined.

TABLE 1

Calculated conditions for the Kompfner dip.

L	CN	$(\beta - \beta_e)l$	b	QC/CN	
0	0·3141	−3·0040	−1·522	0	
3·201	0·2931	−2·9116	−1·581	0	
6·017	0·2755	−2·8369	−1·639	0	
8·527	0·2603	−2·7721	−1·695	0	$QC = 0$
10·79	0·2471	−2·7169	−1·750	0	
12·85	0·2354	−2·6697	−1·805	0	
0	0·3363	−3·1780	−1·504	0·5947	
3·391	0·3105	−3·0492	−1·563	0·6441	
6·318	0·2893	−2·9449	−1·620	0·6913	
8·898	0·2716	−2·8620	−1·677	0·7364	$QC = 0·2$
11·200	0·25656	−2·7916	−1·732	0·7797	
13·290	0·2434	−2·7332	−1·787	0·8217	
0	0·3141	−3·0040	−1·522	0	
0	0·3363	−3·1780	−1·504	0·5947	
0	0·3434	−3·239	−1·501	0·7280	
0	0·3990	−3·843	−1·533	1·2531	
0	0·4347	−4·438	−1·625	1·3803	
0	0·4659	−5·368	−1·834	1·6098	
0	0·4913	−6·369	−2·072	2·0354	
0	0·5275	−7·549	−2·278	2·3697	
0	0·5522	−8·672	−2·499	2·7164	

[7] JOHNSON; *Proc. I.R.E.*, 1955, **43**, 874.

Table 1 shows Johnson's results. In this table, L represents the total circuit loss, i.e.,

$$d = \frac{0 \cdot 0183L}{CN} \tag{13}$$

To use these results, the total loss and the circuit length l are presumed to be accurately known. The current and voltage are adjusted in steps until a condition of zero output is found, when their values are recorded. Then β follows from the interpolated value of $(\beta - \beta_e)l$ and C from the corresponding CN. Since I_0 is known, Z_c is determined from C.

This technique can be applied to a suitable length of circuit made up into a special test valve and without breaks or attenuating sections to complicate the results. The measured phase velocity and impedance are, of course, relevant to the operation of the circuit in any type of valve and not merely in a T.W.A.

APPENDIX 6

THE FOCUSING OF
LONG ELECTRON BEAMS

NOWADAYS nearly all microwave valves utilize some form of magnetic focusing, the principal exception being low-power reflex klystrons. The reason for this is that the current which can be focused at a given voltage through a given tunnel by magnetic means is much greater than is possible by electrostatic means. For discussion it is useful to talk about the perveance, which is p in the equation

$$I_0 = pV_0^{3/2} \tag{1}$$

The limiting perveances of several systems have been discussed elsewhere[1,2] and it will be sufficient here if we merely quote the limiting perveances for a cylindrical tunnel, of radius a and of length l.

Electrostatic focusing

$$\hat{p} = 38 \cdot 9 \times 10^{-6} \left(\frac{2a}{l} \right)^2 \tag{2}$$

Magnetic, infinite field confined flow

$$\hat{p} = 32 \cdot 5 \times 10^{-6} \tag{3}$$

Thus, unless $(2a/l)^2 = 1$, the limiting magnetic perveance (independent of a or l) is the greater. Since in T.W.T.s and the like $l/2a \gg 1$, the comparison is normally highly in favour of the magnetic system. The limitations in the two cases are due to different causes, Eq. (2) relating purely to the effect of space-charge in spreading the beam. On the other hand, Eq. (3), since the magnetic field prevents transverse motion, expresses the fact that the axial potential is depressed by the electronic charge until it reaches an unstable value, dropping abruptly to zero. Equation (3) therefore involves a

---

[1] BECK; *Velocity-Modulated Thermionic Tubes*, Chapter 4, Cambridge University Press, 1948.

[2] BECK; *Thermionic Valves*, Chapter 6, Cambridge University Press, 1953.

different velocity for peripheral electrons and paraxial electrons. If the velocity spread is restricted to 5% the limiting perveance is reduced to

$$p_{5\%} = 6 \cdot 25 \times 10^{-6} \qquad (4)$$

Today the best guns only reach about two-thirds of this figure so that velocity spreads due to this cause are only a few per cent of the maximum velocity. With annular beams, much higher perveances can be obtained for the same velocity spread. For instance, for a beam extending from the wall inwards to 0·8 times the radius, $p_{5\%} = 30 \times 10^{-6}$.

However, from the system design viewpoint magnetic focusing is weighty, expensive, cumbersome and may have undesirable side effects on adjacent apparatus. Much thought has therefore been applied to improved focusing methods. This Appendix deals with some of this work.

6.1. BRILLOUIN FOCUSING

BRILLOUIN,[3] arising out of his work on magnetrons, investigated the field conditions in which stable cylindrical electron beams could be produced. His work was extended by other investigators.[4,5]

If we consider a beam with no angular variation in density, fields, etc., we can write the Lorentz force equation in cylindrical co-ordinates as

$$\ddot{r} - r\dot{\theta}^2 = -\eta(E_r + B_z r\dot{\theta}) \qquad (5)$$

$$\frac{1}{r}\frac{\mathrm{d}}{\mathrm{d}t}(r^2\dot{\theta}) = -\eta(-B_z\dot{r} + B_r\dot{z}) \qquad (6)$$

$$\ddot{z} = -\eta(E_z - B_z r\dot{\theta}) \qquad (7)$$

We may, if we like, now restrict ourselves to the shielded cathode and sudden jump in magnetic field, $0-B_z$, and then investigate the conditions for equilibrium. It will be more informative for future work if we keep our analysis more general. A standard expansion of $\nabla \cdot B = 0$ yields $B_r = (-r/2)(\partial B_z/\partial z)$. Remembering that $\mathrm{d}/\mathrm{d}t = \dot{r}(\partial/\partial r) + \dot{z}(\partial/\partial z)$, we can integrate Eq. (6) to give

$$r^2\dot{\theta} = \eta \int \left(B_z r\dot{r} + \frac{r^2\dot{z}}{2}\frac{\partial B_z}{\partial z} \right) \mathrm{d}t = \eta \frac{B_z r^2}{2} + C \qquad (8)$$

---

[3] BRILLOUIN; *Phys. Rev.*, 1945, **67**, 260.
[4] SAMUEL; *Proc. I.R.E.*, 1949, **37**, 1252.
[5] WANG, *Proc. I.R.E.*, 1950, **38**, 135.

At the cathode, $r = r_0$, $\theta = 0$ and $B_z = B_0$.

Therefore
$$r^2\theta = \frac{\eta}{2}(B_z r^2 - B_0 r_0^2) \qquad (9)$$

This result is known as Busch's theorem in electron optics. Also the Larmor angular frequency ω_L is defined by $\eta(B_z/2)$, so we put $\eta(B_0/2) = \omega_0$ and rewrite Eq. (9) as

$$\theta = \left(\omega_L - \omega_0 \frac{r_0^2}{r^2}\right) \qquad (10)$$

We now put this into Eq. (5) to obtain

$$\ddot{r} = -\eta E_r + r\left(\omega_0^2 \frac{r_0^4}{r^4} - \omega_L^2\right) \qquad (11a)$$

But, from Gauss's theorem for a uniform cylindrical beam of (conventional) current I_0, $E_r = -I_0/2\pi\epsilon_0 u_0 r$

therefore
$$\ddot{r} = \frac{\eta I_0}{2\pi\epsilon_0 u_0 r} + r\left(\frac{\omega_0^2 r_0^4}{r^4} - \omega_L^2\right) \qquad (11b)$$

From Eq. (11b) it is obvious that the magnetic field is most effective when $\omega_0^2 = 0$, i.e., when the cathode is completely shielded. If this is the case, we can achieve a cylindrical beam by putting $\ddot{r} = 0$,† i.e., making

$$B_B^2 = \frac{2I_0}{\pi\eta\epsilon_0 u_0 r^2} = \frac{2\omega_p^2}{\eta^2} = \frac{\sqrt{2}I_0}{\pi\eta^{3/2}\epsilon_0 r^2 V_a^{1/2}} \qquad (12)$$

$$\doteqdot 7\cdot0 \times 10^{-7}\frac{I_0}{V_a^{1/2}r^2}$$

B_B is the Brillouin field value. Since $I_0 = pV_a^{3/2}$, $B \propto \sqrt{(pV_a)}/r$. From Eq. (10) we see that $\theta_B = \omega_L$ when $\omega_0 = 0$. We shall also use the result $-\eta E_r = r\theta_B^2$, which follows from Eq. (11a). This can be rewritten as

$$\frac{\partial V}{\partial r} = \frac{r\theta_B^2}{\eta}$$

or
$$V = V_a + \frac{r^2\theta_B^2}{2\eta} \qquad (13)$$

---

† The solution $\dot{r}$ constant, is obviously not allowable in a magnetic field.

where $V_a =$ the potential on the axis. We can now find the longitudinal velocity by equating the kinetic and potential energies, i.e.,

$$(\dot{z})^2 + (r\dot{\theta})^2 = 2\eta V$$

Inserting the expression for V:

$$\dot{z} = u_0 = \sqrt{2\eta V_a} \qquad (14)$$

Therefore all the electrons have the same longitudinal velocity, corresponding with the potential on the axis, and *not* with the wall potential V_0. Equation (12) anticipated this result. Substituting for θ_B^2 in Eq. (13) we find

$$I_0 = \frac{\pi \epsilon_0 \eta^{3/2} B_B^2 r^2}{\sqrt{2}} \left(V_0 - \eta \frac{B_B^2 r^2}{8} \right)^{1/2} \qquad (15)$$

The maximum current or perveance follows from maximizing this, when we find

$$\eta \frac{B_B^2 r^2}{8} = \tfrac{2}{3} V_0$$

and

$$\hat{I}_0 = \frac{16}{3\sqrt{6}} \pi \epsilon_0 \eta^{1/2} V_0^{3/2} \qquad (16)$$

or

$$\hat{p} = 25 \cdot 4 \times 10^{-6} \qquad (17)$$

When Eq. (17) obtains, the electrons travel at the velocity equivalent of $\tfrac{1}{3} V_0$ only.

We now discuss briefly the effect of the aperture in the magnetic shield, shown in Chapter 4, Fig. 8. The magnetic field does not jump sharply from 0–B_z but changes over a distance of around three aperture diameters. To establish the qualitative behaviour of the beam in this region we assume that the beam radius is nearly constant over this length. Then, if the space-charge forces are just compensated by the magnetic force at exit from this region, the outward space-charge will dominate the magnetic force until the exit is reached. Then the beam will diverge while travelling through the region of increasing B. To overcome this the beam must be given an initial convergence at entry to the region. Closer analysis[6] shows that the beam should be designed so that, in the absence of magnetic field, all the electrons will move parallel to the axis

[6] M. Müller; *Telefunken Z.*, 1953, **26**, 95.

at the plane where B reaches about 70% of the uniform value B_B. Brillouin focusing represents the maximum economy in field strength. In practice, it has grave disadvantages which have led to a preference for confined flow. These disadvantages include:

(i) The practical difficulty of obtaining accurately cylindrical beams unless great care in gun design and manufacture is exercised.

(ii) The fact that it is usually found necessary to work with $B_z = 1 \cdot 5 - 2 \cdot 0 B_B$ for the best results.

(iii) The large defocusing noted when large r.f. drives are imposed on the beam.

(iv) The high noise levels observed with Brillouin beams.

Moreover the development of cathodes with high values of specific emission has rendered the achievement of large values of r_0/r temporarily less important.

6.2. CONFINED FOCUSING

Two versions of confined focusing are used. These are the "brute-force" solution in which a cathode of substantially the required beam diameter is completely immersed in a purely longitudinal magnetic field which is made strong enough to restrict the transverse motion to an acceptable amount. This solution has a lot to be said for it, especially in experimental work, as it prevents time being spent on electron-optical development which could be better spent on tube research. However, even with the best modern cathodes[7,8] increasing operating frequency eventually imposes a limit beyond which the cathode emission density is insufficient.

A more sophisticated form of confined flow is that in which the electron paths in the gun region are designed to lie along the lines of magnetic field. This system is both more economical of magnetic field and gives useful convergence ratios.

6.2.1. "Infinite" field confined flow

We have already developed the fundamental equations in Section 1. The magnetic field on the cathode is now the same as that at any plane along the beam. Equation (11) therefore becomes

$$= \eta \frac{\partial V}{\partial r} + r\eta^2 \frac{B_z^2}{4}\left(\frac{r_0^4}{r^4} - 1\right) \tag{18}$$

Now, the developed paths of the peripheral electrons must be

---

[7] BECK, BRISBANE, CUTTING and KING; *Le Vide*, 1954, **9**, 302; reprinted in *Electrical Communication*, 1955, 172.

[8] COPPOLA and HUGHES; *Proc. I.R.E.*, 1956, **44**, 351.

helical so the beam assumes a scalloped form. At the equilibrium radius r_m, $\ddot{r} = 0$. Inserting $\partial V/\partial r$ from Gauss's law as before we find

$$1 - \left(\frac{r_0}{r_m}\right)^4 = \frac{\sqrt{2}I_0}{\pi\epsilon_0\eta^{3/2}B_z^2V^{1/2}r_m^2} \tag{19}$$

Therefore, increasing B_z makes $r_m \to r_0$. Now, following PIERCE,[9] we put

$$k = \frac{I_0}{\sqrt{2}\pi\epsilon_0\eta^{3/2}B_z^2V^{1/2}r_0^2} = \frac{2\omega_p^2}{\eta^2}\frac{r_m^2}{r_0^2} \tag{20}$$

$$\doteq 3\cdot5 \times 10^{-7}\frac{I_0}{B_z^2V^{1/2}r_0^2}$$

Then Eq. (19) becomes

$$\left(\frac{r_m}{r_0}\right)^4 - 2k\left(\frac{r_m}{r_0}\right)^2 - 1 = 0$$

or

$$\frac{r_m}{r_0} = [(k^2 + 1) + k]^{1/2} \tag{21}$$

Since, to be useful, $r_m \doteq r_0$, k must be small and

$$\frac{r_m}{r_0} \doteq 1 + \frac{k}{2} \tag{22}$$

This calculation obviously makes no allowance for the unavoidable electron lens at entry to a drift tube or helix. If we assume that this lens causes a sudden jump in radial velocity, given by $u_r = -ru_0/F_1$ where F_1 = focal length given by Davisson's formula, we can show that r_m is increased to

$$r_m\left\{1 + \frac{u_0}{\eta B_z|F_1|}\left(1 + \frac{u_0}{\eta B_z|F_1|}\right)\right\} \tag{23}$$

I have not investigated Eq. (23) experimentally.

We now investigate the ripple on the beam, i.e., the departures from r_m. This we do using the method of KLEEN and PÖSCHL.[10] We put

$$r = r_m(1 + \delta) \tag{24}$$

[9] PIERCE; *Theory and Design of Electron Beams*, 2nd Ed., Van Nostrand, 1954.
[10] KLEEN and PÖSCHL; *A.E.U.*, 1955, 9, 295.

δ is assumed to be small, so that we can expand r^{-1} and r^{-3} by the binomial theorem. These substitutions are made in Eq. (11a) yielding

$$\frac{d^2\delta}{dt^2} + 2\left(1 + \frac{r_0^4}{r_m^4}\right)\omega_L^2\delta = 0 \tag{25}$$

to which the solution is

$$\delta = C_1 \cos \sqrt{2\left(1 + \frac{r_0^4}{r_m^4}\right)}\,\omega_L t + C_2 \sin \sqrt{2\left(1 + \frac{r_0^4}{r_m^4}\right)}\,\omega_L t \tag{26}$$

At the cathode $t = 0$ and $r = r_0$ or $r_0 = r_m(1 - \delta)$

$$\therefore \delta = \frac{r_m - r_0}{r_m} \cos \sqrt{2\left(1 + \frac{r_0^4}{r_m^4}\right)}\omega_L t \tag{27}$$

The maximum beam diameter is then $r_m(1 + \delta)$ or

$$r_m\left(2 - \frac{r_0}{r_m}\right) \doteq r_m\left(1 + \frac{k}{2}\right) = r_0\left(1 + \frac{k}{2}\right)^2 \tag{28}$$

The minimum beam diameter is r_0 so the ratio of maximum to minimum is $(1 + k/2)^2$. In a good electron optical system this should be kept small and if we adopt 1·2 as a reasonable figure k must not exceed 0·2.

It is interesting to compare this value with the Brillouin value from Eq. (12). For confined flow with a 1·2 scallop ratio the fields must be in the ratio

$$\frac{B_z}{B_B} = \sqrt{\frac{5}{2}\frac{r_0}{r}}\left(\frac{V_a}{V_0}\right)^{1/4} \tag{29}$$

which, for $r = r_0$ and small perveances, is essentially 1·6. By going to twice the Brillouin field the max/min ratio would be decreased to about 1·1. The "brute-force" method is not so bad after all.

6.2.2. Convergent confined flow

The simplest and best treatment is that given by Kleen and Pöschl. The appearance of the system and the new notation is shown in Fig. 1. The magnetic shield is adjusted in position and diameter until the electron trajectories near the cathode surface

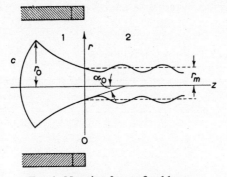

FIG. 1. Notation for confined beam.

lie along the magnetic field lines. The starting point is again Eq. (11) but B_0 does not now equal B_z. After a little manipulation we can write Eq. (11) in the form

$$\frac{B_0{}^2}{B_z{}^2} \frac{r_0{}^4}{r_m{}^4} + \frac{2K}{r_m{}^2} - 1 = 0 \tag{30}$$

where

$$K = kr_0{}^2 = \frac{3\cdot 5 \times 10^{-7} I_0}{B_z{}^2 V^{1/2}} \tag{31}$$

Then

$$r_m = K^{1/2}\left(1 + \sqrt{1 + \frac{B_0{}^2 r_0{}^4}{B_z{}^2 K^2}}\right)^{1/2} \tag{32}$$

As before we put $r = r_m(1 + \delta)$, use binomial expansions and obtain

$$\frac{d^2\delta}{dt^2} + 2(1 + A)\omega_L{}^2\delta = 0 \tag{33}$$

where

$$A = \left(\frac{B_0 r_0{}^2}{B_z r_m{}^2}\right)^2, \qquad 0 \leqslant A \leqslant 1 \tag{34}$$

Then $\delta = C_1 \cos \sqrt{2(1 + A)} \cdot \omega_L t + C_2 \sin \sqrt{2(1 + A)} \cdot \omega_L t$ (35)

In this case the origin is taken at the anode aperture separating region 1 from region 2. Let $r = r_a$ at the origin and let the beam be converging to the axis at angle α_0. Then

$$C_1 = \frac{r_a - r_m}{r_m}, \qquad C_2 = \frac{u_0 \tan \alpha_0}{\sqrt{2(1 + A)} \cdot \omega_L r_m} \tag{36}$$

The maximum beam radius is then given by

$$\frac{r_{max}}{r_{min}} = 1 + \frac{r_a}{r_m} \sqrt{\left(\frac{r_m}{r_a} - 1\right)^2 + \frac{1}{2(1+A)}\left(\frac{u_0 \tan \alpha_0}{\omega_L r_a}\right)^2} \quad (37)$$

Figure 2 shows r_{max}/r_{min} as a function of r_a/r_m with the second term under the radical as parameter. This figure shows that good beam performance can only be achieved by arranging matters so that $r_a/r_m \doteq 1{\cdot}0$, i.e., the electrons enter field free space at the desired

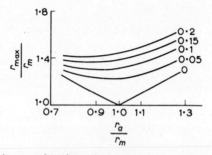

FIG. 2. Ripple as a function of entrance error, with magnetic field function as parameter.

beam diameter. If this is done, sufficiently high fields will give an almost ripple-free beam. Furthermore, we can deduce a relation between the magnetic flux enclosed by the mean beam diameter $2r_m$ and the flux cutting the cathode surface, when the field has been chosen so as to limit the scalloping to an acceptable value. We define the flux ratio α by

$$\pi r_0^2 B_c = \alpha \pi r_m^2 B_z$$

i.e.,
$$\alpha = \frac{r_0^2 B_c}{r_m^2 B_z} = A^{1/2} \quad (38)$$

Then, for $\ddot{r} = 0$, i.e., $r = r_m$ we can write Eq. (11) as

$$\frac{\omega_p^2}{2} = \omega_L^2(1 - \alpha^2)$$

or
$$\alpha^2 = 1 - \frac{\omega_p^2}{2\omega_L^2} \quad (39)$$

In the Brillouin case $\omega_p{}^2 = 2\omega_L{}^2$ so $\alpha^2 = 0$ and no flux must thread the cathode. In the infinite field case $\omega_p{}^2/2\omega_L{}^2 \to 0$ and $\alpha^2 \to 1$ so all the flux must thread the cathode. For twice the Brillouin field $\alpha \doteq 0.86$, so the percentage of flux cutting the cathode increases very rapidly once $2\omega_L > \omega_p{}^2$. Equation (10) gives the corresponding value of θ as

$$\theta = \omega_L(1 - \alpha) \tag{40}$$

so that the angular velocity is normally a small percentage of the Larmor value.

6.3. CROSSED-FIELD ELECTRON GUNS

We now consider guns of the type used in "M" Carcinotrons and "M" type T.W.A.s. Here the electrons are accelerated from the cathode to an anode with the direction of magnetic field normal to the direction of motion, instead of along it. A gun of this type

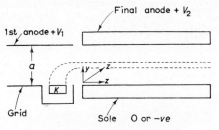

FIG. 3. Gun for crossed field tube.

is sketched in Fig. 3 which gives the notation used. The magnetic field is in the x direction, i.e., into the plane of the paper.

When $E_x = 0$ we have, using the Lorentz equation in rectangular co-ordinates,

$$\ddot{y} = -\eta(E_y + B_x \dot{z}) \tag{41}$$

$$\ddot{z} = -\eta(E_z - B_x \dot{y}) \tag{42}$$

With the substitutions

$$y = y' + \frac{E_z}{B_x}t, \qquad z = z' - \frac{E_y}{B_x}t$$

these become

$$\left.\begin{array}{l} \ddot{y}' = -\eta B_x \dot{z}' \\ \ddot{z}' = \eta B_x \dot{y}' \end{array}\right\} \tag{43}$$

or

$$y' = -R \cos\left(\omega_c t - \phi\right)$$

$$z' = -R \sin\left(\omega_c t - \phi\right)$$

where $\omega_c = \eta B_x$ = cyclotron angular frequency, and R and ϕ are constants.

Then

$$y = C_1 + \frac{E_z}{B_x}t - R \cos\left(\omega_c t - \phi\right) \tag{44}$$

$$z = C_2 - \frac{E_y}{B_x}t - R \sin\left(\omega_c t - \phi\right) \tag{45}$$

Equations (44) and (45) show that there is a translational velocity $u_y = E_z/B_x$, $u_z = -E_y/B_x$, superposed on the cycloidal motion. If we consider the cathode-first anode system as a planar diode, $E_y = -V_1/d$ and $u_z = V_1/B_x d$.

In the guns under discussion it is desired to set up a beam which approximates, as closely as possible, to the dotted lines. Clearly this requires that $u_y = 0$, i.e., $E_z = 0$. Let the initial conditions at $z = 0 = t$, be $y = y_0$, $\dot{y} = \dot{y}_0$, $\dot{z} = \dot{z}_0$

Then

$$C_2 = -R \sin\phi \tag{46}$$

$$C_1 = y_0 + R \cos\phi \tag{47}$$

$$\tan\phi = \frac{\dot{y}_0}{\dot{z}_0 + E_y/B_x} \tag{48}$$

and

$$R = \pm\sqrt{\frac{\dot{y}_0{}^2 + (\dot{z}_0 + E_y/B_x)^2}{\omega_c{}^2}} \tag{49}$$

From Eq. (49) it is obvious that R can be made zero, for example $\dot{y}_0 = 0$, $\dot{z}_0 + E_y/B_x = 0$ is one sufficient condition. The consequences of this can be further examined, but there seems little point in so doing because, owing to the neglect of space-charge and the somewhat artificial nature of the assumption that we are somehow able to make E_z zero, it is unlikely that the deductions would have any relevance for practical guns. It must be admitted that the present methods of design are based on art rather than on science.

BRILLOUIN[11] has carried out calculations on the double-stream steady state in the planar magnetron, with space-charge. These show that a stable solution is possible under the following conditions

$$y = \text{constant} \tag{50}$$

$$\dot{x} = 2\omega_L y \tag{51}$$

$$\rho_0 = -\frac{4\epsilon_0 \omega_L^2}{\eta} \tag{52}$$

$$V = \frac{2\omega_L^2 y^2}{\eta} \tag{53}$$

These, at any rate, serve to show that a linear flow can be obtained with space-charge and the correct input conditions which are not, necessarily, those obtaining in real planar magnetrons.

6.4. STRONG FOCUSING

We now consider a method of focusing long electron beams which is radically different from those described above. In its most general form this consists of the use of a large number of short electron lenses distributed along the length of the beam. Such lenses may be either magnetic or electric, although applications made up to the present have mainly used magnetic lenses. We do not, for the moment, require to differentiate between the two possibilities.

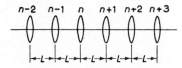

FIG. 4. Periodic focusing.

Consider the system of Fig. 4. PIERCE[12] gives the following analysis. The convergence of each lens is C. The radius and slope of a paraxial

[11] BRILLOUIN; *Advances in Electronics*, Vol. 3, p. 98, Academic Press, 1951.
[12] PIERCE; *Theory and Design of Electron Beams*, 2nd Ed., Van Nostrand, 1954.

ray, measured just to the right of the nth lens, are r_n and r'_n. Then

$$r_{n+1} = r + Lr'_n \tag{54}$$

$$r'_{n+1} = r'_n - Cr_{n+1} \tag{55}$$

whence

$$r'_n = \frac{1}{L}(r_{n+1} - r_n)$$

$$r'_{n+1} = \frac{1}{L}(r_{n+2} - r_{n+1})$$

and

$$r_{n+2} - (2 - CL)r_{n+1} + r_n = 0 \tag{56}$$

This difference equation has solutions of the form

$$r = A \cos n\theta + B \sin n\theta \tag{57}$$

If we only consider the cosine term and $n = 0$, Eq. (56) yields

$$\theta = \cos^{-1}\left(1 - \frac{CL}{2}\right) \tag{58}$$

which shows that θ is real for $CL < 4$ and the electrons follow a
path which oscillates sinusoidally through the system. If $CL > 4$.
the paths diverge exponentially. The reader will note the similarity
between such a system and a low-pass filter. This can be understood physically as follows. When the lenses are weak the electrons
are converged a little more towards the axis by each lens. As the
strength of each lens is increased, a stage is reached when the electron
crosses the axis between each pair of lenses. This means that it
reaches successively greater radius until it is lost from the system
on to the walls or other surrounding structure.

When the current density is large enough for space-charge forces
to be important, the trajectories between lenses are modified as
shown in Fig. 5. The space-charge repulsion, acting outwards,

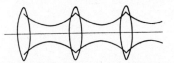

FIG. 5. Periodic focusing with space-charge.

first reduces the inwards velocity gained inside one of the lens
regions, brings it to zero and then causes an outward velocity, which

is destroyed in the next lens and so on. The paths between lenses are symmetrical about the planes $z = nL \pm L/2$ and may be represented by parts of the universal beam spread curve, well known in the theory of electrostatic focusing. The presence of space-charge complicates the theory but does not change its main features.

We now wish to give the salient points in the behaviour of the system most employed in valves.

6.4.1. Periodic magnetic focusing

In this system magnetic lenses are used to perform the focusing function and they are usually provided with permanent magnets. Now, there would be very little advantage in focusing a beam with an array of short magnetic lenses if it were not for the fact that when the sense of the z component of the magnetic field is reversed in each successive section, the stray magnetic field at a distance outside the system is vastly reduced. Put in other words the reluctance of the system as a whole is much increased. The total amount of permanent magnet material required to produce a given axial field is therefore reduced and large decreases in the weight and price of the magnet result. By a scaling argument MENDEL *et al.*[13] show that if N opposed magnets are used instead of a single continuous magnet, the gain in weight is proportional to N^2. In practice, the gain factor lies between N and N^2.

The operation of the system can be understood by reference to Fig. 6. Suppose that an electron beam of a specified density can be focused by the continuous Brillouin field, illustrated in Fig. (6)a. The focusing effect of a Brillouin system depends on B^2, so the direction of B is immaterial and the beam would be focused just as well by the periodic field shown in Fig. (6)b. At every plane where the magnetic field changes sign, the direction of electron rotation will reverse and the compensation will be exactly as before. It may then be shown that the behaviour of the cosine distribution, shown in Fig. 6(c) is the same provided the peak field is increased to $\sqrt{(2)}H_B$, in which case the R.M.S. fields are equal. Practical magnet systems, as shown in Fig. 6(e), tend to give the field shown in Fig. 6(d), at the edge of the pole pieces. However, Fourier analysis shows that this shape can be expressed as a cosine series, which clearly has a strong fundamental component. The fundamental operates in the same way as does the cosine wave, Fig. 6(c).

The notation is given in Figs. 6(d) and 6(e). The magnetic

---

[13] MENDEL, QUATE and YOCOM; *Proc. I.R.E.*, 1954, **42**, 800.

A *

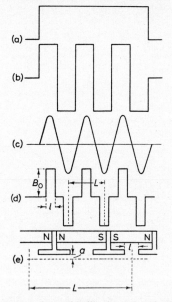

FIG. 6. Comparison of Brillouin and periodic fields.

induction B_z obeys Laplace's equation and in cylindrical co-ordinates can be expressed as

$$B_z(z, r) = \sum_{1 \ (n \ \text{odd})}^{\infty} A_n I_0 \left(\frac{2\pi n r}{L}\right) \cos \frac{2\pi n z}{L} \qquad (59)$$

Then
$$A_n = \frac{4}{l I_0(2\pi n a/L)} \int_0^l B_0 \cos \frac{2\pi n z}{L} \, dz$$

$$= \frac{4 B_0(l/L)}{I_0(2\pi n a/L)} \frac{\sin(n\pi l/L)}{n\pi l/L} \qquad (60)$$

These equations already disclose one of the difficulties with this method of focusing: the field on the axis is inversely proportional to $I_0(2\pi n a/L)$, a function which increases exponentially for values of the argument in excess of about 2·5. a/L must therefore be kept small, <0·2, if the field is to be constant over the beam radius.

When space-charge is neglected, Eq. (58) is still true if we re-define L to denote the complete period of the lens system, i.e., L is now twice the value used in Eq. (58).

Then,
$$\theta = \cos^{-1}\left(1 - \frac{CL}{4}\right)$$

and[14]
$$C = \frac{\eta}{8V_0}\int_0^{L/2} B_z^2\,dz \qquad (61)$$

If we put $B_z = B_1 \cos 2\pi z/L$ we find $CL = \eta/8V_0\,B_1^2L^2/4$. Thus, the pass-band, defined as $CL < 8$, is determined by

$$\frac{\eta B_1^2 L^2}{V_0} < 256 \qquad (62)$$

MENDEL et al.[15] show experimentally that when space-charge is important, the stop and pass-bands still occur but that Eq. (62) is modified to

$$\frac{\eta B_1^2 L^2}{V_0} < 418 \qquad (63)$$

Since the publication of this pioneering work there has grown up a large literature devoted to the details of periodic focusing, which need not concern us here. The reader may be interested by a general treatment, including electric field systems, by CLOGSTON and HEFFNER.[16]

We conclude this work with a few practical remarks. The Brillouin focusing condition is (beam radius $= b$)

$$I_0 = 1\cdot45 \times 10^6 B^2_{rms}\,b^2\,V_0^{1/2}$$

Thus, B has to be increased as I_0 is made larger. But Eq. (63) shows that $BL = $ constant. Therefore L has to be decreased to maintain this condition and must vary as $I_0^{-1/2}$. At the same time, a/L has to be kept small so that a should be decreased in the same ratio. The focusing of high currents therefore demands a short period, strong fields and very small apertures for the beam. These requirements are contradictory and the system is not universally applicable,

---

[14] PIERCE; *Theory and Design of Electron Beams*, 2nd Ed., Chap. 7, Van Nostrand, 1954.
[15] MENDEL, QUATE and YOCOM; *Proc. I.R.E.*, 1954, **42**, 800.
[16] CLOGSTON and HEFFNER; *J. Appl. Phys.*, 1954, **25**, 436.

especially when attention is paid to the limitations of existing permanent magnet materials.

6.4.2. Periodic electrostatic focusing of a spinning electron beam

Periodic electrostatic focusing has not found much practical application because the limiting perveances are, in general, lower than with magnetic field, and theoretical studies such as that by TIEN[17] indicate that such schemes do not work well with a uniform radial charge distribution. A more promising idea is to set the beam spinning by operating the accelerating region, the gun proper, in a magnetic field which decreases to zero in the region where the electrons reach their final velocity. This is done by passing the beam through an aperture in a magnetic screen at this point. The beam then enters the region of periodic electrostatic focusing fields, set up by, for instance, a set of charged rings or a bifilar helix. In this region an equilibrium can be established between the centrifugal force due to the rotation and the electrostatic forces due to the lenses. If the other forces are made sufficiently large the space-charge forces can be ignored and focusing achieved without any special requirement on the radial charge density. This system has been considered by CHANG[18] and we proceed to outline his analysis.

In the cathode-anode region, Eq. (9) shows that the electrons emerge from the magnetic field with an angular velocity given by

$$\dot{\theta}_0 = -\frac{\eta}{r_0^2} \int_0^{r_c} B_0(r) r \, dr \tag{64}$$

where we have now allowed the induction to vary over the cathode surface.

In the region of periodic fields, Eqs. (5), (6) and (7) have to be modified, first to take account of the imposed electric field components $E_r = -\partial V/\partial r$, $E_\theta = -\partial V/\partial \theta$ in addition to the space-charge component of E_r and secondly because the magnetic components are all zero. It is convenient to transform the space-charge part of E_r, by using Eq. (12) to obtain

$$E_{rs} = -\eta \frac{B_B^2}{4} \cdot \frac{r_0^2}{r} \tag{65}$$

where B_B is the Brillouin field referred to the radius at the cathode.

[17] TIEN; *J. Appl. Phys.*, 1954, **25**, 1281.
[18] CHANG; *Proc. I.R.E.*, 1957, **45**, 66.

Then, Eqs. (5), (6) and (7) give

$$\ddot{r} - r\dot{\theta}^2 - \eta\frac{\partial V}{\partial r} = \frac{\eta^2}{4}B_B^2\frac{r_0^2}{r} \tag{66}$$

$$\frac{1}{r}\frac{d}{dt}(r^2\dot{\theta}) = \frac{\eta}{r}\frac{\partial V}{\partial\theta} \tag{67}$$

$$\ddot{z} = \eta\frac{\partial V}{\partial z} \tag{68}$$

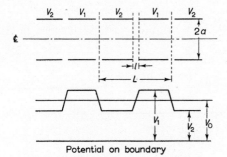

Potential on boundary

FIG. 7. Periodic electrostatic focusing.

The electrostatic field, Fig. 7, is subjected to a Fourier expansion, leading to the analogue of Eq. (60)

$$V = V_0 + \hat{V}_{(r)}\cos\left(\frac{2\pi z}{L} - \theta\right) \tag{69}$$

$$\hat{V}_{(r)} = \frac{2}{\pi}(V_1 - V_2)\frac{\sin\pi l_1/L}{\pi l_1/L}\frac{I_n(2\pi r/L)}{I_n(2\pi a/L)} \tag{70}$$

Here, $n = 0$ for short cylinders, $n = 1$ for the bifilar helix, while θ in Eq. (69) is a constant for cylinders but depends on the helix parameters.

The equations of motion are solved by a perturbation method, assuming

$$r = r_m + r_1\cos\left(\frac{2\pi z}{L} - \theta\right) \tag{71}$$

$$\theta = \theta_0 + \theta_1\cos\left(\frac{2\pi z}{L} - \theta\right) \tag{72}$$

where θ_0 is the initial angular velocity given by Eq. (64). Using

$$\ddot{r} = \frac{\partial^2 r}{\partial z^2}\,\dot{z}^2 + \frac{\partial^2 r}{\partial \theta^2}\cdot\dot{\theta}^2 + 2\dot{\theta}\dot{z}\,\frac{\partial^2 r}{\partial \theta\,\partial z} + \ddot{z}\,\frac{\partial r}{\partial z} + \ddot{\theta}\,\frac{\partial r}{\partial \theta} \qquad (73)$$

carrying out the differentiations, and using Taylor expansions for the radial variation of $\hat{V}(r)$ and $\hat{V}'(r)$ the following relation is proved, subject to the condition $(2\pi/L)u_0 \gg \theta_0$

$$\left[\left(\frac{L}{2\pi}\right)^2\hat{V}'' + V + \left(\frac{L}{2\pi r_m}\right)^2\hat{V}\right]\frac{\hat{V}'}{V_0} = \frac{1}{r_m}\left(\frac{L}{2\pi r_m}\right)^2\frac{\hat{V}}{V_0} + 4r_m\left(\frac{2\pi}{L}\right)^2 V_0$$

$$\times\left[\left(\frac{L}{\lambda_b}\right)^2\left(\frac{r_0}{r_m}\right)^2 + \left(\frac{L}{\lambda_0}\right)^2\left(\frac{r_0}{r_m}\right)^4\left(\frac{\psi_0}{\bar{\psi}_0}\right)^2\right] \qquad (74)$$

where $\lambda_B = \dfrac{4\pi\sqrt{V_0}}{\sqrt{\eta}B_B}$ (plasma wavelength)

$\lambda_0 = \dfrac{4\pi\sqrt{V_0}}{\sqrt{\eta}B_0(r_0)}$ (scallop wavelength)

$\psi_0 = 2\pi\displaystyle\int_\theta^{r_0}B_0(r_0)r\,\mathrm{d}r$

$\bar{\psi}_0 = \pi\,.\,B_0(r_0)r_m^2$

Equation (74) represents the force equilibrium. On the left-hand side we have, respectively, the forces due to the radial, axial and angular focusing fields. On the right-hand side we have forces due

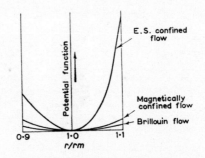

FIG. 8. Stability of various focusing systems.

to the rotation, set up both by the θ component of the electric field, and the initial magnetic field and the space-charge force.

Often, the first term in the R.H. square bracket can be neglected in comparison with the second, and Chang calls this condition "electrostatically confined flow".

Consideration of the potential function around the equilibrium beam radius r_m shows that this type of flow is much more stable than other types of flow (see Fig. 8). This type of focusing thus seems to be of very great practical value.

CONCLUDING REMARKS

It will not have escaped the reader that the theory of this Appendix is based on the hypothesis that the beam exhibits laminar flow, i.e., the electron trajectories do not cross one another. This hypothesis must now be regarded as disproven, at least for the case of a magnetically focused electron beam originating at a completely shielded cathode, by the work of HARKER.[19] By traversing a small pin-hole along the beam, Harker demonstrated that electrons cross the axis in such beams, since ring images are formed. Harker's explanation of ring formation implies that non-laminar flow is set up by the aberrations of the magnetic lens formed at the transition region from zero to finite magnetic field. It is clearly of the utmost importance that this work be extended to magnetically confined beams.

---

[19] HARKER; *J. Appl. Phys.*, 1957, **28**, 645.

APPENDIX 7

ANNULAR BEAMS AND BESSEL FUNCTION EXPANSIONS

WE DERIVE here the results of Section 4.5.
At $r = c$ we have

$$\frac{\gamma_0 I_1(\gamma_0 c)}{I_0(\gamma_0 c)} = \frac{-\gamma r(B J_1(\gamma r . c) + C Y_1(\gamma r . c))}{B J_0(\gamma r . c) + C Y_0(\gamma r . c)} \tag{1}$$

At $r = b$

$$\frac{\gamma_0 (D I_1(\gamma_0 b) - E K_1(\gamma_0 b))}{D I_0(\gamma_0 b) + E K_0(\gamma_0 b)} = \frac{-\gamma r(B J_1(\gamma r . b) + C Y_1(\gamma r . b))}{B J_0(\gamma r . b) + C Y_0(\gamma r . b)} \tag{2}$$

and, since $E_z = 0$ at $r = a$, $D I_0(\gamma_0 a) = -E K_0(\gamma_0 a)$.
Solve Eqs. (1) and (2) for C/B and we obtain

$$\frac{C}{B} = \frac{-\gamma r/\gamma_0 \{I_0(\gamma_0 c)/I_1(\gamma_0 c)\, J_1(\gamma r c)\} - J_0(\gamma r c)}{Y_0(\gamma r c) + \gamma r/\gamma_0 \{I_0(\gamma_0 c)/I_1(\gamma_0 c)\, J_1(\gamma r c)\}} \tag{3}$$

$$\frac{C}{B} = \frac{-\dfrac{\gamma r}{\gamma_0}\left\{\dfrac{I_1(\gamma_0 b)K_0(\gamma_0 a) + I_0(\gamma_0 a)K_1(\gamma_0 b)}{I_0(\gamma_0 b)K_0(\gamma_0 a) - I_0(\gamma_0 a)K_0(\gamma_0 b)}\right\} J_1(\gamma r b) - J_0(\gamma r b)}{Y_0(\gamma r b) + \dfrac{\gamma r}{\gamma_0}\left\{\dfrac{I_1(\gamma_0 b)K_0(\gamma_0 a) + I_0(\gamma_0 a)K_1(\gamma_0 b)}{I_0(\gamma_0 b)K_0(\gamma_0 a) - I_0(\gamma_0 a)K_0(\gamma_0 b)}\right\} Y_1(\gamma r b)} \tag{4}$$

Equating these two expressions for C/B and solving for $\gamma r/\gamma_0$ we obtain the relations given in the text, when the relations discussed below are inserted.

These relations depend on the asymptotic forms for the Bessel functions which are valid for large arguments. These are

$$J_0(X) = \sqrt{\frac{2}{\pi X}} \cos\left(X - \frac{\pi}{4}\right) \tag{5}$$

$$J_1(X) = \sqrt{\frac{2}{\pi X}} \sin\left(X - \frac{\pi}{4}\right) \tag{6}$$

$$Y_0(X) = \sqrt{\frac{2}{\pi X}} \sin\left(X - \frac{\pi}{4}\right) \qquad (7)$$

$$Y_1(X) = -\sqrt{\frac{2}{\pi X}} \cos\left(X - \frac{\pi}{4}\right) \qquad (8)$$

The lowest value of X for which these are valid depends, of course, on the particular purpose, but for most engineering calculations we may use them for $X > 10$. They are tolerably accurate for $X > 6$. Using these expansions we find that, for instance,

$$Y_0(Y)J_0(X) - Y_0(X)J_0(Y) \to \sqrt{\frac{4}{\pi^2 XY}} \sin(Y - X)$$

or $\quad$ bsn $(Y - X) = \dfrac{\pi}{2} \sqrt{XY} \left[Y_0(Y)J_0(X) - Y_0(X)J_0(Y) \right] \qquad (9)$

where bsn may be read as Bessel sine.

$$\text{bcs }(Y - X) = \frac{\pi}{2} \sqrt{XY} \left[Y_0(Y)J_1(X) - Y_1(X)J_1(Y) \right]$$
$$\text{(Bessel cosine)} \quad (10)$$

$$\text{Bsn }(Y - X) = \frac{\pi}{2} \sqrt{XY} \left[Y_1(Y)J_1(X) - Y_1(X)J_1(Y) \right] \qquad (11)$$

$$\text{Bcs }(Y - X) = \frac{\pi}{2} \sqrt{XY} \left[J_1(Y)Y_0(X) - Y_1(Y)J_0(X) \right] \qquad (12)$$

$$\text{btn }(Y - X) = \frac{Y_0(Y)J_0(X) - Y_0(X)J_0(Y)}{Y_0(Y)J_1(X) - Y_1(X)J_0(Y)} \qquad (13)$$

$$\text{Btn }(Y - X) = \frac{Y_1(Y)J_1(X) - Y_1(X)J_1(Y)}{Y_0(X)J_1(Y) - Y_1(Y)J_0(X)} \qquad (14)$$

Similarly, the I and K functions are related to hyperbolic functions

$$\text{bsnh }(Y - X) = \sqrt{XY}[K_0(X)I_0(Y) - K_0(Y)I_0(X)] \qquad (15)$$

$$\text{bcsh }(Y - X) = \sqrt{XY}[K_0(Y)I_1(X) + K_1(X)I_0(Y)] \qquad (16)$$

$$\text{Bsnh }(Y - X) = \sqrt{XY}[K_1(X)I_1(Y) - K_1(Y)I_1(X)] \qquad (17)$$

$$\text{Bcsh }(Y - X) = \sqrt{XY}[K_0(X)I_1(Y) + K_1(Y)I_0(X)] \qquad (18)$$

$$\text{btnh }(Y - X) = \frac{K_0(X)I_0(Y) - K_0(Y)I_0(X)}{K_0(Y)I_1(X) + K_1(X)I_0(Y)} \qquad (19)$$

$$\text{Btnh }(Y - X) = \frac{K_1(X)I_1(Y) - K_1(Y)I_1(X)}{K_0(X)I_1(Y) + K_1(Y)I_0(X)} \qquad (20)$$

The use of these relations greatly simplifies the handling of complicated expressions involving Bessel functions, but the range $0 - X_{min}$, where X_{min} is the lowest value of X for which the asymptotic expressions are valid, still has to be treated by graphical methods.

Example

Solve

$$\frac{J_0(B) - \alpha B J_1(B)}{Y_0(B) - \alpha B Y_1(B)} = \frac{\beta C J_1(C) + J_0(C)}{\beta C Y_1(C) + Y_0(C)} \tag{21}$$

for large arguments.

Using the asymptotic forms we have

$$\frac{1 - \alpha B \tan B'}{\tan B' + \alpha B} = \frac{1 + \beta C \tan C'}{-\beta C + \tan C'}$$

where $B' = (B - \pi/4)$, $C' = (C - \pi/4)$

Putting $\alpha B = \tan A$, $\beta C = \tan D$, we get

$$\cot (A + B') = \cot (C' - D)$$

or $\tan^{-1} (\alpha B) + B = C - \tan^{-1} (\beta C) + n\pi$

that is, $\qquad B - C = n\pi - (\tan^{-1} (\alpha B) + \tan^{-1} (\beta C))$

Suppose now that α and β are both of order one. Then since B and C are by definition large, the bracketed terms are both nearly $\pi/2$.

Then $\qquad\qquad\qquad B - C = (n - 1)\pi \qquad\qquad$ *Answer.*

This approximation can be refined by iteration, if necessary.

The reader should be cautioned that the use of these asymptotic expansions may need special investigation in the immediate vicinity of the zeros of the asymptotic values.

APPENDIX 8

SOLUTION OF EQUATION (134), CHAPTER 4

FOLLOWING Muller we put $u_0 = KZ^\alpha$ to obtain solutions valid for several practical field variations. This transforms Eq. (134) to

$$\frac{d^2P}{dz^2} + \frac{dP}{dz}\frac{3\alpha}{z} + \frac{P\eta J_0}{\epsilon_0 K^3 Z^{3\alpha}} = 0 \tag{1}$$

Then put $x = z^\beta$, $\beta = 2 - 3\alpha/2$, $\gamma = (\eta J_0/\epsilon_0 K^3 \beta^2)^{1/2}$, to obtain

$$\frac{d^2P}{dx^2} + \frac{dP}{dx}\cdot\frac{1}{x}\cdot\frac{3\alpha}{2-3\alpha} + P\gamma^2 = 0 \tag{2}$$

Equation (2) excludes the special case $\alpha = \frac{2}{3}$, which makes the second term infinite.

The solution of Eq. (2) is

$$P = x^{-p}[AJ_p(\gamma x) + BY_p(\gamma x)] \tag{3}$$

where $p = (3\alpha - 1)/(2 - 3\alpha)$.

The constants A and B are determined by putting Eq. (3) into the integrating factor definition of J_1 and into Eq. (133) for u and then inserting the initial conditions $u(x_1) = u_1$, $i(x_1) = i_1$ at the plane of entry to the system. The result is

$$E = \frac{\pi\gamma x_1}{2}\left(\frac{x_1}{x}\right)^p [J_{p+1}(\gamma x_1)Y_p(\gamma x) - Y_{p+1}(\gamma x_1)J_p(\gamma x)] \tag{4}$$

$$F = j\cdot G\cdot\frac{\pi\gamma}{2}\frac{1}{(xx_1)^p}[J_p(\gamma x_1)Y_p(\gamma x) - Y_p(\gamma x_1)J_p(\gamma x)] \tag{5}$$

$$H = j\cdot\frac{\pi\gamma}{2G}(xx_1)^{1/2\beta}[J_{p+1}(\gamma x_1)Y_{p+1}(\gamma x) - Y_{p+1}(\gamma x_1)J_{p+1}(\gamma x)] \tag{6}$$

$$I = \frac{\pi\gamma x_1}{2}\left(\frac{x}{x_1}\right)^{1/2\beta}[Y_p(\gamma x_1)J_{p+1}(\gamma x) - J_p(\gamma x_1)Y_{p+1}(\gamma x)] \tag{7}$$

where $G = \omega(\epsilon_0\eta J_0/K^3)\,|2 - 3\alpha|/(2 - 3\alpha)$, $\alpha \neq \frac{2}{3}$.

The results given in the text can be derived from these by putting $\alpha = \frac{1}{2}$ and altering the notation.

APPENDIX 9

ORTHOGONAL EXPANSIONS IN
BESSEL FUNCTIONS

IN THIS appendix we show that the cylinder function $B_0(pr)$ can be used to obtain orthogonal functions over the region $a < r < b$ with three different types of boundary condition. The reader is left to prove the simpler case, for $J_0(pr)$ himself.

We define

$$B_0(pr) = J_0(pr)Y_0(pb) - Y_0(pr)J_0(pb) \tag{1}$$

$B_0(pb)$ is identically zero.

We put $u = B_0(p_q r)$
$$v = B_0(p_p r)$$

Then, from Bessel's equation with $n = 0$

$$v \frac{\mathrm{d}}{\mathrm{d}r}\left(r \frac{\mathrm{d}u}{\mathrm{d}r}\right) + p_q{}^2 ruv = 0$$

$$u \frac{\mathrm{d}}{\mathrm{d}r}\left(r \frac{\mathrm{d}v}{\mathrm{d}r}\right) + p_p{}^2 ruv = 0$$

Therefore

$$(p_q{}^2 - p_p{}^2)\int_a^b ruv \,\mathrm{d}r = \int_a^b \left[v \frac{\mathrm{d}}{\mathrm{d}r}\left(r \frac{\mathrm{d}u}{\mathrm{d}r}\right) - u \frac{\mathrm{d}}{\mathrm{d}r}\left(r \frac{\mathrm{d}v}{\mathrm{d}r}\right) \right]\mathrm{d}r$$

$$= b\left[v \frac{\mathrm{d}u}{\mathrm{d}r} - u \frac{\mathrm{d}v}{\mathrm{d}r} \right]_{r=b} - a\left[v \frac{\mathrm{d}u}{\mathrm{d}r} - u \frac{\mathrm{d}v}{\mathrm{d}r} \right]_{r=a}$$

$$= b[p_p B_0(p_q b)B'_0(p_p b) - p_q B_0(p_p b)B'_0(p_q b)] - $$
$$- a[p_p B_0(p_q a)B'_0(p_p a) - p_q B_0(p_p a)B'_0(p_q a)]$$

The first square bracket vanishes since $B_0(p_q b) = 0 = B_0(p_p b)$. The second square bracket can be made to vanish in three different ways.

(i) By putting $B_0(p_q a) = 0 = B_0(p_p a)$, i.e., by choosing the p's as the roots of $B_0(pa) = 0$.

(ii) By putting $B'_0(p_q a) = 0 = B'_0(p_p a)$, i.e., by making the p's roots of $B'_0(pa) = 0$.

(iii) By making $p_p[B'_0(p_p a)/B_0(p_p a)] = h$, h being constant, i.e., by choosing the p's as the roots of $pa[B'_0(pa)/B_0(pa)] = ha$.

Thus, for any of these choices $\int_a^b ruv \, dr = 0$, for $p_q{}^2 - p_p{}^2 \neq 0$. This ensures that cross-product terms vanish from a series expansion in the functions $B_0(pr)$.

To use the expansion

$$f(r) = a_1 B_0(p_1 r) + a_2 B_0(p_2 r) \ldots a_n B_0(p_n r)$$

we multiply both sides by $rB_0(p_n r)$ and integrate over a–b, thus determining a_n by

$$a_n = \frac{\int_a^b rf(r)B_0(p_n r) \, dr}{\int_a^b rB_0{}^2(p_n r) \, dr} \tag{2}$$

The evaluation of the lower integral involves the use of the particular boundary condition required. The first and third conditions are interesting to us, the second is not used here

(i) $$\int_a^b rB_0{}^2(pr) \, dr = \frac{1}{2}\left[r^2 B'_0{}^2(pr) + r^2 B_0{}^2(pr) \right]_a^b \tag{3}$$

The second term on the right vanishes at both limits.

Also, $$bB'_0(pb) = b(-J_1(pb)Y_0(pb) + Y_1(pb)J_0(pb)$$

$$= -\frac{2}{\pi p}$$

The last expression is derived using the Wronskian determinant.

$$aB'_0(pa) = a[-J_1(pa)Y_0(pb) + J_0(pb)Y_1(pa)]$$

But, since $B_0(pa) = 0$, $Y_0(pb)/Y_0(pa) = J_0(pb)/J_0(pa) = W$

Therefore $$aB'_0(pa) = -\frac{2W}{\pi p}$$

Therefore

$$\int_a^b rB_0{}^2(pr) \, dr = \frac{2}{\pi^2 p^2}(1 - W^2) = \frac{2}{\pi^2 p^2}\left[\frac{J_0{}^2(pa) - J_0{}^2(pb)}{J_0{}^2(pa)} \right] \tag{4}$$

Finally,

$$a_n = \frac{\pi^2 p^2}{2}\left[\frac{1}{1-W^2}\right]\int_a^b rf\cdot(r)B_0(pr)\,dr \tag{5}$$

(iii) Equation (3) still holds. $B_0(pb) = 0$ but $B_0(pa) \neq 0$. Also $B'_0(pb) = -2/\pi pb$ as before. From the boundary condition

$$pa[-J_1(pa)Y_0(pb) + J_0(pb)Y_1(pa)] = h[J_0(pa)Y_0(pb) - Y_0(pa)J_0(pb)]$$

or $\quad pa\left[\dfrac{Y_1(pa)}{Y_0(pb)} - \dfrac{J_1(pa)}{J_0(pb)}\right] = \left[h\dfrac{J_0(pa)}{J_0(pb)} - \dfrac{Y_0(pa)}{Y_0(pb)}\right]$

and $\quad \dfrac{paY_1(pa) + hY_0(pa)}{Y_0(pb)} = \dfrac{paJ_1(pa) + hJ_0(pa)}{J_0(pb)} = W \tag{6}$

Therefore $WB'_0(pa) = [-J_1(pa)\{paY_1(pa) + hY_0(pa)\} +$
$$\qquad\qquad\qquad + Y_1(pa)\{paJ_1(pa) + hJ_0(pa)\}]$$
$$\qquad\qquad = h[-J_1(pa)Y_0(pa) + Y_1(pa)J_0(pa)]$$

or $\quad B'_0(pa) = -\dfrac{2h}{\pi Wpa}$

Again, using the boundary condition

$$B_0(pa) = \frac{paB'_0(pa)}{h} = -\frac{2}{\pi W}$$

Therefore $\quad \displaystyle\int_a^b rB_0^2(pr)\,dr = \frac{2}{\pi^2 p^2}\left[1 - \left(\frac{h^2}{W^2} + \frac{p^2 a^2}{W^2}\right)\right] \tag{7}$

Then $\quad a_n = \dfrac{\pi^2 p^2}{2}\left[1 - \left(\dfrac{h^2}{W^2} + \dfrac{p^2 a^2}{W^2}\right)\right]^{-1}\displaystyle\int_a^b rfr(r)B_0(pr)\,dr \tag{8}$

W is, of course, given by Eq. (6) in this case.

To my knowledge the expansion shown in Eq. (8) has not been given before. Equation (5) is well known, being given, for example, in CARSLAW and JAEGER.[1]

---

[1] CARSLAW and JAEGER; *Conduction of Heat in Solids*, Oxford University Press, 1947.

APPENDIX 10

COUPLING OF MODES OF PROPAGATION

PIERCE[1] has recently suggested some useful generalizations of the idea of coupling between modes. These modes might, for instance, be voltages and currents on a transmission line, in which case a somewhat new physical picture of the stop-band emerges, or they might be a circuit mode observed in the absence of a beam and a space-charge mode observed in the absence of waves on the circuit. These ideas have been applied by Pierce and Tien (Chapter 3) in discussing the physics of the tape helix, and by GOULD[2] in discussing the B.W.O. This appendix outlines the development.

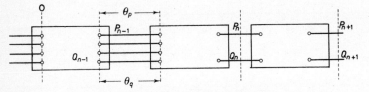

FIG. 1. Coupling of modes of propagation.

We consider a chain of linear transducers, as shown in Fig. 1, in which we suppose there are only two modes of propagation, that is that both lines are terminated in their characteristic impedances. The modes have complex amplitudes P and Q so that the powers are given by PP^*, $\pm QQ^*$. The plus sign applies if the group velocities of both modes are in the same direction, the minus sign otherwise. The coupling is localized in the transducers, but we later go to the case in which the spacing between transducers is very small. The phase shifts between transducers are θ_p for mode P, θ_q for mode Q and the coupling coefficient in the transducer is K. Then

$$\begin{vmatrix} P_{n+1} \\ Q_{n+1} \end{vmatrix} = \begin{vmatrix} A \exp(-j\theta_p), & B \exp(-j\theta_q) \\ D \exp(-j\theta_p), & C \exp(-j\theta_q) \end{vmatrix} \cdot \begin{vmatrix} P_n \\ A_n \end{vmatrix} \qquad (1)$$

[1] PIERCE; *J. Appl. Phys.*, 1954, **25**, 179, and *Bell Syst. Tech. J.*, 1954, **33**, 1343.
[2] GOULD; *Trans. I.R.E.*, ED–2, 1955, **4**, 37.

This equation can be solved by diagonalization of the matrix. We write $M = ADA^{-1}$, where M is the matrix multiplying the column matrix P_n, Q_n. A is a matrix whose elements, though easily determined, do not here concern us. D is the diagonal matrix

$$D = \begin{vmatrix} \lambda_1 & 0 \\ 0 & \lambda_2 \end{vmatrix}$$

where λ_1, λ_2 are the roots of

$$\lambda^2 - [A \exp(-j\theta_p) + C \exp(-j\theta_q)]\lambda + (AC - BD) \exp[-j(\theta_p + \theta_q)] \tag{2}$$

Then by successive multiplication we have

$$\begin{vmatrix} P_{n+1} \\ Q_{n+1} \end{vmatrix} = M^2 \begin{vmatrix} P_{n-1} \\ Q_{n-1} \end{vmatrix} = M^3 \begin{vmatrix} P_{n-2} \\ Q_{n-2} \end{vmatrix} \text{ etc.}$$

or $\begin{vmatrix} P_{n+1} \\ Q_{n+1} \end{vmatrix} = ADA^{-1} \cdot ADA^{-1} \cdot ADA^{-1} \begin{vmatrix} P_{n-2} \\ Q_{n-2} \end{vmatrix} = AD^3A \begin{vmatrix} P_{n-2} \\ Q_{n-2} \end{vmatrix}$ etc.

Finally $\qquad\qquad \begin{vmatrix} P_{n+1} \\ Q_{n+1} \end{vmatrix} = AD^{n+1}A^{-1} \begin{vmatrix} P_0 \\ Q_0 \end{vmatrix}$ (3)

Of course D^{n+1} is simply $\begin{vmatrix} \lambda_1^{n+1} & 0 \\ 0 & \lambda^{n+1} \end{vmatrix}$

But Eq. (3) is just the matrix form of the transmission line equations, in which case the λ's are the forward and backward wave functions $\exp(\pm\gamma)$. Thus, the λ's determined by Eq. (2) are wave functions for the propagation of two coupled modes and the periodic coupling has modified the propagation constants of the original uncoupled modes.

We now turn our attention to the matrix $\begin{vmatrix} A & B \\ D & C \end{vmatrix}$ which characterizes the transducer proper. Network theory tells us that a lossless passive network has a network determinant equal to unity and real coefficients. Symmetry further demands that the diagonal elements be equal. A form which satisfies these requirements is

$$\begin{vmatrix} A & B \\ D & C \end{vmatrix} = \begin{vmatrix} (1 \mp K^2)^{1/2}, & K \\ \mp K & (1 \mp K^2)^{1/2} \end{vmatrix} \tag{4}$$

and Pierce shows directly that this is a statement of the conservation of energy.

We next generalize Eq. (4) by allowing the reference planes of P_{n+1}, P_n, Q_{n+1} and Q_n to be shifted by θ_I, θ_II, θ_III, and θ_IV, respectively. The most general form of Eq. (4) then becomes:—

$$\begin{vmatrix} P_{n+1} \\ Q_{n+1} \end{vmatrix} = \begin{vmatrix} (1 \mp K^2)^{1/2} \exp(j\theta_1), & K \exp(j\theta_2) \\ \mp K \exp[j(\theta_1 - \theta_2 + \theta_3)], & (1 \mp K^2) \exp(j\theta_3) \end{vmatrix} \begin{vmatrix} P_n \\ Q_n \end{vmatrix} \quad (5)$$

where $\theta_1 = \theta_\mathrm{I} - \theta_\mathrm{II}$

$\theta_2 = \theta_\mathrm{III} - \theta_\mathrm{II}$

$\theta_3 = \theta_\mathrm{III} - \theta_\mathrm{IV}$

and therefore $\theta_1 - \theta_2 + \theta_3 = \theta_\mathrm{I} - \theta_\mathrm{IV}$.

If the values of A, B, C, D in Eq. (3) are substituted by those in Eq. (5) into Eq. (1) we find that

$$M^2 - 2M(1 \mp K^2)^{1/2} \cos\left(\frac{(\theta_1 - \theta_p - \theta_3 + \theta_q)}{2}\right) + 1 = 0 \quad (6)$$

where $\qquad M = \lambda \exp\left\{-j\left(\frac{\theta_1 - \theta_p + \theta_3 - \theta_q}{2}\right)\right\} \quad (7)$

When the group velocities are in the same direction the top sign applies and the radical is <1, in which case M must be complex and of unit magnitude. Power surges back and forth between the two original modes without any net loss. This situation can either be described by the matrix (5) or by the much more convenient matrix (2) where the λ's are given by Eqs. (6) and (7).

When one of the group velocities is reversed, real values of M are obtained when

$$(1 + K^2)^{1/2} \cos\left(\frac{\theta_1 - \theta_p - \theta_3 + \theta_q}{2}\right) > 1 \quad (8)$$

and the waves change exponentially with distance along the system. Conservation of energy in this case demands that the power fed in by one mode is led out by the other. In network terminology we are in a stop-band of our network.

The transition to the case of continuous coupling is made by Gould as follows. The distance between transducers is put equal to Δz; P and Q are defined through relations of the form

$$P_n \to P(z), \qquad P_{n+1} \to P(z) + \mathrm{d}P;$$

and $\qquad\qquad\qquad K \to k\Delta z$

B*

while the phase angles are defined through

$$\theta_p - \theta_1 \to \beta_p \Delta z, \qquad \theta_q - \theta_3 \to \beta_q \Delta z$$

If we now expand the exponentials and square-roots in the explicit form of Eq. (1), (A, B, C, D defined by Eq. (5)), and retain only the first terms, we find

$$\frac{\partial P}{\partial z} + j\beta_p P_z - kQ = 0$$

$$\frac{\partial Q}{\partial z} + j\beta_q Q \pm kP = 0 \tag{9}$$

The solution of Eqs. (9) is easily found to be

$$P = C_1 \exp(-j\beta_1 z) + C_2 \exp(-j\beta_2 z)$$

$$Q = -jC_1 \left(\frac{\beta_1 - \beta_p}{k} \right) \exp(-j\beta_1 z) - jC_2 \left(\frac{\beta_2 - \beta_p}{k} \right) \exp(-j\beta_2 z) \tag{10}$$

where

$$\beta_1, \beta_2 = \frac{\beta_p + \beta_q}{2} \pm \sqrt{\left(\frac{\beta_p - \beta_q}{2} \right)^2 \pm k^2} \tag{11}$$

To illustrate the use of Eq. (11), Pierce has drawn Figs. 2 and 3 which illustrate the situation in a T.W.A. without coupling and the behaviour when the coupling is taken into account by the results of this section. Fig. 2 shows the space-charge waves β_s, $\beta_f = \omega/u_0 \pm \frac{1}{2}$ and the circuit wave, arbitrarily put equal to 1. Fig. 3 shows the situation for $k = 0 \cdot 1$. Consider first the coupling between the slow space-charge wave and the circuit wave. Here the group velocities are opposed and we take the lower sign inside the root in Eq. (11). We immediately see that at $\beta_e = 0 \cdot 5$, $\beta_s = 1$ or $\beta_p = \beta_q$ and Eq. (11) gives

$$\beta_1, \beta_2 = 1 \cdot 0 \pm jk$$

If we put $\beta_e = 0 \cdot 5 \pm \delta$, $\beta_s = 1 \pm \delta$, and

$$\beta_1 = \left(1 \pm \frac{\delta}{2} \right) + \sqrt{\frac{\delta^2}{4} - 0 \cdot 01}, \qquad \beta_2 = \left(1 \pm \frac{\delta}{2} \right) - \sqrt{\frac{\delta^2}{4} - 0 \cdot 01}$$

so that both the perturbed modes have equal phase constants and opposite attenuation constants. When δ exceeds 0·2 both β's become purely real.

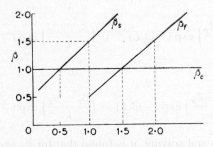

FIG. 2. Uncoupled helix and beam modes.

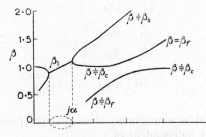

FIG. 3. The same, when coupled.

If we next consider interaction between the fast space-charge wave and the circuit wave, the sign of k is positive and the expression for β, around $\beta_e \doteq 1\cdot5$ is $\beta_1 = 1 \pm \delta/2 + \sqrt{(\delta^2/4 + 0\cdot01)}$ which is always real.

We thus note that to obtain gain, i.e., complex β's, the group velocity of one of the original modes must be reversed with respect to that of the other.

APPLICATION TO THE B.W.O.

Here P is used to denote the slow space-charge wave with power flow in the backward direction. Q is the circuit mode which is obviously also backwardly directed and the upper signs are therefore used in Eq. (9), and the square root in Eq. (11). The boundary conditions follow; they are $P = 0$ at $z = 0$, from the fact that there is no input modulation while, if the circuit is correctly terminated at $z = L$, Q will there be zero. Thus, from Eq. (10):—

$$C_1 + C_2 = 0$$

$$C_1\left(\frac{\beta_1 - \beta_p}{k}\right) \exp\left(-j\beta_1 L\right) + C_2\left(\frac{\beta_2 - \beta_p}{k}\right) \exp\left(-j\beta_2 L\right) = 0$$

and therefore

$$\left(\frac{\beta_1 - \beta_p}{k}\right) \exp\left(-j\beta_1 L\right) = \left(\frac{\beta_2 - \beta_p}{k}\right) \exp\left(-j\beta_2 L\right) \tag{12}$$

Using Eq. (11) and solving, it is found that for β_p and β_q both real,

$$\beta_p = \beta_q$$

Then

$$kL = (2n + 1)\frac{\pi}{2}$$

$$\beta_1 = \beta_p + k$$

$$\beta_2 = \beta_p - k$$

$$\left.\begin{matrix} P \\ Q \end{matrix}\right\} = -2jC_1 \exp\left(-j\beta_p z\right) \begin{cases} \sin kz \\ \cos kz \end{cases} \tag{14}$$

From Eq. (14) it is immediately clear that the power flow is just $4C_1^2$, a constant independent of z.

We next have to identify k. This is done by returning to the analysis of Chapter 7, Section 7. When $4QC$ is large, Eq. (79) suggests that we should have δ's of the form $\pm j\sqrt{(4QC)}$ so that

$$\Gamma_{1,2} = j\beta_e(1 \pm C\sqrt{4QC}) \tag{15}$$

If we substitute this and $\Gamma_0 = j\beta_e$ into Eq. (76) we find

$$(\beta - \beta_e - \beta_c\sqrt{4QC})(\beta - \beta_e) = \frac{\beta_e^2 C^2}{2\sqrt{4QC}} \tag{16}$$

whereas the coupled mode analysis yields

$$(\beta - \beta_p)(\beta - \beta_q) - k^2 = 0$$

Thus

$$k^2 \equiv \frac{\beta_e^2 C^2}{2\sqrt{4QC}} \tag{17}$$

and the starting condition for the lowest, $n = 0$, mode using Eq. (13) is

$$\frac{\beta_e{}^2 C^2 L^2}{2\sqrt{4QC}} = \frac{\pi^2}{4}$$

which in our earlier notation becomes

$$CN = \tfrac{1}{2}(QC)^{1/4} \tag{18}$$

Gould finds that this result is in good agreement with the usual, three wave theory when $CN > \{2\sqrt{(4QC)}\}^{-1}$. Using Eq. (22) of Chapter 7 we find that this is equivalent to saying that the length of the B.W.O. must exceed one half plasma wavelength for the present theory to apply.

The reader will be able to think of other applications.

APPENDIX 11

EXCITATION OF THE WAVES IN T.W.A.s AND B.W.O.s

THIS appendix gives a general treatment of the determination of the amplitudes of the three major waves in the T.W.A. and B.W.O. The elementary treatment for the T.W.A. was given in chapter 7, section 3.4. Here we use the a.c. voltages defined by $E_n = +\Gamma_n V_n$ and retain terms in $C\delta$ compared with unity. Also $\Gamma_n = j\beta_e(1 + jC\delta_n)$. We can then write down the equations relating the component voltages to the total voltage, initial r.f. velocity and initial r.f. current in matrix form, viz.,

$$
\begin{vmatrix}
1 & 1 & 1 \\
\dfrac{1 + jC\delta_1}{\delta_1} & \dfrac{1 + jC\delta_2}{\delta_2} & \dfrac{1 + jC\delta_3}{\delta_3} \\
\dfrac{1 + jC\delta_1}{\delta_1{}^2} & \dfrac{1 + jC\delta_2}{\delta_2{}^2} & \dfrac{1 + jC\delta_3}{\delta_3{}^2}
\end{vmatrix}
\begin{vmatrix} V_1 \\ V_2 \\ V_3 \end{vmatrix}
=
\begin{vmatrix} V \\ j\dfrac{u_0 C}{\eta} u_1 \\ \dfrac{-2V_0 C^2}{I_0} i_1 \end{vmatrix}
\tag{1}
$$

This equation is easily solved by the usual procedure of forming the adjoint, then transposing rows and columns to form the reciprocal. The result is Eq. (4) below, where Δ is the determinant of the matrix in Eq. (1), i.e.,

$$
\Delta = (1 + jC\delta_2)(1 + jC\delta_3)\left(\frac{1}{\delta_2\delta_3{}^2} - \frac{1}{\delta_2{}^2\delta_3}\right) + (1 + jC\delta_1)(1 + jC\delta_3)
$$

$$
\times \left(\frac{1}{\delta_3\delta_1{}^2} - \frac{1}{\delta_1\delta_3{}^2}\right) + (1 + jC\delta_1)(1 + jC\delta_2)\left(\frac{1}{\delta_1\delta_2{}^2} - \frac{1}{\delta_2\delta_1{}^2}\right)
\tag{2}
$$

For example, we may write down the explicit relation for V_1/V. This equals

$$
\left[1 + \left(\frac{1 + jC\delta_1}{1 + jC\delta_2}\right)\left(\frac{\delta_2}{\delta_1}\right)^2\left(\frac{\delta_3 - \delta_1}{\delta_2 - \delta_3}\right) + \left(\frac{1 + jC\delta_1}{1 + jC\delta_3}\right)\left(\frac{\delta_3}{\delta_1}\right)^2\left(\frac{\delta_1 - \delta_2}{\delta_2 - \delta_3}\right)\right]^{-1}
$$

$$
\tag{3}
$$

which proves Eq. (66) of Chapter 7 in the text.

378

$$
\begin{vmatrix} V_1 \\ V_2 \\ V_3 \end{vmatrix} =
\begin{vmatrix}
\begin{aligned}
&(1 + jC\delta_2)(1 + jC\delta_3)\left(\dfrac{1}{\delta_2\delta_3{}^2} - \dfrac{1}{\delta_2{}^2\delta_3}\right), \\
&\qquad -\left(\dfrac{1 + jC\delta_3}{\delta_3{}^2} - \dfrac{1 + jC\delta_2}{\delta_2{}^2}\right), \\
&\qquad\qquad \left(\dfrac{1 + jC\delta_3}{\delta_3} - \dfrac{1 + jC\delta_2}{\delta_2}\right)
\end{aligned} \\[2mm]
\begin{aligned}
&-(1 + jC\delta_1)(1 + jC\delta_3)\left(\dfrac{1}{\delta_3\delta_1{}^2} - \dfrac{1}{\delta_1\delta_3{}^2}\right), \\
&\qquad \dfrac{1 + jC\delta_3}{\delta_3{}^2} - \dfrac{1 + jC\delta_1}{\delta_1{}^2}, \\
&\qquad\qquad -\left(\dfrac{1 + jC\delta_3}{\delta_3} - \dfrac{1 + jC\delta_1}{\delta_1}\right)
\end{aligned} \\[2mm]
\begin{aligned}
&(1 + jC\delta_2)(1 + jC\delta_1)\left(\dfrac{1}{\delta_1\delta_2{}^2} - \dfrac{1}{\delta_2\delta_1{}^2}\right), \\
&\qquad -\left(\dfrac{1 + jC\delta_2}{\delta_2{}^2} - \dfrac{1 + jC\delta_1}{\delta_1{}^2}\right), \\
&\qquad\qquad \left(\dfrac{1 + jC\delta_2}{\delta_2} - \dfrac{1 + jC\delta_1}{\delta_1}\right)
\end{aligned}
\end{vmatrix}
\begin{vmatrix} \dfrac{V}{\varDelta} \\[3mm] j\dfrac{u_0 C}{\eta\varDelta}u_1 \\[3mm] -\dfrac{2V_0 C^2}{I_0\varDelta}i_1 \end{vmatrix}
$$

$$(4)$$

The total voltage after the beam has travelled a distance z is simply

$$
V = \sum_{n=1}^{3} V_n \exp\left(-\beta_e C\delta_n z\right)\exp j(\omega t - \beta_e z) \tag{5}
$$

Similarly

$$
u = \frac{-j\eta}{u_0 C}\sum\left(\frac{1 + jC\delta_n}{\delta_n}\right)V_n \exp\left(-\beta_e C\delta_n z\right)\exp j(\omega t - \beta_e z) \tag{6}
$$

$$
i = \frac{-I_0}{2V_0 C^2}\sum\left(\frac{1 + jC\delta_n}{\delta_n{}^2}\right)V_n \exp\left(-\beta_e C\delta_n z\right)\exp j(\omega t - \beta_e z) \tag{7}
$$

With the relations developed here we can write down voltages, velocities and currents anywhere in the tube, starting from the most general input conditions.

In the B.W.O. the relations are very similar but we are now given that the voltage at the collector end of the tube is the specified value, usually zero, and the current and velocity are specified at the start of the circuit. Thus the right analogue of Eq. (1) is

$$
\begin{vmatrix}
\exp(-\Gamma_1 L) & \exp(-\Gamma_2 L) & \exp(-\Gamma_3 L) \\
\dfrac{1+jC\delta_1}{\delta_1} & \dfrac{1+jC\delta_2}{\delta_2} & \dfrac{1+jC\delta_3}{\delta_3} \\
\dfrac{1+jC\delta_1}{\delta_1{}^2} & \dfrac{1+jC\delta_2}{\delta_2{}^2} & \dfrac{1+jC\delta_3}{\delta_3{}^2}
\end{vmatrix}
\begin{vmatrix}
V_1(0) \\
V_2(0) \\
V_3(0)
\end{vmatrix}
=
\begin{vmatrix}
V(L) \\
j\dfrac{u_0 C}{\eta} u_1(0) \\
-\dfrac{2V_0 C^2}{I_0} i_1(0)
\end{vmatrix}
\tag{8}
$$

leading to

$$
\begin{vmatrix}
V_1(0) \\[3.5em]
V_2(0) \\[3.5em]
V_3(0)
\end{vmatrix}
=
\begin{vmatrix}
(1+jC\delta_2)(1+jC\delta_3)\left(\dfrac{1}{\delta_2\delta_3{}^2}-\dfrac{1}{\delta_2{}^2\delta_3}\right), \\
-\left(\dfrac{e^{-\Gamma_2 L}(1+jC\delta_3)}{\delta_3{}^2}-\dfrac{e^{-\Gamma_3 L}(1+jC\delta_2)}{\delta_2{}^2}\right), \\
\dfrac{e^{-\Gamma_2 L}(1+jC\delta_3)}{\delta_3}-\dfrac{e^{-\Gamma_3 L}(1+jC\delta_2)}{\delta_2} \\[1.5em]
\hline
-(1+jC\delta_1)(1+jC\delta_3)\left(\dfrac{1}{\delta_3\delta_1{}^2}-\dfrac{1}{\delta_3{}^2\delta_1}\right), \\
\left(\dfrac{e^{-\Gamma_3 L}(1+jC\delta_1)}{\delta_1{}^2}-\dfrac{e^{-\Gamma_1 L}(1+jC\delta_3)}{\delta_3{}^2}\right), \\
\dfrac{e^{-\Gamma_3 L}(1+jC\delta_1)}{\delta_1}-\dfrac{e^{-\Gamma_1 L}(1+jC\delta_3)}{\delta_3} \\[1.5em]
\hline
(1+jC\delta_1)(1+jC\delta_2)\left(\dfrac{1}{\delta_1\delta_2{}^2}-\dfrac{1}{\delta_1{}^2\delta_2}\right), \\
-\left(\dfrac{e^{-\Gamma_1 L}(1+jC\delta_2)}{\delta_2{}^2}-\dfrac{e^{-\Gamma_2 L}(1+jC\delta_1)}{\delta_1{}^2}\right), \\
\dfrac{e^{-\Gamma_1 L}(1+jC\delta_2)}{\delta_2}-\dfrac{e^{-\Gamma_2 L}(1+jC\delta_1)}{\delta_1}
\end{vmatrix}
\begin{vmatrix}
\dfrac{V(L)}{\varDelta} \\[3.5em]
j\dfrac{u_0 C}{\eta\varDelta} u_1(0) \\[3.5em]
-\dfrac{2V_0 C^2}{I_0\varDelta} i_1(0)
\end{vmatrix}
\tag{9}
$$

where $\varDelta$ now equals

$$
\exp(-\Gamma_1 L)(1+jC\delta_2)(1+jC\delta_3)\left(\dfrac{1}{\delta_2\delta_3{}^2}-\dfrac{1}{\delta_2{}^2\delta_3}\right)+
$$

$$
+\exp(-\Gamma_2 L)(1+jC\delta_1)(1+jC\delta_3)\left(\dfrac{1}{\delta_3\delta_1{}^2}-\dfrac{1}{\delta_3{}^2\delta_1}\right)+
$$

$$
+\exp(-\Gamma_3 L)(1+jC\delta_1)(1+jC\delta_2)\left(\dfrac{1}{\delta_1\delta_2{}^2}-\dfrac{1}{\delta_1{}^2\delta_2}\right)
$$

Simplified versions of Eqs. (9) in which $C\delta_n \ll 1$, and the circuit voltage modified for space-charge is used are given by CURRIE and WHINNERY.[1]

In conclusion, we may note that if the space-charge correction is made by using Eq. (14) instead of using Pierce's method, our current equations take the form

$$\sum_{n=1}^{3} \left(\frac{1 + jC\delta_n}{\delta_n{}^2 + F^2\omega_p{}^2/C^2\omega^2} \right) V_n(0) = -\frac{2V_0C^2}{I_0} i_1(0) \qquad (10)$$

but $F^2\omega_p{}^2/C^2\omega^2 = 4QC$; therefore in Pierce's notation

$$\sum_{n=1}^{3} \left(\frac{1 + jC\delta_n}{\delta_n{}^2 + 4QC} \right) V_n(0) = -\frac{2V_0C^2}{I_0} i_1(0) \qquad (11)$$

Similarly, the velocity equation becomes

$$\sum_{n=1}^{3} \frac{\delta_n(1 + jC\delta_n)}{\delta_n{}^2 + 4QC} V_n(0) = j\frac{u_0C}{\eta} u_1(0) \qquad (12)$$

We may therefore introduce Eqs. (11) and (12) and (8) as an alternative to calculating the total voltage and then correcting to obtain the circuit part of the voltage. This is a somewhat more natural procedure which has not been adopted above because of the almost prohibitive difficulty in writing the relevant equations.

---

[1] CURRIE and WHINNERY; *Proc. I.R.E.*, 1955, **43**, 1617.

c*

APPENDIX 12

LLEWELLYN'S ELECTRONIC EQUATIONS

SPACE does not permit us to give more than the essential form of the coefficients. For complete accounts the reader should consult LLEWELLYN and PETERSON[1] or BECK.[2] The equations are here used in the form given by PETERSON.[3] The relation between the b matrix and the earlier one is

$$
\|b_{ik}\| = \begin{vmatrix} \dfrac{1}{A'} & -\dfrac{B}{A'} & -\dfrac{C}{A} \\[2ex] \dfrac{D}{A'} & E - \dfrac{BD}{A'} & F - \dfrac{CD}{A} \\[2ex] \dfrac{G}{A'} & H - \dfrac{BG}{A'} & K - \dfrac{CG}{A} \end{vmatrix} \tag{1}
$$

The b_{ik} are, in general, functions of the space-charge parameter ζ which is zero in the absence of electrons and unity in complete space-charge limitation, e.g., a space-charge limited diode. We give below values for the b_{ik} appropriate (a) to $\zeta = 1$, (b) to small ζ, as encountered in high-velocity beam problems.

The values of case (b) are obtained by neglecting terms in ζ^2 everywhere and ζ in terms of the form $1 - \zeta$.

	$\zeta \ll 1$	$\zeta = 1$
b_{11}	$j\omega C_0 + \dfrac{2\eta I_0}{(u_a + u_b)^2}\,\beta\phi_4(\beta)$	$\dfrac{3I_0\eta}{(u_a + u_b)^2}\dfrac{1}{\phi_6(\beta)}$
b_{12}	$\left[\dfrac{u_a}{u_a + u_b}\,\phi_2(\beta) + \dfrac{u_b}{u_a + u_b}\,\phi_3(\beta)\right]$	$\dfrac{u_a}{u_a + u_b} \cdot \dfrac{\phi_4(\beta)}{\phi_6(\beta)}$
b_{13}	$\dfrac{I_0}{u_a + u_b}\,\beta\phi_3(\beta)$	$\dfrac{3I_0}{u_a + u_b}\dfrac{\phi_3(\beta)}{\phi_6(\beta)}$

[1] LLEWLLYN and PETERSON; *Proc. I.R.E.*, 1944, 32, 144.
[2] BECK; *Thermionic Valves*, Chapter 7, Cambridge University Press, 1953.
[3] PETERSON; *Proc. I.R.E.*, 1947, 35, 1264.

b_{21} $\dfrac{\eta I_0}{u_a + u_b}\, \beta \phi_3(\beta)$ $\left|\ \dfrac{3I_0\eta}{u_b(u_a + u_b)}\, \dfrac{\phi_3(\beta)}{\phi_6(\beta)}\right.$

b_{22} $e^{-\beta}$ $\dfrac{u_a}{u_b}\left[-e^{-\beta} + \dfrac{\phi_3(\beta)\phi_4(\beta)}{\phi_6(\beta)}\right]$

b_{23} $\dfrac{I_0}{u_b}\, \beta\, e^{-\beta}$ $\dfrac{I_0}{u_b}\left[\beta\, e^{-\beta} + \dfrac{3\phi_3^2(\beta)}{\phi_6(\beta)}\right]$

b_{31} $\dfrac{\eta}{u_b}\left[\dfrac{u_b}{u_a + u_b}\,\phi_2(\beta) + \dfrac{u_a}{u_a + u_b}\,\phi_3(\beta)\right]$ $\dfrac{\eta}{u_a + u_b}\, \dfrac{\phi_4(\beta)}{\phi_6(\beta)}$

b_{32} $\dfrac{\eta}{j\omega C_0 u_b}\left\{e^{-\beta} +\right.$ $\dfrac{u_a}{3I_0}\, \dfrac{\phi_4^2(\beta)}{\phi_0(\beta)}$

$\qquad + \left[\dfrac{u_b}{u_a + u_b}\,\phi_2(\beta) + \dfrac{u_a}{u_a + u_b}\,\phi_3(\beta)\right]$

$\qquad \times \left.\left[\dfrac{u_a}{u_a + u_b}\,\phi_2(\beta) + \dfrac{u_b}{u_a + u_b}\,\phi_3(\beta)\right]\right\}$

b_{33} $\dfrac{u_a}{u_b}\, e^{-\beta}$ $-e^{-\beta} + \dfrac{\phi_3(\beta)\phi_4(\beta)}{\phi_6(\beta)}$

Here C_0 is the cold capacitance per unit area, $\beta = \omega\tau$

$$\left.\begin{aligned}
\phi_2(\beta) &= \frac{2}{\beta^2}(-1 + \beta + e^{-\beta}) = \frac{2}{\beta^2}(\beta - Q)\\[4pt]
\phi_3(\beta) &= \frac{2}{\beta^2}(1 - e^{-\beta} - \beta\, e^{-\beta}) = \frac{P}{\beta^2}\\[4pt]
\phi_4(\beta) &= \frac{6}{\beta_3}(-2 + \beta + 2\, e^{-\beta} + \beta\, e^{-\beta}) = \frac{-6S}{\beta_3}\\[4pt]
\phi_6(\beta) &= \frac{12}{\beta^4}\left(\frac{\beta^3}{6} + 2 - \beta - 2\, e^{-\beta} - \beta\, e^{-\beta}\right)\\[4pt]
&= \frac{12}{\beta^4}\left(\frac{\beta^3}{6} + S\right)
\end{aligned}\right\} \to 1 \text{ as } \beta \to 0$$

The ϕ's are, as mentioned in the text, forms introduced by Bakker and de Vries; they have the useful property of tending to unity as $\beta \to 0$, indicated above.

Care should be taken to distinguish between writers who use densities, following Llewellyn (as we do) and those who use currents. For instance, we put $I_0 = [2\epsilon_0(u_a + u_b)/\eta\tau^2]$, while other writers multiply this by the area under consideration.

The reader can write down other useful forms of these coefficients, examples being $\zeta = 1$, $u_a \to 0$ as used in the text and $\zeta \ll 1$, $u_a = u_b$, suitable for beam problems. In the latter case, the recognition of the coefficients is eased by remembering that

$$\omega_p{}^2 = \frac{\eta I_0}{\epsilon_0 u_0}$$

It is also worth noting that the function $\phi_2(\beta) + \phi_3(\beta)$, which appears in several coefficients, when $u_a = u_b$, is $2M\,e^{-\beta/2}$, M being the gap coupling factor.

As there seems little risk of confusion, I have not thought fit to depart from the use of $\dot{\beta} = j\omega\tau$, in spite of the conflict with our usual meaning for β.

PROBLEMS ON CHAPTER 1

1. Find an expression for $\omega_p{}^2$ involving only the beam voltage, current and area and a numerical constant. Klystrons and T.W.A.s using solid beams usually work with beam radii b such that $\omega b/u_0 \doteq 1{\cdot}0$. For a gun with a perveance of $1{\cdot}0 \times 10^{-6}$ evaluate $\omega_p{}^2$ for voltages of 1, 3 and 10 kV at frequencies of 1, 3, 10 and 30 kMc/s, respectively. If $F = 0{\cdot}5$ what are the corresponding space-charge wavelengths?

PROBLEMS ON CHAPTER 2

1. If $\partial/\partial t \equiv j\omega$, derive the following vector wave equations:

$$\nabla^2 \mathbf{E} + \frac{\omega^2}{C^2}\mathbf{E} = \text{grad}\,\frac{\rho}{\epsilon_0} + j\omega\mu_0\mathbf{J}$$

Find the corresponding expression for $\mathbf{H}$.

2. Find an expression for the power flow in the TE_{10} mode in a rectangular waveguide.

3. Prove the expression given in Eq. (82) for the power in the TM_{01} mode in circular guide.

4. A wave-guide system is used to transmit power at two widely different frequencies using two modes. Will any new effects be observed with detectors tuned to the two frequencies. Why are such systems not, in fact, used?

5. Write down explicit expressions for the fields in a cylindrical pill-box resonator excited in the TM_{001} mode. Why is such a resonator suitable for excitation by an electron beam?

6. Exponential functions and Bessel functions of real arguments are examples of functions yielding complete orthogonal sets. What other such functions do you know? Are hyperbolic functions and the I_0 and K_0 functions in this class?

PROBLEMS ON CHAPTER 3

1. Travelling-wave tubes are to be designed to operate at 3600 V, 1600 V and 400 V respectively. By what factors must c be reduced by the corresponding slow-wave circuits?

2. For the circuit of Fig. 7(a), derive Eqs. (14).

3. Using the fields of Appendix 3 write down the explicit values of the fields in the sheath helix. From the canonical boundary conditions, tangential electric field continuous over the surface, tangential field zero in the direction of the conductor and tangential magnetic field in the direction of the helix continuous in the direction of the conductor, deduce the determinantal equation for this case.

4. For the structure of Fig. 34 show that, on the same assumptions used in the text,

$$\frac{W}{W_0} = \frac{1}{2}\frac{\theta_L}{\theta_g} \cdot \frac{(\theta_g/2)^2}{\sin^2(\theta_g/2)} \cdot \frac{1}{\sin^2 \theta/2}$$

where $\theta = \beta_n(l + T)$.

5. Determine the dimensions of an interdigital line circuit for a 2500 V beam and wavelengths of 3 cm and 1 cm, respectively. Which of these, if either, is practicable mechanically?

6. For the voltages given in Problem 1, find the pitch angles for helices all designed for cold propagation constants of $\gamma_0 a = 1\cdot0$ at 3000 Mc/s. What are the corresponding wire diameters if the wire diameter is made equal to the spacing? What are the coupling impedances? Scale these helices to 10 and 35 kMc/s. Comment on the practicability of the resulting structures.

7. Plot the Brillouin diagram for a low-pass filter in which $L = 1$ mH, $C = 1000$ pF. Up to what frequency does g depart from p by less than 10%? What variation is there in the impedance over this range?

8. The functions $J_0(\beta_n d/2)$, $\sin (\beta_n d/2)/(\beta_n d/2)$, appear in several field problems. Plot these functions over the range $0 < \beta_n d/2 < 2\pi$.

PROBLEMS ON CHAPTER 4

1. An electron beam has a current density of 1 A/cm² at a voltage of 2·5 kV. What is the plasma frequency (a) when the beam travels through an infinite plane parallel electrode system in an infinite magnetic field. (b) When an infinite field is used to focus the beam through a cylindrical tunnel or normalized radius 0·8 radian. (c) When Brillouin focusing is used, the beam diameter being the same as in (b), but the tunnel diameter being increased to 1·0 radian. (d) What proportion of the magnetic induction threads the cathode when the space-charge wavelength is half-way between the value of (b) and (c)?

2. Prove that the transverse propagation constant on an electron beam of thickness t, between parallel walls spaced a distance d apart, is given by

$$\gamma_t \cdot t \tan\left(\frac{\gamma_t \cdot t}{2}\right) = \beta t \coth\frac{\beta d}{2}$$

3. Find the expression analogous to Eq. (45) for the case in which a central conductor extends throughout the length of the beam.

4. Explain carefully why one might expect longer space-charge wavelengths in finite than in infinite magnetic fields.

5. Find the expressions analogous to Eqs. (36) and (37) if it be assumed that $\rho_{10} = 0$ and $i_{10} \neq 0$. Show that the extra term in i_1 is negligible.

6. Show that, for a normal beam as used in practical valves, the reduced plasma frequency is, very approximately, $0\cdot1\, pu_0$, where p is the beam perveance, in micropervs.

PROBLEMS ON CHAPTER 5

1. In the case of a beam filling a circular tunnel derive, from the T.M. wave equations, an expression for the current induced in the walls of the tunnel and show that it is equal and opposite to the conduction current in the beam, if $F^2 \ll 1$.

2. In the text it is stated that E_r can be derived from E_z by termwise differentiation of an infinite series. What are the considerations which make this procedure legitimate?

3. How could one excite a single space-charge wave on an electron beam focused by a very strong magnetic field?

4. Consider a beam which is velocity modulated between a pair of perfect grids, when the beam does not fill the tunnel. Derive the expression analogous to Eq. (28) of the text.

5. Prove that if Y_a given by Eq. (77) is put in place of Y_s in Eq. (44) the result can be reduced to Eq. (76).

PROBLEMS ON CHAPTER 6

1. Prove that the gain of a six-cavity klystron with equal resonator spacings is given by

$$\frac{i_{T(6)}}{u_1} = j\frac{M^8}{Z_0^5}\frac{\sin^5 L}{Y_2 . Y_3 . Y_4 . Y_5} - \frac{M^6}{Z_0^4}\sin^3 L \sin 2L$$

$$\left(\frac{1}{Y_2 . Y_3 . Y_4} + \frac{1}{Y_2 . Y_3 . Y_5} + \frac{1}{Y_2 . Y_4 . Y_5} + \frac{1}{Y_3 . Y_4 . Y_5}\right)$$

$$-j\frac{M^4}{Z_0^3}\sin^2 L \sin 3L\left(\frac{1}{Y_2 . Y_3} + \frac{1}{Y_2 . Y_5} + \frac{1}{Y_4 . Y_5}\right)$$

$$-j\frac{M^4}{Z_0^3}\sin^2 L \sin L\left(\frac{1}{Y_2 . Y_4} + \frac{1}{Y_3 . Y_5} + \frac{1}{Y_3 . Y_4}\right)$$

$$+\frac{M^2}{Z_0^2}\sin L \sin 4L\left(\frac{1}{Y_2} + \frac{1}{Y_5}\right)$$

$$+\frac{M^2}{Z_0^2}\sin 2L \sin 3L\left(\frac{1}{Y_3} + \frac{1}{Y_4}\right) + j\frac{\sin 5L}{Z_0}$$

2. Calculate the maximum gain and the length between resonator centres for a two-resonator klystron for $f = 3\cdot0\,\text{kMc/s}$. The beam voltage is 10 kV, the perveance 1×10^{-6}, the gaps are to have $L = 1$, $A = 1$ and the unloaded parallel impedance of the resonators is $8 \times 10^4\,\Omega$. Calculate the corresponding gain for a three-cavity klystron. What modifications would be introduced in the performance if $A = 0\cdot5$ and $2\cdot0$?

3. Derive expressions giving the ratio of the loaded Q of the output

388   SPACE-CHARGE WAVES

gap of a klystron working in the large-signal régime to the loaded Q's of the input and intermediate gaps.

4. Show that the optimum load resistance for a klystron working in the high-efficiency régime is 1–2 times the d.c. beam impedance.

5. Discuss the statement, "The more power one puts into a klystron the better the performance".

6. Using the data of Problem 2, redesign the klystron for maximum output according to the analysis if Section 6.5 and recompute the gain.

PROBLEMS ON CHAPTER 7

1. Using the current expression of Eq. (13) write down a modified wave equation similar to Eq. (58) Chapter 5.

2. Using the data given in Figs. 9–12 compute the gain at optimum voltage for a T.W.A. in which $V = 2\cdot5$ kV, $p = 0\cdot5 \times 10^{-6}$, $Z_c = 70\ \Omega$, $f_0 = 4000$ Mc/s and $\beta_e b = 1\cdot0$. Compare these results with the simple theory of Sections 7.3.3 and 7.3.4.

3. By direct numerical methods compute some values of the δ's from Eq. (59).

4. Write down the first order δ's ignoring loss and space-charge for the B.W.O. and compare them with the analogous expressions for the T.W.A.

5. Write a short memorandum on the desirable properties of circuits for very high-frequency B.W.O.s.

PROBLEMS ON CHAPTER 8

1. Why are crossed field devices fundamentally more efficient than "O" type devices?

2. Justify Eq. (43).

PROBLEMS ON CHAPTER 9

1. Calculate the stage gain and lengths required in a velocity jump amplifier working between 500 and 2500 V.

2. Calculate the stage gain and lengths required in a space-jump amplifier working between $\beta_e b = 0\cdot1$ and $\beta_e b = 1\cdot0$. Comment on the relative practical difficulties of velocity and space-jump amplification.

3. Consider the possible variations of the cascade B.W.A. and note their possible operational features.

PROBLEMS ON CHAPTER 10

1. Discuss the noise currents induced in the output circuit of a grounded grid triode. What components are observed as the midband frequency of observation is increased?

2. Equation (4) shows that the mean square noise velocity varies as I_0^{-1}. Is this physically reasonable?

3. Derive Eq. (21).

4. Prove that no choice of $Z - Z_2$ will give a lower noise figure than those obtained in Sections 10.3.1 and 10.3.2.

5. What modifications are introduced into the dimensioning of a low noise gun by the inclusion of higher order modes?

6. An amplifier has a noise figure of 6 dB. What improvement in signal to noise will result if it is replaced by one of 0·5 dB N.F? What will be the effect in each case if the aerial temperature is dropped from 300°K to 150°K?

7. Why are low noise T.W.A.s usually made with very low beam currents? What value of gain is necessary to avoid effects due to subsequent stages for second stage N.F.s of 10, 15 and 25 dB? What considerations beside gain set a value to the minimum beam current?

RECENT REFERENCES

CHAPTER 3

1. CHODOROW and CRAIG; Some new circuits for high-power T.W.T.s, *Proc. I.R.E.*, 1957, **45**, 1106.
2. WALDRON; Theory of the helical waveguide of rectangular cross-section, *J. Brit. Instn. Radio Engrs.*, 1957, **17**, 577.
3. A treatment of the round wire helix is given by KOGAN; *Dokl. Akad. Nauk, SSSR*, 1949, **66**, 867; 1956, **107**, 541.
4. CHIAO-MIN CHU; Propagation of waves in helical waveguides, *J. Appl. Phys.*, 1958, **29**, 88.
5. BUTCHER; A theoretical study of propagation along tape ladder lines, *Onde Élect.*, 1957, **37**, 850.
6. BUTCHER; On the coupling impedance of tape structures, *Onde Élect.*, 1957, **37**, 863.

CHAPTER 4

1. LABUS; Space-charge waves along magnetically focused electron beams, *Proc. I.R.E.*, 1957, **45**, 854. A refutation of this paper is contained in RIGROD; *Proc. I.R.E.*, 1958, **46**, 358.
2. HAUS and BOBROFF; Small signal power theorem for electron beams, *J. Appl. Phys.*, 1957, **28**, 694.
3. WANG; Linear beam tube theory, *Trans. I.R.E.*, 1957, *ED–4*, 92.
4. STIX; Oscillations of a cylindrical plasma, *Phys. Rev.*, 1957, **106**, 1146.
5. STURROCK; Non-linear effects in electron plasmas, *Proc. Roy. Soc.*, 1957, **242**, 277.

CHAPTER 7

1. DUNN; Traveling-wave amplifiers and backward-wave oscillations for V.H.F., *Trans. I.R.E.*, 1957, *ED–4*, 246.
2. GITTINS, ROCK and SULLIVAN; An experimental high power pulsed travelling-wave tube, *J. Electronics*, 1957, **3**, 267.
3. VAIHNSTEIN; Théorie non linéaire du tube à propagation d'onde, *Onde Élect.*, 1957, **37**, 824.
4. PURL, ANDERSON and BREWER; A high-power periodically focused T.W.T., *Proc. I.R.E.*, 1958, **46**, 441.

CHAPTER 8

1. GOULD; Space-charge effects in beam type magnetrons, *J. Appl. Phys.*, 1957, **28**, 599.
2. BROWN; Description and operating characteristics of the Platinotron—a new microwave tube device, *Proc. I.R.E.*, 1957, **45**, 1209.

3. HOCH and WATKINS; A gun and focusing system for crossed field T.W.T.s, *I.R.E. Westcon. Convention Record*, 1957, Pt. 3, 122.
4. FEINSTEIN and KINO; Large signal behaviour of crossed field travelling-wave devices, *Proc. I.R.E.*, 1957, **45**, 1364.

CHAPTER 10

1. RIGROD; Noise spectrum of electron beams in longitudinal magnetic fields· Pt. 1. The growing noise phenomenon. Pt. 2. The U.H.F. noise spectrum, *Bell Syst. Tech. J.*, 1957, **36**, 831, 855.
2. BEAM; Noise wave excitation at the cathode of a microwave beam amplifier, *Trans. I.R.E.*, 1957, *ED*–4, 226.
3. BUCHMILLER, DE GRASSE and WADE; Design and calculation procedures for low-noise T.-W.T.s, *Trans. I.R.E.*, 1957, *ED*–4, 234.
4. SIEGMAN and BLOOM; Equivalent circuit for microwave noise at the potential minimum, *Trans. I.R.E.*, 1957, *ED*–4, 295.
5. BRIDGES; A parametric electron beam amplifier, *Proc. I.R.E.*, 1958, **46**, 494.
6. CURRIE and FORSTER; Low noise tunable preamplifiers for microwave receivers, *Proc. I.R.E.*, 1958, **46**, 570.

APPENDIX 6

1. WATERS; Rippling of thin electron beams, *J. Appl. Phys.*, 1958, **29**, 100.
2. COOK, KOMPFNER and YOCOM; Slalom focusing, *Proc. I.R.E.*, 1957, **45**, 1517.
3. CHANG; Biperiodic electrostatic focusing for high density electron beams, *Proc. I.R.E.*, 1957, **45**, 1522.

LIST OF MAJOR SYMBOLS

M.K.S. units are used throughout. Linear dimensions are denoted by lower case letters, a, b, c etc., and normalized dimensions, i.e. transit angles, by the corresponding capitals, A, B, C, etc. In cylindrical systems a is the tunnel radius, b the outer radius of the beam, c the inner radius of an annular beam, d the radius of a central conductor.

The notation for propagation constants is based on history rather than on logic. The complex propagation constant $\Gamma = \alpha + \mathrm{j}\beta$, and this is used when a complex value is expected. However, $\Gamma \doteq \mathrm{j}\beta$ in many cases and we often use a lower case γ instead of β. Lower case γ's are usually, but not invariably, real numbers therefore.

$\mathbf{A} =$ Magnetic vector potential
$B =$ Susceptance
$\mathbf{B} =$ Magnetic induction
$C =$ Pierce's T.W.T. parameter. $C^3 = I_0 Z_c / 4V_0$
$c =$ Velocity of light
$\mathbf{E} =$ Electric field
$e =$ Electronic charge
$F =$ Space-charge reduction factor
$G =$ Conductance
$g =$ Group velocity
$\mathbf{H} =$ Magnetic field
$I, i =$ Current
$I_n, K_n =$ Bessel functions with imaginary arguments
$J, j =$ Current density
$J_n, Y_n =$ Bessel functions of first kind
$k =$ Wave-number, $(2\pi f/p)$ or Boltzmann's constant
$\ln =$ Napierian logarithm
$M, M^1 =$ Gap coupling coefficient (pp. 134–135)
$m =$ Electronic mass
$P =$ Klystron parameter ($P = 4V_0/I_0 RM^2 + 2M^1/M$)
$p =$ Phase velocity and beam perveance
$Q =$ Pierce's space-charge parameter
$\mathbf{S} =$ Poynting's vector
$T =$ Absolute temperature, °K

t = time co-ordinate. The dot notation for differentiation is used

u = Velocity, u_0 is the unmodulated velocity

V_0 = D.C. voltage

V = A.C. kinetic voltage

W = Power

X = Reactance

Y = Admittance

Z = Impedance

Z_c = Coupling impedance

Z_0 = Characteristic impedance

α = Attenuation constant, also depth of modulation in klystron theory

β = Phase constant

βe = Phase constant of electrons = ω/u_0

Γ = Propagation constant.

ϵ, ϵ_0 = Permittivity, for dielectric and vacuum

η = e/m

λ = Wave-length

λ_c = Cut-off wave-length

λ_g = Guide wave-length

μ, μ_0 = Permeability, of dielectric and vacuum

ρ = charge density

Σ = Cross-sectional area of beam

σ = Conductivity

π = Hertzian vector

τ = Transit time

ϕ = Electric scalar potential

ω = Angular frequency

ω_L = Larmor frequency $(\eta B/2)$

ω_p = Plasma frequency $(\eta I_0/\epsilon_0 u_0 \Sigma)^{1/2}$

ω_c = Cyclotron frequency (ηB)

PHYSICAL CONSTANTS

$e = 1\cdot60 \times 10^{-19}$ C

$m = 9\cdot11 \times 10^{-31}$ kg

$\eta = 1\cdot76 \times 10^{-9}$ C/kg

$\mu_0 = 4\pi \times 10^{-7}$ H/m

$\epsilon_0 = 1/36\pi \times 10^{-9}$ F/m

$k = 8\cdot61 \times 10^{-5}$ eV/°K

INDEX